Gradient Optimization
and Nonlinear Control

Gradient Optimization and Nonlinear Control

LAWRENCE HASDORFF

University of Houston
Clear Lake City, Texas

A WILEY-INTERSCIENCE PUBLICATION

JOHN WILEY & SONS, New York · London · Sydney · Toronto

Copyright © 1976 by John Wiley & Sons, Inc.

All rights reserved. Published simultaneously in Canada.

No part of this book may be reproduced by any means, nor transmitted, nor translated into a machine language without the written permission of the publisher.

Library of Congress Cataloging in Publication Data:

Hasdorff, Lawrence, 1929-
   Gradient optimization and nonlinear control.
   "A Wiley-Interscience publication."
   Includes bibliographical references and index.
   1. Control theory. 2. Mathematical optimization.
3. Nonlinear theories. I. Title.
QA402.3.H35   629.8′36   75–40187
ISBN 0–471–35870–3

Printed in the United States of America

10 9 8 7 6 5 4 3 2 1

Preface

This book is intended to serve as an introduction to computation in control by an iterative, gradient, numerical method. This general approach is thought to be important, since it permits one to attack problems in control without an assumption of linearity. In effect it permits one to do for nonlinear systems many of the things that have heretofore been possible only for linear systems. The importance of being able to deal with nonlinear systems is readily evident to anyone who has to deal with any real system.

Fundamental in taking an iterative, gradient, numerical approach to control problems is the assumption of an enormous computational capability, basically to integrate the system differential equations involved. The modern, large-scale, digital computer makes all this possible. There are of course many different approaches to solving control problems with the digital computer. The gradient approach is felt to be a good one since it is a simple, generally well understood method that permits the solution of a truly large class of optimization problems, a class that extends well outside the area of control.

The general language and approach used here are those of elementary functional analysis. This selection was made because it is very general and because it is receiving increasing acceptance in a wide variety of fields. Also, from a functional analysis standpoint the basic ideas in gradient methods stand out with clarity and simplicity.

The particular gradient method that is emphasized and used here is conjugate gradient descent; it is by now a well known method and it exhibits quadratic convergence while requiring very little more computation than simple steepest descent. So far as convergence is concerned, it generally does much better than steepest descent.

It may be noted by scanning the table of contents that there is very little said about constraints directly. This is done because it is felt that constraints are a thicket that it is best not to get into deeply at the introductory level intended here. The importance of constraints is recognized, however they do tend to obscure the generally beautiful simplicity that one has with a gradient approach. Also, in control problems constraints can and are often handled as part of the nonlinearity of the dynamics. For instance, a magnitude constraint on a control input may be treated as a constraint on the control input or it may be treated as a saturation nonlinearity in series with the control input. Another approach, and one used in the text, is to introduce the constraints as penalty terms in the criterion.

The text falls naturally into two parts. Chapters 1 to 3 treat the general method of the iterative gradient approach. Here the general mathematical tools are introduced and applied to the development of the underlying theorems on conjugate gradient descent. The second part discusses the application of the general methods, developed in the first three chapters, specifically to problems in control. Those individuals interested only in control applications may limit themselves to Chapters 4 to 6. On the other hand, those interested only in the theory of conjugate gradient descent may limit themselves to the first three chapters. The author, of course, feels that the two parts complement each other, and in general neither part can be fully appreciated without the other.

A few words concerning the level of rigor intended are also in order here. In the first three chapters the basic mathematical tools are developed with some care. In the second part, which deals with applications almost entirely, a great deal of this care has been set aside with more emphasis placed on obtaining and applying specific results.

The level of the text is that of a first-year graduate student in applied mathematics or engineering. No real background in control is assumed, although this will be helpful in understanding and appreciating the choice of criteria used and the initial guesses made in doing the examples. Every method introduced is illustrated by an example. There has been a real attempt to choose an approach and to use mathematical tools that make the material both appealing and accessible to an audience outside the control field.

LAWRENCE HASDORFF

Clear Lake City, Texas
October 1975

Acknowledgments

As in the writing of any text, there are many people, mainly students, who make a real and solid contribution and make the entire task possible and whose names must go unmentioned. To all of these, the author is indeed grateful and gives first acknowledgment.

Special mention must go to the following individuals who had the most immediate effect upon the form and direction of the manuscript. To begin, as in all scholastic attempts, first there must be a teacher. In this case it was Prof. C. A. Desoer of the University of California, Berkeley, who first introduced me to the "method of Bryson and Kelley" and in his own gentle way guided the first halting steps in the application of gradient optimization in control systems. Next, special recognition must go to two men of NASA/ Langley. The first of these is Alper Caglayan, who read the manuscript, gave many helpful comments on the theory, and suggested numerous problems. The second is Raymond Montgomery, who reviewed the manuscript and offered much helpful and constructive criticism. The author acknowledges a major improvement in the quality of the manuscript due to their efforts.

Special appreciation must also be expressed to G. Allan Smith of NASA/ Ames. Though his contributions were indirect, his encouragement, support, and example over the past 6 years have made more of a contribution than I have ever heretofore had the opportunity to acknowledge.

Very special thanks must go to Carole Lewis and Martha Esleeck who cheerfully and efficiently turned rough, mostly illegible, handwritten notes and sketches into manuscript.

There are several organizations whose contribution must also be recognized. Virginia Polytechnic Institute and State University, The National Aeronautics and Space Administration, and The National Research Council provided the financial and administrative support through the period of the manuscript's production. This support is gratefully acknowledged. On the immediate operating level, the members of the Department of Electrical Engineering of VPI and SU and of the Flight and Systems Research Branch at Ames Research Center have supported my work on a day by day basis as the work progressed and I would like to express my appreciation to all of them.

And finally, recognition is hereby expressed to my wife Ruth and our children Deborah, Henry, and Karen for their understanding in giving up all the weekends and evenings of my time that this effort required.

L. H.

Contents

Symbols

Symbol	Description	Where First Found
$\mathscr{H}$	Hilbert space	Fig. 1.1
$\mathscr{R}^n$	n-Dimensional real space	Fig. 1.1
x	Element of a space	(1.1)
$F(x)$	Value of a functional at x	(1.1)
x^*	Minimizing element of a functional	(1.2)
t_0	Initial time of the time interval of interest	Under (1.5)
t_f	Final time of the time interval of interest	Under (1.5)
$\phi(\cdot)$	Cost function for the control system of interest	(1.6)
$\langle x, y \rangle$	Scalar product between elements x and y	Section 2.1
$\mathscr{C}_{[a,b]}$	Space of continuous functions over the closed interval $[a, b]$	Section 2.1
$[a, b]$	Closed interval in $\mathscr{R}^1$ beginning at a and ending at b	Section 2.1
$\|x\|$	Norm of vector x	(2.4)
$\|\cdot\|_{\mathscr{E}}$	Norm of space $\mathscr{E}$	(2.10)
$\mathscr{E} \times \mathscr{L}$	Cross-product space obtained from space $\mathscr{E}$ and space $\mathscr{L}$	Under (2.7)
$\mathscr{L}^2_{[a,b]}$	Space of functions square integrable over $[a, b]$	Under (2.7)
A	Linear operator	(2.9)
sup	Supremum, least upper bound	(2.10)
$\lambda(A)$	Eigenvalue of matrix A	(2.11)
$\|A\|$	Norm of linear operator A	(2.10)
$\forall x$	For all x	(2.14)

$B(x, y)$	Value of bilinear operator B at (x, y)	(2.18)
$\langle \cdot, \cdot \rangle_{\mathscr{E}}$	Scalar product of space $\mathscr{E}$	(2.8)
A^*	Adjoint of linear operator A	(2.24)
A^+	Transpose of matrix A	(2.11)
x^+	Transpose of n-vector x	(2.15)
$F'(x_0)$	Derivative of operator F at x_0	Above Fig. 2.7
$o(\cdot)$	The order operator	(2.38)
$F''(x_0)$	Second derivative of operator F at x_0	(2.45)
A^{-1}	Inverse of the linear operator A	(2.68)
$\{p_i\}$	Set with typical element p_i	(3.2)
CGD	Conjugate gradient descent	Section 3.3
SCGD	Scaled conjugated gradient descent	Section 3.5
∇_x	Gradient operator on $\mathscr{R}^n$, w.r.t. x	(4.8)
$f(x, u)$	n-Valued function giving the dynamics $(\dot{x} = f(x, u))$ of the control system of interest	(4.9), (1.5)
$f_x(x, u)$	$n \times n$ matrix of partial derivatives of components of f w.r.t. components of x	(4.19a)
$f_u(x, u)$	$n \times m$ matrix of partial derivatives of components of f w.r.t. components of u	(4.19b)
$1(t)$	Unit step function $1(t) = 0, t < 0$ $1(t) = 1, t \geq 0$	(4.72)
$\mathscr{P}\mathscr{C}^M_{[t_0, t_f]}$	Space of piecewise continuous functions over $[t_0, t_f]$ with M discontinuities	Above (5.4)
$\operatorname{sgn} \tau$	$\operatorname{sgn} \tau = \dfrac{\tau}{|\tau|}$	(5.42)
$x_d(t)$	$x(t)$ delayed by T	(5.98)
x_p	Precondition on x	(5.125)
θ_{ss}	Steady-state value of θ	Under (6.8)
$y_d(t)$	The desired output signal	Above (6.1)
$\Phi_{rr}(s)$	Power spectral density of signal $r(t)$	Above (6.53)
σ_r^2	Variance of signal $r(t)$	Below (6.56)
$\bar{e}^2$	Mean square value of signal $e(t)$	Fig. 6.20

Gradient Optimization
and Nonlinear Control

PART ONE

Chapter 1

Introduction

1.1. STATEMENT OF THE GENERAL PROBLEM

Our object here is to lay a general foundation in optimization theory that can be used to optimize the responses of the control systems that are considered subsequently. Our main aid is the digital computer, so our aim is to develop a theory that anticipates the use of the computer.

To this end we postulate a mapping, or an operator, or a transformation, or whatever from a Hilbert space $\mathcal{H}$ to the real line $\mathcal{R}^1$. This shown in Fig. 1.1. Let us call this operator F since it is a functional. F assigns to every element $x \in \mathcal{H}$ a real value $F(x)$. Now any two elements x_1 and x_2 can be ranked relative to one another depending on whether

$$F(x_1) < F(x_2)$$

or

$$F(x_1) > F(x_2) \tag{1.1}$$

Of course if $F(x_1) = F(x_2)$, then x_1 and x_2 rank equally. The functional F is thus seen to be simply a device for ordering the elements of $\mathcal{H}$.

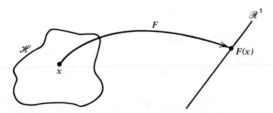

Figure 1.1 A functional F from Hilbert space $\mathcal{H}$ to the real line $\mathcal{R}^1$.

3

An additional and basic assumption here is that the functional F is a continuous, smooth operator. Therefore if x moves around at some fixed rate in $\mathcal{H}$, $F(x)$ does not change erratically or abruptly in $\mathcal{R}^1$.

The Problem

With these basic assumptions the basic problem is now

To find x^* in $\mathcal{H}$ such that

$$F(x^*) \le F(x) \tag{1.2}$$

for all $x \in \mathcal{H}$ in a neighborhood of x^*.

It should be noted here that the problem is minimization. We can as well consider maximization by simply exchanging $-F$ for F and this is done in the sequel when a maximization problem arises.

Also, it can be appreciated that it would be better to choose as the problem finding the x^* such that (1.2) is satisfied for all $x \in \mathcal{H}$. That is, our problem states that we are seeking a relative minima when it would be better to seek an absolute minima. There is really no short, good explanation for this since one usually does want the absolute minimum. Suffice it to say that seeking the absolute minimum extends the problem beyond the range of the gradient methods studied here. From a practical standpoint, the relative minima techniques are usually sufficient for the control problem for which the theory is intended.

The Method of Attack

The basic method used here for finding a minimizing argument x^* of F in $\mathcal{H}$, termed descent, consists of the following steps:

1. Making an initial guess.
2. Constructing a sequence $x_0, x_1, x_2, \ldots$ such that

$$F(x_{i+1}) < F(x_i) \tag{1.3}$$

The sequence is extended until (1) no x_{i+1} can be found such that (1.3) is satisfied or (2) until the sequence $\{x_i\}$ approaches a limit. In case 1 $x_i = x^*$ and in case 2 x^* is the limit of the sequence. It is seen that we obtain either x^* or a value very near x^*.

This basic method has been chosen because it is particularly adaptable to the use of the computer. One has only to program the computer to find x_{i+1}

from x_i. The computer generally accomplishes the iteration very well for our control problems. And, though this method does introduce additional problems, it does avoid many of the problems of the more direct methods.

Thus it can be understood why a Hilbert space has been chosen as the space in which a minimizing argument for F is sought. The distinguishing features of a Hilbert space are as follows:

1. It is *linear*.
2. It is *complete*.
3. It has a *scalar product*.

1. We recall that if a space is *linear* and if x_1 and x_2 are in the space, then the element $y = ax_1 + bx_2$ is also in the space (a and b are scalar constants). Therefore our series is constructed so that

$$x_{i+1} = x_i + \alpha_i z_i \tag{1.4}$$

where z_i is also a member of the space under consideration and α_i is a scalar constant. Thus x_{i+1} is also a member of the space under consideration and the whole sequence is in the space.

2. A space is *complete* if every cauchy sequence in the space has a limit in the space. If we wish to construct a sequence that approaches a limit, it is desirable to have that limit in the space in which we are working.

3. The *scalar product* (see Chapter 2 for a definition of the scalar product) is very fundamentally involved in the way the direction of step is chosen in going from x_i to x_{i+1} (i.e., choosing z_i to be used in 1.4). How the scalar product comes into play becomes obvious in the following sections where expansion of a functional (such as F) about a given point is discussed.

Our plan for the chapters ahead is as follows:

Part One: To lay the mathematical foundation required and to develop the general algorithm to be used in constructing the sequence that is to converge on the solution to the general minimization problem stated above.

Part Two: To specialize the theory of Part One to the case of optimization of the inputs to a control system. Specifically we consider a control system whose dynamics are given by

$$\dot{x} = f(x, u) \tag{1.5}$$

where $x \in \mathscr{R}^n$, u is in Hilbert space $\mathscr{H}$, and f is a vector-valued function on $\mathscr{R}^n \times \mathscr{H}$. The initial time t_0 and final time t_f are assumed to be given. The cost of operating this system over the time interval $[t_0, t_f]$ is assumed to be given by

$$\text{cost} = J = \phi(x(t_f)) \tag{1.6}$$

where ϕ is a real-valued function on $\mathscr{R}^n$. The cost is thus a function of the final state reached. The problem then is to find $u \in \mathscr{H}$ using the general method developed in Part One, that produces minimum cost. The u considered can take many specific forms. It may be a set of initial conditions, an input control function that may take on several different forms, or a set of parameters, or it may be combinations of these.

Part Three: To use the techniques developed in Parts One and Two to attack the still more specialized problem of controller design for the class of control systems considered in Part Two.

Chapter 2

Basic Mathematical Concepts

2.1. SOME FUNDAMENTAL DEFINITIONS

We consider here definitions of the fundamental mathematical quantities and terms and introduce the notation that is used in all subsequent work. Our basic problem is finding the minimizing argument of a functional on a Hilbert space. Let us begin by defining the terms needed.

A Linear Space

A space $\mathscr{S}$ is a collection of elements; it is said to be linear if $x_1 \in \mathscr{S}$, $x_2 \in \mathscr{S}$ then $(ax_1 + bx_2) \in \mathscr{S}$ where a and b are scalar constants. We see in particular that if $x \in \mathscr{S}$, then $ax \in \mathscr{S}$ and so are $-x \in \mathscr{S}$ and $0 \in \mathscr{S}$, which correspond to $a = -1$ and $a = 0$, respectively. We shall in general adhere to the convention of denoting spaces by script capitals and elements of spaces by italic lowercase letters.

Examples of linear spaces are the real numbers, denoted by $\mathscr{R}^1$. Real, n-dimensional euclidean space is denoted by $\mathscr{R}^n$, and the space of continuous functions over an interval of the real line $[a, b]$, by $\mathscr{C}_{[a, b]}$. Examples of collections of elements that are not linear spaces are any finite set, any proper subset of $\mathscr{R}^n$, and the numbers in the interval $[0, 1]$.

The Scalar Product

A scalar product on a space $\mathscr{S}$ is an operation that assigns a real number to every pair of elements in $\mathscr{S}$. If the scalar product of two elements $x, y \in \mathscr{S}$ is denoted by $\langle x, y \rangle$, the scalar product has the following properties:

1. $\langle x, y \rangle \in \mathscr{R}^1$ for $x, y \in \mathscr{S}$.
2. $\langle x, y \rangle = \langle y, x \rangle$.
3. $\langle ax + bz, y \rangle = a\langle x, y \rangle + b\langle z, y \rangle$ (linear, where a and b are scalar constants).
4. $\langle x, x \rangle > 0$ if $x \neq 0$.
5. $\langle 0, x \rangle = 0$ where 0 is the null element.   (2.1)

Examples of scalar products are as follows:

1. In $\mathscr{R}^1$, ordinary multiplication.
2. In $\mathscr{R}^n$ where

$$x - \begin{bmatrix} x_1 \\ x_2 \\ \vdots \\ x_n \end{bmatrix} \qquad y - \begin{bmatrix} y_1 \\ y_2 \\ \vdots \\ y_n \end{bmatrix}$$

$$\langle x, y \rangle = \sum_{i=1}^{n} x_i y_i \tag{2.2}$$

3. In $\mathscr{C}_{[a, b]}$, with elements $x(t)$ and $y(t)$

$$\langle x, y \rangle = \int_a^b x(t) y(t) \, dt \tag{2.3}$$

Scalar Product Norm

The norm, is, obviously, a measure of the magnitude (or length) of an element in a space. For spaces on which a scalar product is defined, the most convenient and usual definition of norm for a typical element x, written $\|x\|$, is

$$\|x\| = \sqrt{\langle x, x \rangle} \tag{2.4}$$

This is the norm used in this text, since all interest centers on the Hilbert space, which by definition has a scalar product. Some examples of scalar product norms are as follows:

1. For $x \in \mathscr{R}^1$, $\|x\| = |x|$
2. For $x \in \mathscr{R}^n$, $\|x\| = \left(\sum_{i=1}^{n} x_i^2 \right)^{1/2}$
3. For $x \in \mathscr{C}_{[a, b]}$, $\|x\| = \left[\int_a^b x^2(t) \, dt \right]^{1/2}$

We say two elements x and y of a space are orthogonal if $\langle x, y \rangle = 0$.

Two Norm Inequalities

Two very useful inequalities involving norms are Schwarz's inequality and the triangle inequality. *Schwarz's inequality* for two elements x and y from a *scalar product space* is

$$|\langle x, y \rangle| \leq \|x\| \cdot \|y\| \tag{2.5}$$

The *triangle inequality* is

$$\|x + y\| \leq \|x\| + \|y\| \tag{2.6}$$

We offer no proof for these inequalities; any elementary text in functional analysis (see, for example, [1] or [2]) or linear spaces should have one. These inequalities, shown in Fig. 2.1, have a good geometrical interpretation in $\mathscr{R}^2$. It should be realized from the figure that the inequalities hold as well in $\mathscr{R}^n$ for the plane on which Fig. 2.1 is drawn can simply be taken as the plane in $\mathscr{R}^n$ determined by the two vectors (elements) x and y. As a simple exercise, these two inequalities may be shown to hold in $\mathscr{R}^1$, $\mathscr{R}^n$, and $\mathscr{C}_{[a, b]}$.

A Cluster Point

A point or element y is a cluster point of a sequence $\{x_n\}$ if every ε neighborhood of y contains an infinite number of members of the sequence. This means in our case, given any $\varepsilon > 0$ there are an infinite number of x_n for which

$$\|y - x_n\| < \varepsilon$$

where we assume the norm is as defined by (2.4). A cluster point is also commonly called a limit point if it is in the space in which the sequence occurs. If a sequence has a cluster point y in the sequence space, it is obvious that there is a sub-sequence that has limit y in the conventional sense of the limit.

A Complete Space

A space $\mathscr{S}$ is said to be complete if every sequence in that space with cluster point y has $y \in \mathscr{S}$. One might assume that every linear space that has a scalar product defined upon it and a corresponding norm as in (2.4) would be complete. This is true for the very important practical case of $\mathscr{R}^n$ with scalar products as in (2.2) and norm as in (2.4). However an important exception, that is, a linear, scalar-product space that is not complete, is $\mathscr{C}_{[a, b]}$ with scalar product as in (2.3) and corresponding norm as in (2.4).

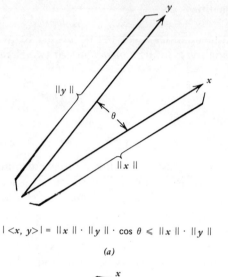

$$|<x, y>| = \|x\| \cdot \|y\| \cdot \cos\theta \leqslant \|x\| \cdot \|y\|$$

(a)

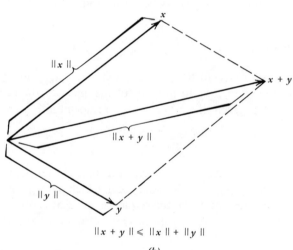

$$\|x + y\| \leqslant \|x\| + \|y\|$$

(b)

Figure 2.1 (a) Schwarz's inequality in $\mathscr{R}^2$. (b) Triangle inequality in $\mathscr{R}^2$.

To see this, we consider the functions in Fig. 2.2. Let us consider the sequence of functions $\{x_n(t)\} \in \mathscr{C}_{[a, b]}$. It is obvious how to extend the sequence of continuous functions of which $x_1(t)$, $x_2(t)$, $x_3(t)$, and $x_4(t)$ are the starting members so that

$$\int_a^b [y(t) - x_n(t)]^2 \, dt < \varepsilon$$

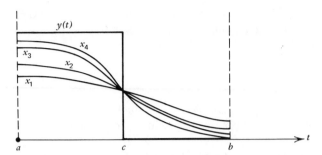

Figure 2.2   A sequence of continuous functions converging to a discontinuous function.

for an infinite number of $x_n(t)$ and arbitrary ε. $y(t)$ is the function shown by the heavy line in Fig. 2.2. But $y(t)$ has a jump at $t = c$, and thus is discontinuous and hence $y \notin \mathscr{C}_{[a,b]}$. The conclusion is that $\mathscr{C}_{[a,b]}$ with the integral square norm is not complete. As it turns out, if we want a complete space we must choose a different norm, for example,

$$\|x(t)\| = \max_{t \in [a,b]} |x(t)| \tag{2.7}$$

will make $\mathscr{C}_{[a,b]}$ a complete space. The other alternative if we want to keep the integral square norm and have a complete space is to increase the number of functions included in our space. As a matter of fact, we must increase $\mathscr{C}_{[a,b]}$ to include all functions square integrable over $[a,b]$ (this space is called $\mathscr{L}^2_{[a,b]}$) to get a complete space with the integral square norm (see [3]).

Linear, scalar-product spaces that are not complete are sometimes called pre-Hilbert spaces. $\mathscr{C}_{[a,b]}$ with scalar product as in (2.3) and corresponding norm is a pre-Hilbert space.

A Hilbert Space

A complete, linear, scalar product space is called a Hilbert space. Examples of Hilbert spaces are $\mathscr{R}^1$, $\mathscr{R}^n$, and $\mathscr{L}^2_{[a,b]}$.

The Cartesian or Cross Product of Two Spaces

A very useful notion from set theory is the notation of the cartesian product or cross product, or simply product of two sets. Given two sets A and B, the product of these two sets, written $A \times B$, is the set of ordered pairs (x, y) such that $x \in A$ and $y \in B$. The ordering is important here; $(x, y) = (y, x)$

only if $A = B$ and $y = x$. We extend this notion straightforwardly to linear spaces and define the product of two spaces $\mathscr{E}$ and $\mathscr{F}$ to be $\mathscr{E} \times \mathscr{F}$, which has elements that are ordered pairs of the form (x, y) where $x \in \mathscr{E}$ and $y \in \mathscr{F}$. An obvious example of this concept is the product of two real lines $\mathscr{R}^1 \times \mathscr{R}^1$, which is just $\mathscr{R}^2$. This is shown in Fig. 2.3. This concept can be extended easily to multiproduct spaces, for example, $\mathscr{R}^1 \times \mathscr{R}^1 \times \cdots \times \mathscr{R}^1$ n times is $\mathscr{R}^n$. These are obvious examples of product spaces. A less obvious one, but one that will be seen to be useful in control work, is the product $\mathscr{R}^n \times \mathscr{C}_{[a, b]}$ where the typical element is a pair (x, u), where $x \in \mathscr{R}^n$, and u is a function over the interval $[a, b]$. We write $u_{[a, b]}$ to mean the function u over the closed interval $[a, b]$.

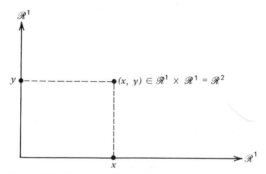

Figure 2.3   The cartesian product of two real lines.

If the product of two spaces is formed, such as $\mathscr{E} \times \mathscr{F}$, and if $\mathscr{E}$ and $\mathscr{F}$ both have scalar products defined on them, the scalar product on $\mathscr{E} \times \mathscr{F}$ is easily defined as

$$\langle \, , \, \rangle_{\mathscr{E} \times \mathscr{F}} = \langle \, , \, \rangle_{\mathscr{E}} + \langle \, , \, \rangle_{\mathscr{F}} \tag{2.8}$$

that is, the scalar product on $\mathscr{E} \times \mathscr{F}$ is just the sum of the scalar product on $\mathscr{E}$ and the scalar product on $\mathscr{F}$. The norm on the cross-product space can then be naturally defined using this scalar product in (2.4).

2.2   LINEAR AND BILINEAR OPERATORS

Linear operators underlie our whole approach to solving control problems, so let us now consider them in the detail that is warranted.

An operator, or transformation, or mapping as we shall think of it here, is simply a relationship between the elements of two spaces. An operator T assigns, or relates, to each element of a space $\mathscr{E}$, an element of another space $\mathscr{F}$.

If $x \in \mathscr{E}$ then $T(x)$ is an element (or possibly elements) in $\mathscr{F}$, $T(x) \in \mathscr{F}$, as shown in Fig. 2.4. Of course the operator T may be specialized to consider only a set of elements in $\mathscr{E}$ (which is called the *domain* of T) to another set in $\mathscr{F}$ (which is called the *range*). However, for our purpose, we are mainly interested in operators in which the domain is the whole space $\mathscr{E}$. The range may or may not be the whole space $\mathscr{F}$.

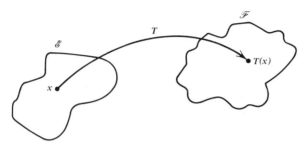

Figure 2.4 An operator from space $\mathscr{E}$ to space $\mathscr{F}$.

The Constant Operator

It should be appreciated that an operator can be complicated, so to be tractable we must immediately put restrictions on the ones to be considered. Starting with the simplest possible case, we consider first the constant operator. Let us consider an operator from $\mathscr{E}$ to $\mathscr{F}$ as in Fig. 2.4; a constant operator is one that takes every element in $\mathscr{E}$ into a single element in $\mathscr{F}$, that is, to every element in $\mathscr{E}$ a single element in $\mathscr{F}$ is assigned. Possibly the most obvious operator in this class is the *null* operator, which takes every element in $\mathscr{E}$, the domain, into the null or zero element in the range space $\mathscr{F}$.

The Linear Operator

The constant operator is really too simple to be of much interest, although it does find use.

Going up to the next order of complexity, we consider the linear operator. A linear operator A is one that satisfies

$$A(ax + by) = aAx + bAy \qquad (2.9)$$

for all x and y in its domain and all scalar constants a and b. It might seem at first glance at (2.9) that linear operators might also be too simple to be of much interest. This is not the case, for discussion of these linear operators occupies a great deal of space both here and in every other text that considers operators.

The first thing to note about a linear operator A that satisfies (2.9) is that the null operator is a trivial case of a linear operator. If $Ax = Ay = 0 \in \mathscr{F}$ is satisfied for all $x, y \in \mathscr{E}$, (2.9) is also satisfied. The most often encountered example of a linear operator is the case of $\mathscr{E} = \mathscr{R}^n$, $\mathscr{F} = \mathscr{R}^m$ where the linear operator A is multiplication by an $m \times n$ real matrix.

The Norm of a Linear Operator

If the domain and range space ($\mathscr{E}$ and $\mathscr{F}$) of a linear operator A have a norm, then a norm for A can also be defined. The norm of a linear operator $\|A\|$ is then given by

$$\|A\| \triangleq \sup_{\|x\|_{\mathscr{E}} = 1} \|Ax\|_{\mathscr{F}} \qquad (2.10)$$

where $\| \cdot \|_{\mathscr{E}}$ and $\| \cdot \|_{\mathscr{F}}$ are the norms on $\mathscr{E}$ and $\mathscr{F}$, respectively. Since the spaces considered here are Hilbert spaces with a scalar product and norm as given by (2.4), all linear operators here have well defined norms. As an example of a norm of an operator we note that the norm of a constant operator is just the norm of the element in $\mathscr{F}$ into which all elements of $\mathscr{E}$ are transformed. Another interesting case is where the operator A is multiplication by a matrix which we simply call A. Use of the scalar product norm in $\mathscr{R}^n$ as in (2.4) gives

$$\|A\| = \sqrt{\max \lambda(A^+ A)} \qquad (2.11)$$

where $\lambda(A^+ A)$ is the eigenvalue of $A^+ A$. If A is real, symmetric and positive definite then this reduces to

$$\|A\| = \max |\lambda(A)| \qquad (2.12)$$

From (2.10) a very useful relationship is

$$\|Ax\|_{\mathscr{F}} \leq \|A\| \cdot \|x\|_{\mathscr{E}} \qquad (2.13)$$

A Continuous Linear Operator

For operators from one normed linear space to another, continuity is a natural concept defined as in the case of real-valued functions of a real variable.

Continuity at a point

An operator, for example, T from $\mathscr{E}$ to $\mathscr{F}$, is said to be continuous at $x_0 \in \mathscr{E}$ if for any $\varepsilon > 0$ a $\delta > 0$ can be found such that for any x such that $\|x - x_0\|_{\mathscr{E}} < \delta$, $\|T(x) - T(x_0)\|_{\mathscr{F}} < \epsilon$. And again as in the case of functions, an operator is said to be continuous on a set if it is continuous at every point in that set. If an operator is said to be continuous without any qualification, it is continuous at every point in its domain.

For linear operators, the norm of the operator tells whether or not the operator is continuous since a linear operator A is continuous if $\|A\| < \infty$. This fact follows immediately from the use of (2.13) and $\|A\|$ bounded with the definition of continuity.

A Linear Functional on a Hilbert Space

A functional is the special case of an operator that assigns a number to every element of a space. It is thus a special case of an operator with range in $\mathscr{R}^1$. The case of interest here is one where the domain space is a Hilbert space. For this special case there is a useful theorem[†]:

Theorem 2.1.   A continuous, linear functional F, from a Hilbert space $\mathscr{H}$ to $\mathscr{R}^1$ can be considered to be the scalar product of $x \in \mathscr{H}$ with another vector $z \in \mathscr{H}$ for all x, that is,

$$F(x) = \langle z, x \rangle \qquad \forall\ x \in \mathscr{H} \tag{2.14}$$

Thus a continuous, linear functional on a Hilbert space $\mathscr{H}$ is completely characterized by one element $z \in \mathscr{H}$. Theorem 2.1 is a direct paraphrasing of Theorem 1.1 of [4]. The reader is referred there for the proof.

As an example of the use of Theorem 2.1 let us consider a linear function $y = F(x)$ where $x \in \mathscr{R}^n$. In this case

$$x = [x_1 x_2 \ldots x_n]^+ \tag{2.15}[‡]$$

and the most general form for a linear functional is

$$y = F(x) = a_1 x_1 + a_2 x_2 + \cdots + a_n x_n \tag{2.16}$$

where $a_1, a_2, \ldots, a_n$ are scalar constants. It is easily seen here that

$$y = \langle z, x \rangle \tag{2.17}$$

[†] This is called the theorem of F. Riesz in [2].
[‡] To save space column vectors as in (2.15) are written here with the superscript $+$ indicating transpose. Row vectors do not have the $+$.

using the scalar product of (2.2) with

$$z = [a_1 a_2 \ldots a_n]^+$$

and $z \in \mathcal{R}^n$.

Bilinear Operators

The next level of complexity in operators is the bilinear operator, which has a cross-product space domain. A bilinear operator B is a relationship of elements in the domain space $\mathcal{D} \times \mathcal{E}$ to elements in the range space $\mathcal{F}$, that is, for $x \in \mathcal{D}$, $y \in \mathcal{E}$, $B(x, y) \in \mathcal{F}$ (this is as shown in Fig. 2.5) such that

$$B(ax + bw, cy + dz) = acB(x, y) + adB(x, z) + bcB(w, y) + bdB(w, z)$$

$$(2.18)$$

where $x, w \in \mathcal{D}$, $y, z \in \mathcal{E}$, and a, b, c, d are scalar constants. A bilinear operator $B(x, y)$ is linear in x for fixed y and likewise linear in y for fixed x. Stated another way, a bilinear operator is a linear operator on one of its operands while the other is fixed.

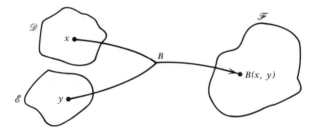

Figure 2.5   The domain and range spaces of a Bilinear operator.

The Norm of a Bilinear Operator

For a bilinear operator, whose domain and range spaces have a norm defined, the definition of the norm of the operator is similar to that of the norm of a linear operator:

$$\|B\| = \sup \|B(x, y)\|_{\mathcal{F}}$$

$$\|x\|_{\mathcal{D}} = 1$$

$$\|y\|_{\mathcal{E}} = 1 \qquad\qquad (2.19)$$

For this choice of norm, the following useful relationship applies:

$$\|B(x, y)\| \leq \|B\| \cdot \|x\| \cdot \|y\| \tag{2.20}$$

$\|B\|$ is the smallest number for which (2.20) holds for arbitrary x and y. A bilinear operator is continuous if $\|B\| < \infty$. In general the bilinear operators considered here involve only Hilbert spaces and have bounded norms and hence are continuous.

The Continuous Bilinear Functional on Hilbert Space

Let us for the moment consider a bilinear operator on $\mathscr{D} \times \mathscr{E}$, where $\mathscr{D}$ and $\mathscr{E}$ are Hilbert spaces, to the range space $\mathscr{R}^1$. This is a straightforward generalization of the linear functional, so let us call it a bilinear functional.

Let us consider such a functional and call it $B. B \cdot (x, y) \in \mathscr{R}^1$ for $x \in \mathscr{D}$ and $y \in \mathscr{E}$. All spaces involved are assumed Hilbert spaces so that a scalar product and corresponding norm exist. For $\|B\|$ bounded and B hence continuous, we have for fixed $x \in \mathscr{D}$

$$B \cdot (x, y) = \langle z, y \rangle_{\mathscr{E}} \tag{2.21}$$

from Theorem 2.1 since B is linear in y. But B is also linear in x for a given y, hence z must be linearly related to x. Thus

$$z = Ax$$

where A is linear operator from $\mathscr{D}$ to $\mathscr{E}$.

Using this in (2.21) we get

$$B \cdot (x, y) = \langle Ax, y \rangle_{\mathscr{E}} \tag{2.22}$$

By the same argument we get

$$B \cdot (x, y) = \langle x, A^*y \rangle_{\mathscr{D}} \tag{2.23}$$

where A^* is the adjoint† operator to A. Using the results of (2.22) and (2.23) we have Theorem 2.2.

Theorem 2.2 A continuous, bilinear functional $B \cdot (x, y)$ with $x \in \mathscr{D}$ and $y \in \mathscr{E}$, $\mathscr{D}$ and $\mathscr{E}$ Hilbert spaces, is of the form

$$B \cdot (x, y) = \langle Ax, y \rangle_{\mathscr{E}} = \langle x, A^*y \rangle_{\mathscr{D}} \tag{2.24}$$

---

† For a linear operator A on one Hilbert space to another, the adjoint operator to A, let us call it A^*, is the operator for which

$$\langle x, Ay \rangle = \langle A^*x, y \rangle$$

for all x and y.

where A and A^* are continuous, linear operators from $\mathscr{D}$ to $\mathscr{E}$ and $\mathscr{E}$ to $\mathscr{D}$, respectively.

A useful relationship that we get by applying Schwarz's inequality to (2.24) is

$$\|B \cdot (x, y)\| = |\langle Ax, y \rangle| \leq \|Ax\| \cdot \|y\|$$

and using the definition of $\|A\|$ we have

$$\|B \cdot (x, y)\| \leq \|A\| \cdot \|x\| \cdot \|y\| \tag{2.25}$$

that is $\|B\| \leq \|A\|$.

Examples of bilinear functionals of interest here are the cases where $\mathscr{D} = \mathscr{R}^m$, $\mathscr{E} = \mathscr{R}^n$, for which

$$B \cdot (x, y) = \sum_{i=1}^{n} y_i \sum_{j=1}^{m} a_{ij} x_j = \langle Ax, y \rangle_{\mathscr{R}_n} \tag{2.26}$$

where A is the $n \times m$ matrix given by

$$A = (a_{ij}) \, i = 1, 2, \ldots, n$$
$$j = 1, 2, \ldots, m$$

A^* in this case is just the transpose of A, that is, A^+. Another frequently appearing example of a bilinear functional is the case where $\mathscr{D} = \mathscr{L}^2_{[a, b]}$ and $\mathscr{E} = \mathscr{L}^2_{[c, d]}$, in which case the functional has the form

$$B \cdot (x, y) = \int_c^d y(t) \left[\int_a^b k(t, s) x(s) \, ds \right] dt = \langle Ax, y \rangle_{\mathscr{E}}$$

$$= \int_a^b x(s) \left[\int_c^d k(t, s) y(t) \, dt \right] ds = \langle x, A^* y \rangle_{\mathscr{D}}$$

where $k(t, s)$ is called the kernel function.

2.3. TANGENCY AND THE DERIVATIVE OF AN OPERATOR

With the structure that has been introduced so far we can define tangency between two operators, and from tangency comes the very important optimization concept of the derivative of an operator.

Let us assume now that we have two operators F and G both from Hilbert space $\mathscr{E}$ to Hilbert space $\mathscr{F}$. Using the norms corresponding to these two spaces, we define tangency.

Tangency

F and G are tangent at $x_0 \in \mathscr{E}$ if

$$\lim_{\substack{x \to x_0 \\ x \neq x_0}} \frac{\|F(x) - G(x)\|}{\|x - x_0\|} = 0 \qquad (2.27)$$

From (2.27) it is obvious that $F(x_0) = G(x_0)$ if F and G are tangent at x_0. The concept of tangency is shown in two dimensions in the case $\mathscr{E} = \mathscr{F} = \mathscr{R}^1$ in Fig. 2.6. It can be seen from the figure that in the case of the two curves F and G, tangency as defined by (2.27) conforms to the ordinary notions of tangency. Here tangency means that $\|F(x) - G(x)\|$ decreases faster than $\|x - x_0\|$ as $x \to x_0$.

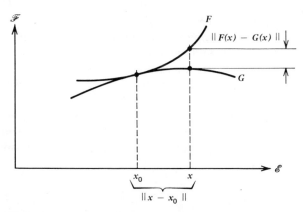

Figure 2.6   Tangency of two operators.

Our interest is in linear operators that are tangent to some generally nonlinear operator. To this end we note that if $F(x)$ is tangent to $H(x)$, and $G(x)$ is tangent to $H(x)$ at some x_0 then $F(x)$ is tangent to $G(x)$ at x_0. To see this we note that

$$\frac{\|F(x) - G(x)\|}{\|x - x_0\|} \leq \frac{\|F(x) - H(x)\| + \|G(x) - H(x)\|}{\|x - x_0\|}$$

If $F(x)$ and $G(x)$ are both tangent to $H(x)$ at x_0, the limit as $x \to x_0$ on the right is zero, as is thus the left-hand side (LHS). Let us consider now two tangent linear operators.

If two linear operators are tangent at some x_0 then the two operators are equivalent.   (2.28)

To see this, we consider tangent linear operators A_1 and A_2. From (2.27)

$$\lim_{x \to x_0} \frac{\|A_1(x - x_0) - A_2(x - x_0)\|}{\|x - x_0\|} = 0$$

$$\lim_{y \to 0} \frac{\|A_1 y - A_2 y\|}{\|y\|} = \lim_{y \to 0} \left\| A_1 \frac{y}{\|y\|} - A_2 \frac{y}{\|y\|} \right\| = 0$$

$$= \|A_1 z - A_2 z\|$$

where $y = x - x_0$ and $z = y/\|y\|$ are arbitrary, and $\|z\| = 1$. Thus $A_1 z = A_2 z$ for arbitrary z and hence $A_1 = A_2$.

Let us consider now a mapping of the form $F(x_0) + A$. That is, a constant plus a linear operator tangent to an operator $F(x)$ at x_0. If such an operator A exists, then F is said to be differentiable at x_0. The operator A is the derivative, written $F'(x_0)$, of the operator F at x_0. We note especially that the derivative of an operator from spaces $\mathscr{E}$ to $\mathscr{F}$ is in turn another operator from $\mathscr{E}$ to $\mathscr{F}$ and not an element of $\mathscr{F}$. The basic concepts here are shown for the case of $\mathscr{E} = \mathscr{F} = \mathscr{R}^1$ in Fig. 2.7. From the figure we note that the derivative of the operator F at x_0, $F'(x_0)$, is the linear operator that

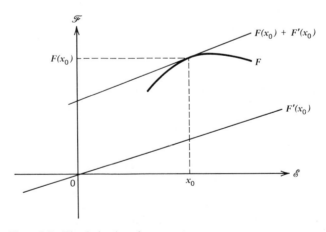

Figure 2.7 The derivative of an operator.

passes through the origin. $F'(x_0)$ is itself not tangent to F at x_0, but $F(x_0)$ + $F'(x_0)\cdot$ is. $F'(x_0)$ is a function of x_0. Thus

If F is differentiable at x_0, the derivative $F'(x_0)$ is the linear operator that satisfies

$$\lim_{x \to x_0} \frac{\|F(x) - F(x_0) - F'(x_0)(x - x_0)\|}{\|x - x_0\|} = 0 \tag{2.29}$$

or equivalently

$$\lim_{t \to 0} \frac{\|F(x_0 + t) - F(x_0) - F'(x_0)t\|}{\|t\|} = 0 \tag{2.30}$$

Let us consider a few basic properties of the derivative of an operator. First we note that $F'(x_0)$ is unique, for if $F(x_0) + F'_1(x_0)\cdot$ and $F(x_0) + F'_2(x_0)\cdot$ are both tangent to F at x_0, they are tangent to each other. From (2.28) they are then equivalent and hence $F'_1(x_0) = F'_2(x_0)$. Secondly, if F is a continuous operator from $\mathscr{E}$ into $\mathscr{F}$, then $F'(x_0)$ is a continuous, linear operator from $\mathscr{E}$ into $\mathscr{F}$. To see this, if F is continuous at x_0 then

$$\|F(x) - F(x_0)\| < \varepsilon \tag{2.31}$$

for $\|x - x_0\| < \delta$. If $F'(x_0)$ is the derivative of F at x_0 then

$$\frac{\|F(x) - F(x_0) - F'(x_1)(x - x_0)\|}{\|x - x_0\|} < \varepsilon$$

for $\|x - x_0\| < \delta$. Thus

$$\|F(x) - F(x_0) - F'(x_0)(x - x_0)\| < \varepsilon \tag{2.32}$$

for $\delta < 1$. From (2.31) and (2.32) we have

$$\|F'(x_0)(x - x_0)\| = \|F'(x_0)x - F'(x_0)x_0\| < 2\varepsilon$$

which means $F'(x_0)$ is continuous.

Summarizing:

Theorem 2.3. If F is continuous and differentiable at x_0 then $F'(x_0)$ is linear, unique, and continuous.

Example 2.1.

The derivative of a constant operator is the null operator. To see this we note that if $F(x) = \zeta$ for all x then

$$\|F(x) - F(x_0)\| = 0 \qquad \forall\, x, x_0$$

Using this in the definition of the derivative in (2.29) we get $F'(x_0) = \mathbf{0}$.

Example 2.2.

The derivative of a continuous linear operator A is the operator A itself. To see this we note that

$$\|Ax - Ax_0 - A(x - x_0)\| = 0 \qquad \forall x, x_0$$

if A is linear. Thus $F(x) = Ax$ implies $F'(x) = A \qquad \forall x$.

Example 2.3.

The derivative of a continuous bilinear operator B from domain space $\mathscr{D} \times \mathscr{E}$ to $\mathscr{F}$ at (x_0, y_0) in $\mathscr{D} \times \mathscr{E}$ is the linear operator $B(x_0, \cdot) + B(\cdot, y_0)$. Here we note that $B(x_0 + s, y_0 + t) - B(x_0, y_0) - B(x_0, t) - B(s, y_0) = B(s, t)$ for all (x_0, y_0) and (s, t) in $\mathscr{D} \times \mathscr{E}$. Thus

$$\lim_{(s,t) \to 0} \frac{\|B(x_0 + s, y_0 + t) - B(x_0, y_0) - B(x_0, t) - B(s, y_0)\|}{\|s, t)\|}$$

$$= \frac{\|B(s, t)\|}{\|(s, t)\|} \leq \frac{\|B\| \cdot \|s\| \cdot \|t\|}{\|(s, t)\|}$$

$$= \frac{\|B\| \cdot \|s\| \cdot \|t\|}{\sqrt{\|s\|^2 + \|t\|^2}}$$

But

$$\lim_{\substack{\|s\| \to 0 \\ \|t\| \to 0}} \frac{\|s\| \cdot \|t\|}{\sqrt{\|s\|^2 + \|t\|^2}} = 0$$

$$\lim_{(s,t) \to 0} \frac{\|B(x_0 + s, y_0 + t) - B(x_0, y_0) - B(x_0, t) - B(s, y_0)\|}{\|(s, t)\|} = 0$$

and thus

$$B'(x_0, y_0) \cdot (s, t) = B(x_0, t) + B(s, y_0)$$

The case of special interest here is a functional F from domain space $\mathscr{E}$, a Hilbert space, to range space $\mathscr{R}^1$. In this special case $F'(x_0)$ is a linear functional and for $z \in \mathscr{E}$, according to Theorem 2.1

$$F'(x_0)z = \langle g(x_0), z \rangle \tag{2.33}$$

Here $g(x_0) \in \mathscr{E}$ is called the *gradient* of the functional F at x_0. The main application of the derivative theory developed here is to find the gradient of a cost functional for a control system. This is discussed in Chapter 4. As a more explicit example of finding the derivative of a functional let us consider

$$F(x) = \langle x, Ax \rangle \qquad (2.34)$$

where $x \in \mathscr{E}$, a Hilbert space, and A is a continuous linear operator from $\mathscr{E}$ and into $\mathscr{E}$. Considering the right-hand side (RHS) of (2.34) as a bilinear operator from $\mathscr{E} \times \mathscr{E}$ into $\mathscr{R}^1$, we may apply the result of Example 2.3 to get

$$F'(x) \cdot = \langle \cdot, Ax \rangle + \langle x, A \cdot \rangle \qquad (2.35)$$

where the $\cdot$ indicates where the argument of the operator is to go. The operator of (2.35) operating on $z \in \mathscr{E}$ gives

$$\begin{aligned} F'(x)z &= \langle z, Ax \rangle + \langle x, Az \rangle \\ &= \langle z, Ax \rangle + \langle A^*x, z \rangle \\ &= \langle Ax + A^*x, z \rangle \end{aligned} \qquad (2.36)$$

where A^* is the adjoint of A. Comparison of (2.36) with (2.33) gives the gradient of the functional of (2.34) as

$$g(x) = (A + A^*)x \qquad (2.37)$$

2.4. THE DERIVATIVE OF A COMPOSITE OPERATOR AND THE SECOND DERIVATIVE OF AN OPERATOR

A very important tool in the consideration of optimization is the notion of the composite operator. A composite operator is really two operators in tandem. We consider an operator F from $\mathscr{E}$ to $\mathscr{F}$ and another operator G from $\mathscr{F}$ to $\mathscr{G}$. This is shown in Fig. 2.8.

The composite operator is the operator from $\mathscr{E}$ to $\mathscr{G}$ which, incidentally, goes through the space $\mathscr{F}$. The composite operator shown in Fig. 2.4b operating on $x \in \mathscr{E}$ is written as $G(F(x))$. This is also written as $GF(x)$, or simply GF when we speak of the operator itself. We assume that all spaces involved are Hilbert spaces and that hence norms are defined for all spaces. Also, F is differentiable w.r.t.† $x \in \mathscr{E}$ and G is differentiable w.r.t. $y \in \mathscr{F}$. The question we seek to answer is: *What is the derivative of the composite operator GF w.r.t. $x \in \mathscr{E}$?*

The Operator $o(\cdot)$

Before getting into a discussion of the derivative of a composite operator, let us introduce a tool to aid in this discussion. This is the operator $o(\cdot)$,

† w.r.t. = with respect to.

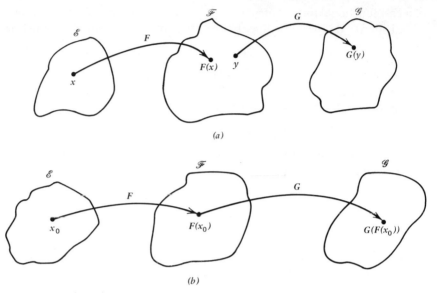

Figure 2.8 (*a*) Two operators F and G from $\mathscr{E}$ to $\mathscr{F}$ and $\mathscr{F}$ to $\mathscr{G}$. (*b*) A composite operator $G(F(x))$.

which is an operator from $\mathscr{E}$ to $\mathscr{F}$ with the property that for $t \in \mathscr{E}$

$$\lim_{t \to 0} \frac{\|o(t)\|}{\|t\|} = 0 \tag{2.38}$$

or equivalently

$$\|o(t)\| < \varepsilon \|t\| \tag{2.39}$$

for $\|t\| < \delta$. This property defines $o(\cdot)$.

An Expansion of an Operator Using $o(\cdot)$

From the definition of the derivative as given in (2.30) and from the definition of $o(\cdot)$, it may be seen that if an operator F is differentiable at x_0 then it may be expanded about x_0 as

$$F(x_0 + t) = F(x_0) + F'(x_0)t + o(t) \tag{2.40}$$

This is a standard Taylor series expansion of the operator F about x_0 and here $o(t)$ is all the terms in the expansion above first order in t. Equation

2.40 is one very practical application of the derivative theory developed here for it shows how to construct a first-order linear approximation to a generally nonlinear operator. Here $F(x_0) + F'(x_0) \cdot t$ is tangent to F at x_0; it is an approximation with error $o(t)$ valid in some neighborhood of x_0.

The Derivative of a Composite Operator

Now let us consider the composite operator GF shown in Fig. 2.8. We assume that $G'(y_0)$, $y_0 \in \mathscr{F}$, and $F'(x_0)$, $x_0 \in \mathscr{E}$ exist. F and G may both be expanded as in (2.40) to get

$$F(x_0 + t) = F(x_0) + F'(x_0)t + o_1(t)$$
$$G(y_0 + s) = G(y_0) + G'(y_0)s + o_2(s) \qquad (2.41)$$

Here the subscripts 1 and 2 have been added to the $o(\cdot)$ operator to show that they are not the same. We now let $y_0 = F(x_0)$ and $s = F'(x_0)t + o_1(t)$ in the expansion of G in (2.41). Thus

$$G(F(x_0 + t)) = GF(x_0 + t) = G(F(x_0)) + G'(F(x_0))F'(x_0)t$$
$$+ G'(F(x_0))o_1(t) + o_2(F'(x_0)t + o_1(t))$$

and therefore

$$\frac{\|GF(x_0 + t) - GF(x_0) - G'(F(x_0))F'(x_0)t\|}{\|t\|}$$

$$= \frac{\|G'(F(x_0))o_1(t) + o_2(F'(x_0)t + o_1(t))\|}{\|t\|}$$

$$\leq \frac{\|G'(F(x_0))\| \, \|o_1(t)\|}{\|t\|} + \frac{\|o_2(F'(x_0)t + o_1(t))\|}{\|t\|}$$

The limit on the RHS is zero as $\|t\| \to 0$ if $\|F'(x_0)\|$ and $\|G'(F(x_0))\|$ are bounded (which is true if F' and G' are continuous) by the definition of the $o(\cdot)$ operator, (2.38). Hence by the definition of derivative of (2.30) the derivative of GF at x_0 is

$$(GF(x_0))' = G'(F(x_0))F'(x_0) \qquad (2.42)$$

This is the result desired and a familiar one from the standard calculus, for it is known that in general for a function of one variable

$$\frac{d}{dx}(f(g(x))) = f'(g(x)) \cdot g'(x)$$

Equation 2.42 gives this result for operators on more general spaces.

Example 2.4.

A frequent application of (2.42) is to find

$$\frac{d}{d\zeta} G(x_0 + \zeta t)$$

where x_0 and t are in $\mathscr{F}$, a Hilbert space, and ζ is in $\mathscr{R}^1$. This is the case in Fig. 2.8 where $\mathscr{E} = \mathscr{R}^1$, $G = G$ and $F(\zeta) = x_0 + \zeta t$, $x_0, t \in \mathscr{F}$. Thus

$$F'(\zeta) = t$$

by application of the result of Examples 2.1 and 2.2. Thus use of (2.42) gives

$$\frac{d}{d\zeta} G(x_0 + \zeta t) = G'(x_0 + \zeta t)t \tag{2.43}$$

Equation 2.42 may be extended straightforwardly to the case of composite operators that go through more than one intermediate space, such as

$$(GFH(x_0))' = G'(FH(x_0))F'(H(x_0))H'(x_0) \tag{2.44}$$

for example.

The Second Derivative of an Operator

Higher derivatives of operators can be defined, as they are in the standard calculus for functions of one variable by repeated application of the rules obtained for first order differentiation. Here no derivatives higher than the second order are dealt with, so we restrict our considerations to this case.

Let us assume we have an operator F on a Hilbert space $\mathscr{E}$ to another Hilbert space $\mathscr{F}$ that is differentiable in some neighborhood of a given $x_0 \in \mathscr{E}$. We can find the second derivative by applying (2.30) to F' in the neighborhood of x_0 to get

$$\lim_{t \to 0} \frac{\|F'(x_0 + t) - F'(x_0) - F''(x_0)t\|}{\|t\|} = 0 \tag{2.45}$$

If $F''(x_0)$ is a linear operator that satisfies (2.45), then it is the second derivative of F at x_0.

It should be noted in (2.45) that $F'(x_0 + t)$, $F'(x_0)$ and hence $F''(x_0)t$ are all linear operators from $\mathscr{E}$ to $\mathscr{F}$ if the operator F is from $\mathscr{E}$ to $\mathscr{F}$. $F''(x_0)$ is in fact a bilinear operator from $\mathscr{E} \times \mathscr{E}$ to $\mathscr{F}$ (Fig. 2.9).

An example, and the one of real interest here, is the case of a functional from a Hilbert space $\mathscr{E}$ to $\mathscr{R}^1$ of the form

$$F(x) = \langle x, Ax \rangle \tag{2.46}$$

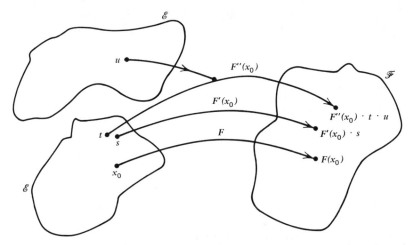

Figure 2.9 The domains and range of an operator and the first and second derivatives of an operator.

where A is a linear operator from $\mathcal{E}$ to $\mathcal{E}$. For $x = x_0$ we have found from (2.36) that

$$F'(x_0)\cdot = \langle Ax_0 + A^*x_0, \cdot \rangle \qquad (2.47)$$

Now to find the second derivation of F at x_0 we need only again take the derivative on the RHS, from Example 2.2.

$$F''(x_0) = \langle (A + A^*)\cdot, \cdot \rangle \qquad (2.48)$$

Equation 2.48 shows that $F''(x_0)$ is indeed a bilinear operator in this case for it is the standard form of a bilinear functional from $\mathcal{E} \times \mathcal{E}$ to $\mathcal{R}^1$. From (2.48) we have that $F''(x_0)$ operating upon an element (s, t) from $\mathcal{E} \times \mathcal{E}$ is then

$$F''(x_0)(s,t) = \langle (A + A^*)s, t \rangle$$
$$= \langle As, t \rangle + \langle s, At \rangle \qquad (2.49)$$

Equation 2.49 illustrates that the second derivative operator is symmetric in s and t. This is a general characteristic of second derivative operators. We have in fact the following theorem.

Theorem 2.4. If F is twice differentiable at x_0, then the bilinear mapping $(s, t) \rightarrow F''(x_0)(s, t)$ is symmetric,

$$F''(x_0)(s, t) = F''(x_0)(t, s) \qquad \forall \, s, t \qquad (2.50)$$

The proof of this theorem is omitted even though it does play a part in the development to follow. The proof is somewhat involved and does not reveal more than the fact that the second derivative is symmetric. The reader is referred to [1] for the proof of Theorem 2.4 (it is Theorem 8.12.2 in this reference).

We now turn to the use of the first and second derivative of an operator in the expansion of such an operator.

2.5. THE TAYLOR SERIES, EXPANSION OF A FUNCTIONAL

The functionals considered in the optimization problems here are assumed smooth enough to permit expansion into series. Let us consider this expansion in more detail.

To begin, we consider a function $g(\cdot)$ from $\mathcal{R}^1$ to $\mathcal{R}^1$. For $\zeta \in \mathcal{R}^1$ if $g(\cdot)$ is a p times differentiable function in an open interval containing the origin and ζ, then†

$$g(\zeta) = g(0) + \zeta g'(0) + \frac{\zeta^2}{2!} g''(0) + \cdots + \frac{\zeta^{p-1}}{(p-1)!} g^{(p-1)}(0)$$

$$+ \int_0^\zeta \frac{(\zeta - \tau)^{p-1}}{(p-1)!} g^{(p)}(\tau) \, d\tau \qquad (2.51)$$

Equation 2.51 is a simple Taylor (Maclaurin) series expansion of $g(\cdot)$ about the origin. To use this to find the expansion of a functional from Hilbert space $\mathcal{E}$ to $\mathcal{R}^1$ we consider the Taylor series expansion of

$$g(\zeta) = F(x_0 + \zeta t) \qquad (2.52)$$

where x_0 and $t \in \mathcal{E}$. $F(x_0 + \zeta t)$ is a composite operator, the linear operator $\zeta \to x_0 + \zeta t$ from $\mathcal{R}^1$ to $\mathcal{E}$, and the operator F from $\mathcal{E}$ to $\mathcal{R}^1$. Using (2.42) to evaluate the derivatives here, we obtain

$$\frac{d}{d\zeta} g(\zeta) = \frac{d}{d\zeta} F(x_0 + \zeta t) = F'(x_0 + \zeta t)t$$

$$\frac{d^2}{d\zeta^2} g(\zeta) = \frac{d}{d\zeta} F'(x_0 + \zeta t)t = F''(x_0 + \zeta t)t \cdot t \qquad (2.53)$$

$$\frac{d^3}{d\zeta^3} g(\zeta) = \frac{d}{d\zeta} F''(x_0 + \zeta t)t \cdot t = F'''(x_0 + \zeta t)t \cdot t \cdot t$$

† See Theorem 8.14.2 of [1].

Using (2.53) in (2.51) and terminating the series at $p = 3$ and evaluating at $\zeta = 1$ we get

$$F(x_0 + t) = F(x_0) + F'(x_0)t + \tfrac{1}{2}F''(x_0)t \cdot t + \int_0^1 \frac{(1 - \tau)^2}{2} F'''(x_0 + \tau t)t \cdot t \cdot t \, d\tau$$

$$= F(x_0) + F'(x_0)t + \tfrac{1}{2}F''(x_0)t \cdot t + o^2(t) \qquad (2.55)$$

where $o^2(t)$ is a functional in t that satisfies

$$\lim_{t \to 0} \frac{\|o^2(t)\|}{\|t\|^2} = 0 \qquad (2.56)$$

Equation 2.55 is the desired result. It is a second order Taylor expansion of a functional F from a Hilbert space $\mathscr{E}$ to $\mathscr{R}^1$ about an $x_0 \in \mathscr{E}$. Of course to be valid the derivatives involved must exist at all $x_0 + \zeta t$, $0 \leq \zeta \leq 1$, that is, along the straight line joining x_0 and $x_0 + t$.

We may now make use of the fact that $F'(x_0)$ and $F''(x_0)$ are linear and bilinear functionals, respectively. Using Theorems 2.1 and 2.2 on these two operators, we may write (2.55) in the form

$$F(x_0 + t) = F(x_0) + \langle g(x_0), t \rangle + \tfrac{1}{2}\langle t, A(x_0)t \rangle + o^2(t) \qquad (2.57)$$

where now $g(x_0) \in \mathscr{E}$ is the gradient of the functional F at x_0 and $A(x_0)$ is a linear operator from $\mathscr{E}$ to $\mathscr{E}$, which is often simply called the second derivative of x_0. Equation 2.57 is the form of the expansion of a functional used in subsequent development.

An obvious example of an expansion of a functional in the form of (2.57) is the case where $\mathscr{E} = \mathscr{R}^n$ and $F = \phi(\cdot)$ is a scalar-valued function on $\mathscr{R}^n$. If we let $x = [x_1, x_2, \ldots, x_n]^+$, $t = [t_1, t_2, \ldots, t_n]^+$, a straightforward Taylor series expansion about x_0 as usually done gives

$$\phi(x_0 + t) = \phi(x_0) + \sum_{i=1}^n t_i \frac{\partial \phi(x_0)}{\partial x_i} + \frac{1}{2} \sum_{i=1}^n \sum_{j=1}^n \frac{\partial^2 \phi(x_0)}{\partial x_i \, \partial x_j} t_i t_j + o^2(t) \quad (2.58)$$

Recalling $\mathscr{E} = \mathscr{R}^n$ we obtain the scalar product

$$\langle x, y \rangle = \sum_{i=1}^n x_i y_i$$

Then (2.58) can be written as

$$\phi(x_0 + t) = \phi(x_0) + \langle g(x_0), t \rangle + \tfrac{1}{2}\langle t, A(x_0)t \rangle + o^2(t) \qquad (2.59)$$

where now the gradient $g(x_0)$ and the second derivative operator $A(x_0)$ can be identified by comparing (2.58) and (2.59).

2.6. THE MINIMUM OF A FUNCTIONAL

The functionals of interest here are assumed to be expandable into a Taylor series of the form (2.57). For $\|t\|$ small, the terms up to and including second order dominate and hence a general functional can be approximated by one of this form. Therefore let us consider this form of quadratic functional in more detail. Specifically we consider the extrema of quadratic functionals of the form

$$F(x) = F_0 + \langle a, x \rangle + \tfrac{1}{2}\langle x, Ax \rangle \qquad (2.60)$$

where now $x, a, Ax \in \mathscr{E}$, a Hilbert space. Since the functional of interest is assumed to be a truncation of a Taylor series let us assume that the operator A is symmetric, that is

$$\langle x, Ay \rangle = \langle Ax, y \rangle \qquad (2.61)$$

This is the case of interest here since we know that $\langle x, Ax \rangle$ term in the series of (2.60) is the second derivative contribution to the Taylor series and by Theorem 2.4, the second derivative is a symmetric operator.

As in the classical extrema problem of the calculus, we consider where the gradient is null to find the extremum. The gradient of F of (2.60) is found by application of the differentiation rules as developed in Examples 2.1, 2.2, and 2.3 to get

$$F'(x) = 0 + \langle a, \cdot \rangle + \tfrac{1}{2}\langle \cdot, Ax \rangle + \tfrac{1}{2}\langle x, A\cdot \rangle$$
$$= \langle a + Ax, \cdot \rangle \qquad (2.62)$$

where the dot on the RHS indicates the position of the argument of the functional. The gradient of the functional F of (2.60) is hence

$$g(x) = a + Ax \qquad (2.63)$$

We consider x^* such that

$$Ax^* = -a \qquad (2.64)$$

and assume for the moment that such an x^* exists. Obviously for such an x^* the gradient is null. If F of (2.60) has an extremum, that is where it is going to be.

We evaluate

$$F(x^*) = F_0 + \langle a, x^* \rangle + \tfrac{1}{2}\langle x^*, Ax^* \rangle$$
$$= F_0 + \tfrac{1}{2}\langle a, x^* \rangle \qquad (2.65)$$

using (2.64). Now let us consider a perturbation about x^* of the form $(x^* + z) \in \mathscr{E}$. For this element

$$
\begin{aligned}
F(x^* + z) &= F_0 + \langle a, x^* + z \rangle + \tfrac{1}{2} \langle x^* + z, A(x^* + z) \rangle \\
&= F_0 + \langle a, x^* \rangle + \langle a, z \rangle + \tfrac{1}{2} \langle x^*, Ax^* \rangle + \tfrac{1}{2} \langle x^*, Az \rangle \\
&\quad + \tfrac{1}{2} \langle z, Ax^* \rangle + \tfrac{1}{2} \langle z, Az \rangle \\
&= F_0 + \tfrac{1}{2} \langle a, x^* \rangle + \tfrac{1}{2} \langle z, Az \rangle
\end{aligned}
\tag{2.66}
$$

from (2.64) and the fact that $\langle z, Ax^* \rangle = \langle Az, x^* \rangle$ since A is symmetric. From (2.65) and (2.66)

$$
F(x^* + z) = F(x^*) + \tfrac{1}{2} \langle z, Az \rangle
\tag{2.67}
$$

From (2.67) we draw the following conclusions about the functional F of (2.60).

1. If the linear operator A is positive definite, that is,

$$
\langle z, Az \rangle > 0 \qquad \forall \, z,
$$

then x^* is a minimum† of F.

2. If A is positive semidefinite, that is,

$$
\langle z, Az \rangle \geq 0 \qquad \forall \, z,
$$

then x^* is a minimum for F but it is not necessarily unique. In fact, for any z for which $\langle z, Az \rangle = 0$, $x^* + z$ is also a minimum.

3. If A is indefinite then x^* does not minimize F.

Similar statements can be made regarding maximizing arguments of F for the case where A is negative definite, negative semidefinite, or indefinite.

We now note from Appendix A that if an operator is positive definite, then it has an inverse, from which we conclude that (2.64) has a solution and x^* does exist. Hence we can state the following theorem.

Theorem 2.5. If for the functional F of (2.60) the operator A is positive definite then a minimum x^* exists, is unique and is given by

$$
x^* = -A^{-1}a
\tag{2.68}
$$

The Minima of Three Times Differentiable Functionals

Now let us turn our attention to functionals that are three times differentiable and hence expandable into a Taylor series of the form of (2.55) and (2.57). For these functionals the quadratic part of the expansion dominates for

† A minimizing argument of a functional is called a minimum.

$\|t\|$ small enough. Let us consider specifically the case of an expansion about an argument x_0^* for which $F'(x_0^*)$ is the null operator, that is,

$$F'(x_0^*) = 0 \tag{2.69}$$

Applying Theorem 2.5 gives us a new theorem.

Theorem 2.6. If at x_0^*, F is a three times differentiable functional from Hilbert space $\mathscr{E}$ to $\mathscr{R}^1$ and $F'(x_0^*) = 0$ and $F''(x_0^*)$ is a positive definite operator then x_0^* is a unique, relative minimum of F.

The minimum is only a relative minimum for the general functional considered here since the Taylor series expansion, and hence the conclusions drawn from its use, are only valid in a small neighborhood of x_0^*.

It is possible to draw slightly more from the derivation of Theorem 2.5, for if the second derivative at x_0^* is indefinite, then by conclusion 3 under (2.67) we can see that a minimum does not exist.

Corollary to Theorem 2.6. If $F''(x_0^*)$ is an indefinite operator then x_0^* is not a minimum of F.

As a further comment, if $F''(x_0^*)$ is only positive semidefinite, that is,

$$F''(x_0^*) t \cdot t = \langle t, A(x_0)t \rangle \geq 0$$

we can draw no conclusions about x_0^*, because the higher order terms in the series expansion dominate for those t where

$$F''(x_0^*) t \cdot t = 0$$

Thus the higher order terms must be investigated to determine whether x_0^* is or is not a minimum. $F''(x_0^*)$ positive semidefinite means that x_0^* may be a minimum but not a unique minimum, or it may not be a minimum at all.

Example 2.5.

As a simple example of the use of Theorems 2.5 and 2.6, let us consider the functional

$$F(x) = \tfrac{3}{2}x_1 + \tfrac{3}{2}x_2 + \tfrac{1}{2}(x_1^2 + x_1 x_2 + x_2^2) \tag{2.70}$$

where now $x = [x_1, x_2]^+ \in \mathscr{R}^2$. This may be put into the form

$$F(x) = \begin{bmatrix} \tfrac{3}{2} & \tfrac{3}{2} \end{bmatrix} \begin{bmatrix} x_1 \\ x_2 \end{bmatrix} + \tfrac{1}{2}[x_1 \quad x_2] \begin{bmatrix} 1 & \tfrac{1}{2} \\ \tfrac{1}{2} & 1 \end{bmatrix} \begin{bmatrix} x_1 \\ x_2 \end{bmatrix}$$

$$= \langle a, x \rangle + \tfrac{1}{2}\langle x, Ax \rangle$$

which is the form of (2.60). The minimum, if there is a minimum, is given by (2.68) as

$$x^* = -A^{-1}a = -\begin{bmatrix} 1 & \frac{1}{2} \\ \frac{1}{2} & 1 \end{bmatrix}^{-1}\begin{bmatrix} \frac{3}{2} \\ \frac{3}{2} \end{bmatrix} = -\begin{bmatrix} 1 \\ 1 \end{bmatrix} \qquad (2.71)$$

x^* is the minimum if the matrix

$$A = \begin{bmatrix} 1 & \frac{1}{2} \\ \frac{1}{2} & 1 \end{bmatrix}$$

is positive definite. Application of Sylvester's criterion shows that it is. Therefore x^* of (2.71) is the unique minimum of F of (2.70).

Example 2.6.

Let us consider the system of Fig. 2.10. The input to the system of interest is the function $u(t)$, which is assumed an element of $\mathscr{L}^2_{[0,\,\infty)}$, and thus square integrable over the interval $[0, \infty)$. $u(t) = 0$ is assumed for $t < 0$. $u(t)$ is fed into a linear, time invariant system which is assumed causal, with impulse

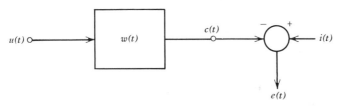

Figure 2.10   System block diagram for Example 2.6.

response $w(t)$. Hence $w(t) = 0$ for $t < 0$ also. The output of the system here is $c(t)$, which, since the system is linear and time invariant, is simply the convolution integral of u and w, that is,

$$c(t) = \int_0^t u(\tau)w(t - \tau)\, d\tau = \int_0^t w(\tau)u(t - \tau)\, d\tau \qquad (2.72)$$

The output $c(t)$ is subtracted from the function $i(t)$, which is the ideal value of the output, to produce the error signal $e(t)$. It is assumed that $i \in \mathscr{L}^2_{[0,\,\infty)}$ also, that is,

$$\int_0^\infty i^2(t)\, dt < \infty$$

We now consider the following problem:

**Find $w(t)$, the impulse response of a real, causal system,
that minimizes integral square error**

$$\int_0^\infty e^2(t)\, dt$$

Integral square error (ISE) defines here a functional on the space of impulse responses of linear, time invariant, causal systems. Since the systems of interest are assumed causal, if $w(t)$ is an impulse response then

$$w(t) = 0 \qquad t < 0 \tag{2.73}$$

However $w(t)$ may or may not be square integrable over $[0, \infty)$, so it may or may not be in $\mathscr{L}^2_{[0,\,\infty)}$.

From Fig. 2.10 and (2.72) we have

$$e(t) = i(t) - c(t)$$

$$= i(t) - \int_0^t w(\tau)u(t - \tau)\, d\tau$$

$$= i(t) - \int_0^\infty w(\tau)u(t - \tau)\, d\tau \tag{2.74}$$

where the integral has been extended to ∞. This is possible since $u(t - \tau) = 0$ for $\tau > t$. Using (2.74), we obtain

$$\text{ISE} = \int_0^\infty e^2(t)\, dt$$

$$= \int_0^\infty \left[i(t) - \int_0^\infty w(\tau)u(t - \tau)\, d\tau \right]^2 dt$$

$$\text{ISE} = \int_0^\infty i^2(t)\, dt - \int_0^\infty 2i(t) \int_0^\infty w(\tau)u(t - \tau)\, d\tau\, dt$$

$$+ \int_0^\infty \int_0^\infty w(\tau)u(t - \tau)\, dt \int_0^\infty w(\tau)u(t - \theta)\, d\theta\, d\tau \tag{2.75}$$

Changing the order of integration and after some minor manipulations (2.75) becomes

$$\frac{1}{2}\,\text{ISE} = \frac{1}{2} \int_0^\infty i^2(t)\, dt - \int_0^\infty w(\tau) \int_0^\infty i(t)u(t - \tau)\, dt\, d\tau$$

$$+ \frac{1}{2} \int_0^\infty w(\tau)\left[\int_0^\infty \int_0^\infty u(t - \tau)u(t - \theta)w(\theta)\, d\theta\, dt \right] d\tau \tag{2.76}$$

Recalling now that the scalar product of two elements x, $y \in \mathscr{L}^2_{[0, \infty)}$ is given by

$$\langle x, y \rangle = \int_0^\infty x(t)y(t) \, dt \tag{2.77}$$

we see that (2.76) is of the form

$$F(w) = F_0 + \langle a, w \rangle + \tfrac{1}{2}\langle w, Aw \rangle \tag{2.78}$$

that is, the form of (2.60). Here $a \in \mathscr{L}^2_{[0, \infty)}$ is

$$a(\tau) = -\int_0^\infty i(t)u(t - \tau) \, d\tau \tag{2.79}$$

and the operator A is given by

$$A \cdot = \int_0^\infty \int_0^\infty u(t - \tau)u(t - \theta) \cdot \, d\theta \, dt \tag{2.80}$$

where the dot indicates the position of the argument. Theorem 2.5 applies here if it can be shown that the operator A is positive definite. By comparing (2.76) and (2.78), we note that

$$\langle w, Aw \rangle = \int_0^\infty \int_0^\infty w(\tau)u(t - \tau) \, d\tau \int_0^\infty w(\theta)u(t - \theta) \, d\theta \, dt$$

$$= \int_0^\infty \left[\int_0^\infty w(\tau)u(t - \tau) \, d\tau \right]^2 dt$$

and therefore

$$\langle w, Aw \rangle > 0$$

for $w \neq 0$, $u \neq 0$. We assume $u \neq 0$ in order to have a nontrivial problem and hence conclude that the operator A is positive definite. Theorem 2.5 hence applies and we arrive at the following conclusions:

1. Aw^*, which produces minimum ISE for the system of Fig. 2.10, exists in $\mathscr{L}^2_{[0, \infty)}$ for $u(t) \neq 0$.
2. $w^* = -A^{-1}a$ where A is the operator given in (2.80) and $a \in \mathscr{L}^2_{[0, \infty)}$ as given by (2.78).

Since A is positive definite we also know from Theorem A.1, Appendix A, that A^{-1} exists.

To complete the problem, that is, find w^*, we need to determine A^{-1}, however this is beyond the scope of this text. Since finding the ISE minimizing impulse response is a popular problem, many solutions exist. See, for example, [7].

PROBLEMS

1. Consider the constant operator $T(x) = \zeta, \zeta \neq 0, \forall x \in \mathscr{E}$; show that T is not a linear operator.

2. In $\mathscr{R}^2$, $\|x\|_p = (|x_1|^p + |x_2|^p)^{1/p}$. In the (x_1, x_2)-plane show the unit sphere $\|x\|_p \leq 1$ for $p = 1$, $p = 2$, and $p \to \infty$.

3. Show that the null operator is linear. (It is thus the only linear, constant operator.)

4. Show that a linear operator A is continuous if $\|A\| < \infty$, that is, if A is bounded.

5. Show Schwarz's inequality
$$|\langle x, y \rangle| \leq \|x\| \|y\|, \quad \|x\| = \sqrt{\langle x, y \rangle}$$
holds for all $x, y \in \mathscr{H}$.

6. Prove the triangle inequality on Hilbert space given by (2.6).

7. Show that the triangle and Schwarz's inequalities hold for the following:
   (a) $x, y \in \mathscr{R}^2$, $x = [1 \quad 2]^+$, $y = [-1 \quad 1]^+$
   (b) $x, y \in \mathscr{C}_{[0, \infty)}$, $x(t) = e^{-t}$, $y(t) = e^{-2t}$,
   (c) $x, y \in \mathscr{C}_{[0, 2\pi]}$, $x(t) = \cos(t)$, $y(t) = \sin(t)$.

8. Give the y values that satisfy the triangle and Schwarz's inequalities with equality for the three x's in problem 7.

9. Let F be a differentiable operator on $\mathscr{E} \to \mathscr{R}^1$. Show that $F'(x_0)$ is continuous at x_0 if and only if the gradient of F is continuous at x_0.

10. Show that if F is differentiable at x_0 then $F(x)$ is continuous at x_0.

11. Find the following quantities:

   (a) $\dfrac{d}{d\zeta} A \cdot (x_0 + \zeta t)$, where A is a linear operator on $\mathscr{E} \to \mathscr{F}, x_0, t \in \mathscr{E}$, $\zeta \in \mathscr{R}^1$.

   (b) $\dfrac{d}{d\zeta} \langle x_0 + \zeta t, A \cdot (x_0 + \zeta t) \rangle$, where A is a linear operator on $\mathscr{E} \to x_0$, $t \in \mathscr{E}, \zeta \in \mathscr{R}^1$,

   (c) $\dfrac{d}{d\zeta} B \cdot (x_0 + \zeta t, y_0 + \zeta s)$ where B is a linear operator on $\mathscr{E} \times \mathscr{F} \to \mathscr{G}$, $x_0, t \in \mathscr{E}, y_0, s \in \mathscr{F}, \zeta \in \mathscr{R}^1$.

12. Let F be a differentiable transformation from $\mathscr{R}^n$ to $\mathscr{R}^m$. Let $(e_1, e_2, \ldots, e_n)$ be a basis for $\mathscr{R}^n$ such that

$$e_1 = [1, 0, \ldots, 0]^+$$
$$e_2 = [0, 1, \ldots, 0]^+$$

Show that

$$F'(x_0)y = \begin{bmatrix} \dfrac{\partial F_1(x_0)}{\partial x_1} & \cdots & \dfrac{\partial F_1(x_0)}{\partial x_n} \\ \vdots & & \vdots \\ \dfrac{\partial F_m(x_0)}{\partial x_1} & \cdots & \dfrac{\partial F_m(x_0)}{\partial x_n} \end{bmatrix} \begin{bmatrix} y_1 \\ y_2 \\ \vdots \\ y_n \end{bmatrix}$$

13. Show the general form of a second order expansion of a functional on $\mathscr{L}^2_{[a, b]}$ about $x_{0[a, b]}$. Here the scalar product is of the form

$$\langle x, y \rangle = \int_a^b x(t)y(t)\, dt$$

14. Find $x^* \in \mathscr{R}^3$ that minimizes

$$F(x) = 1 + x_1 + x_2 + x_3 + x_1^2 + 2x_2^2 + 4x_3^2 - 2x_1x_2$$

verify that the obtained x^* is truly the minimum value.

15. Given the function on $[0, 4]$

$$f_n(x) = n^5x - n \qquad \frac{1}{n^4} \le x \le \frac{2}{n^4}$$

$$f_n(x) = -n^5x + 3n \qquad \frac{2}{n^4} \le x \le \frac{3}{n^4}$$

$$= 0 \qquad \text{everywhere else in } [0, 4].$$

(a) Find $\| f_n(x) \|_2 = \left(\displaystyle\int_0^4 (f_n(x))^2 \, dx \right)^{1/2}$.

(b) Find $\| f_n(x) \|_\infty = \displaystyle\max_{x \in [0, 4]} |f_n(x)|$.

(c) Find $\displaystyle\lim_{n \to \infty} \| f_n(x) \|_2$.

(d) Find $\displaystyle\lim_{n \to \infty} \| f_n(x) \|_\infty$.

REFERENCES

[1]   Dieudonné, J., *Foundations of Modern Analysis*, Chapters I–VII, Academic Press, 1962.

[2]   Collatz, L., *Functional Analysis and Numerical Mathematics*, Chapter 1, Academic Press, 1966.

[3]   *Survey of Applicable Mathematics*, Chapter 22, V. Rektorys, ed., Massachussetts Institute of Technology Press, 1969.

[4]   Friedman, B., *Principles and Techniques of Applied Mathematics*, Wiley, 1956.

[5]   Desoer, C. A., Lecture in Department of Electrical Engineering, University of California, Berkeley, August 17, 1963.

[6]   Halmos, P. R., *Introduction to Hilbert Space*, 2nd ed., Chelsea, 1957.

[7]   Newton, G. C., Jr., L. A. Gould, and J. F. Kaiser, *Analytical Design of Linear Feedback Controls*, Chapter 5, Wiley, 1957.

[8]   Frechét, M., "La Notion de Différentielle dans l'Analyse Générale," *Ann. Ecole Norm. Super*, Ser. 3, **42**, 1925.

[9]   Gateaux, R., "Sur les Fonctionelles Continues et les Fonctionelles Analytiques," *Bull. Soc. Math. France*, **50**, 1–21, 1922.

[10] Luenberger, D. G., *Optimization by Vector Space Methods*, Wiley, 1969.

[11] Tapiz, R. A., "The Differentiation and Integration of Nonlinear Operators," in *Nonlinear Functional Analysis and Applications*, L. B. Rall, ed., Academic Press, 1971.

Chapter 3

Conjugate Gradient Descent

3.1. INTRODUCTION

In the previous chapters we have considered the general problem of optimization of a functional on a Hilbert space. The required mathematical tools
have been introduced and a few restrictions have been placed on the type of
the functional that is to be considered. And finally, conditions required for
these functionals to have minima have been discussed. There has *not* been
any consideration of methods to specifically find that element of a Hilbert
space that minimizes a functional on such a space. We here turn to the development of a method that has some advantages if a computer is available for its
implementation.

As mentioned in Chapter 1 the overall method of solution to the optimization problem is by descent. If we have a functional F on a Hilbert space
$\mathcal{H}$, that is, an operator from $\mathcal{H} \to \mathcal{R}^1$, then by descent we mean the following:

1. To guess an initial $x_0 \in \mathcal{H}$.
2. To construct a sequence $x_0, x_1, \ldots, x_i, \ldots$ such that

$$F(x_{i+1}) < F(x_i)$$

This choice lends itself to implementation on the computer, as we see
below.

The basic idea is as outlined in Fig. 3.1, where the sequence $x_0, x_1, \ldots,$
$x_i, \ldots$, in $\mathcal{H}$ is shown with the corresponding values in $\mathcal{R}^1$, $F(x_0)$, $F(x_1)$, $\ldots$.
The range of F in $\mathcal{R}^1$ [which is often written as $F(\mathcal{H})$] is also indicated in Fig.
3.1. The problem with descent is to choose the sequence so that it converges
to the x^* for which $F(x^*)$ is at the bottom of the range of F in $\mathcal{R}^1$, that is, the

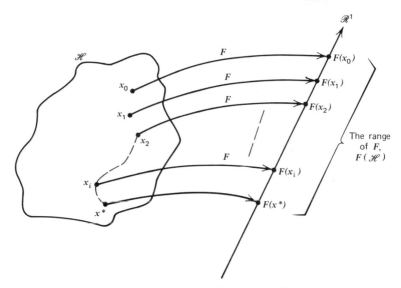

Figure 3.1   Descent with a functional F on Hilbert space $\mathcal{H}$.

minimum. We now turn to the choice of a descent method and to showing what conditions on F must be satisfied to have convergence to the
minimum x^*.

The Choice of Descent Method

Of the many descent methods, the simplest and probably the widest known,
because of its intuitive appeal is the *steepest descent* method, which moves
in the direction of negative gradient. For many problems this method has
been found very useful; however for the type of control problems considered
here, experience has shown that it is not a generally satisfactory method. For
control problems it is usually so slow to converge as to tax even the powers of
the modern digital computer. One control-type problem for which steepest
descent has been found to work well is the brachistochrone problem
or the problem of the path of minimum time of descent. This also, oddly
enough, is one of the problems that can be solved analytically by the methods
of the calculus of variations. It is a point of conjecture why steepest descent
works as well on this problem as it does.

Suffice it to say that because of the shortcomings of steepest descent as a
computational method, there have been a great many other descent methods
proposed. A currently popular one and the one chosen for consideration and

use here is the *conjugate gradient descent* method. There are several reasons for this choice, a few of which follow:

1. It has quadratic convergence properties, that is, for a quadratic functional on an n-dimensional Hilbert space it converges in at most n steps.

2. It requires a relatively small increase in computer time per iteration and memory space over steepest descent methods.

3. It has a well worked out theory; see for example, [1], [3], [6], and [7].

4. Experience has shown it to work well. For a comparison of conjugate gradient descent and steepest descent methods applied to some simple control problems, see [2].

The Plan for this Chapter

With this choice of descent, we devote the rest of this chapter to an exposition of the method. The plan for the chapter is as follows:

1. To consider conjugate descent of which conjugate gradient descent is a special case.

2. To consider conjugate gradient descent with a quadratic functional.

3. To consider conjugate gradient descent with a not necessarily quadratic functional.

4. To consider briefly conjugate gradient descent in $\mathcal{R}^n$ with scaling to speed up the descent rate.

3.2. CONJUGATE DESCENT

We begin by considering descent with a functional F on a Hilbert space $\mathcal{H}$ (as shown in Fig. 3.1) in which F is a Taylor series expansion, as in (2.57), truncated after the second order terms. The form assumed here is as in (2.60),

$$F(x) = F_0 + \langle a, x \rangle + \tfrac{1}{2}\langle x, Ax \rangle \qquad (3.1)$$

where the scalar product is the scalar product of $\mathcal{H}$. The linear operator A is assumed symmetric and positive definite so that by Theorem 2.5 the functional has a unique minimum in $\mathcal{H}$.

Let us first consider what is termed conjugate descent with F of (3.1) (conjugate gradient descent is a special case of conjugate descent). With conjugate descent it is assumed that a sequence

$$\{p_j\} \triangleq [p_0, p_1, \ldots, p_j, \ldots] \qquad (3.2)$$

is available with the members of the sequence conjugate w.r.t. the positive-definite, linear operator A of the second order term in (3.1). By conjugate w.r.t. A is meant

$$\langle p_i, Ap_j \rangle = 0 \qquad \text{if} \quad i \neq j$$
$$\neq 0 \qquad \text{if} \quad i = j \qquad (3.3)$$

In the case here A is assumed positive definite so

$$\langle p_i, Ap_i \rangle > 0 \qquad (3.4)$$

With conjugate descent, the sequence

$$\{x_i\} = [x_0, x_1, \ldots, x_i, \ldots]$$

is constructed by guessing x_0 and then letting

$$x_{i+1} = x_i + \alpha_i p_i \qquad (3.5)$$

where α_i, a scalar constant, is chosen so that it minimizes

$$F(x_i + \alpha_i p_i) = F_0 + \langle a, x_i + \alpha_i p_i \rangle + \tfrac{1}{2}\langle x_i + \alpha_i p_i, A(x_i + \alpha_i p_i) \rangle \qquad (3.6)$$

This means that α_i is chosen so that

$$\frac{d}{d\alpha} F(x_i + \alpha p_i) \bigg|_{\alpha = \alpha_i} = 0$$

$$= F'(x_i + \alpha_i p_i) \cdot p_i$$

$$= \langle g(x_{i+1}), p_i \rangle = 0 \qquad (3.7)$$

where the second line of (3.7), is obtained by applying (2.42), the differentiation rule for composite operators. Equation 3.7 is obtained by applying Theorem 2.1. $g(x_{i+1})$ of (3.7) is the gradient of F evaluated at $x_{i+1} = x_i + \alpha_i p_i$. Equation 3.7 means that x_{i+1} is chosen so that at x_{i+1} the gradient and p_i are orthogonal. The relationship between x_i, x_{i+1}, p_i and the gradient at x_{i+1} is shown in Fig. 3.2, for $x \in \mathscr{R}^2$.

We may find the gradient of F at any given x by taking $F'(x)$ for F of (3.1). Using the results of Examples 2.1, 2.2, and 2.3, we have

$$F'(x) = \langle a, \cdot \rangle + \langle Ax, \cdot \rangle$$
$$= \langle a + Ax, \cdot \rangle$$
$$= \langle g(x), \cdot \rangle \qquad (3.8)$$

where $g(x)$ is the gradient of F at x. Use has been made of the fact that A is symmetric in obtaining (3.8). Using (3.8), we then have

$$g(x_{i+1}) = a + Ax_{i+1}$$

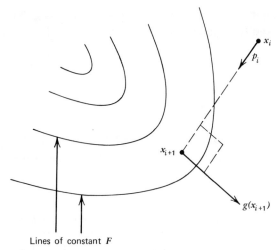

Lines of constant F

Figure 3.2 The relationship of x_i and x_{i+1} in conjugate descent in $\mathscr{R}^2$.

or using a more compact notation

$$g_{i+1} = a + Ax_{i+1} \qquad (3.9)$$

We now show that conjugate descent as described here converges in at most n steps if the Hilbert space we are working in is of dimension n. Thus let us consider

$$x_{j+2} = x_{j+1} + \alpha_{j+1}p_{j+1}$$

by use of (3.5). Continuing this we have

$$x_{j+3} = x_{j+2} + \alpha_{j+2}p_{j+2}$$
$$= x_{j+1} + \alpha_{j+1}p_{j+1} + \alpha_{j+2}p_{j+2}$$

$$x_n = x_{j+1} + \sum_{i=j+1}^{n-1} \alpha_i p_i \qquad 0 \le j \le n-1 \qquad (3.10)$$

Now the gradient at x_n may be found from (3.9) to be

$$g_n = a + Ax_n$$

and using (3.10)

$$g_n = a + Ax_{j+1} + \sum_{i=j+1}^{n-1} \alpha_i Ap_i \qquad 0 \le j \le n-1$$

or

$$g_n = g_{j+1} + \sum_{i=j+1}^{n-1} \alpha_i Ap_i \qquad 0 \le j \le n-1 \qquad (3.11)$$

which expresses the gradient at the nth step as a function of the gradient at the $(j + 1)$st step and the elements of the conjugate set $\{p_i\}$.

Now let us consider

$$\langle g_n, p_j \rangle \qquad 0 \leq j \leq n - 1$$

Use of (3.11) gives

$$\langle g_n, p_j \rangle = \langle g_{j+1}, p_j \rangle + \sum_{i=j+1}^{n-1} \alpha_i \langle p_j, Ap_i \rangle \qquad 0 \leq j \leq n - 1 \quad (3.12)$$

Now we consider the two terms on the RHS of (3.12). $\langle g_{j+1}, p_j \rangle$ in conjugate descent is zero from (3.7). By conjugacy of the elements of the set $\{p_i\}$, $\langle p_j, Ap_i \rangle = 0$ for $j + 1 \leq i \leq n - 1$. Therefore

$$\langle g_n, p_j \rangle = 0 \qquad 0 \leq j \leq n - 1 \quad (3.13)$$

that is, the gradient at the nth step is orthogonal to all elements of $p_0, p_1, \ldots, p_{n-1}$.

We are considering descent with the functional F of (3.1) where A is positive definite. If A is positive definite then $p_0, p_1, \ldots, p_{n-1}$ are linearly independent if $\mathcal{H}$ is of at least dimension n by Theorem A.2 of Appendix A. Let us consider now the case where the Hilbert space $\mathcal{H}$ in which we are working is of dimension n. Then any linearly independent set of n elements, $p_0, p_1, \ldots, p_{n-1}$, for example, forms a basis of $\mathcal{H}$. From Theorem 1 of Section 14 of [4] any vector orthogonal to all elements of the basis of a space can only be the null element $\mathbf{0}$. We conclude then from (3.13) that

$$g_n = \mathbf{0} \quad (3.14)$$

that is, conjugate descent if $\mathcal{H}$ is of dimension n converges to the element in $\mathcal{H}$ that has zero gradient in at most n steps. It may of course converge in fewer than n steps depending on how the initial element x_0 in our sequence is chosen. In fact, if x_0 is chosen as the element for which the gradient as given by (3.9) is the null element then the sequence converges to the zero gradient immediately.

We summarize the above remarks, in the following theorem.

Theorem 3.1. Given a functional F as in (3.1) with the operator A positive definite, on Hilbert space $\mathcal{H}$ of dimension n, then the conjugate descent method converges to the minimum of F in at most n steps.

3.3. CONJUGATE GRADIENT DESCENT OF A QUADRATIC FUNCTIONAL

Conjugate descent as described in the last section exhibits quadratic convergence and is hence a likely candidate for use as a computational descent algorithm. However one question has been left open in the description of the previous section; that is, how are the conjugate descent directions $\{p_i\}$ obtained in the first place? A method that constructs the conjugate set $\{p_i\}$ and one that fits our needs very well is called conjugate gradient descent. It is basically a conjugate descent method that constructs the conjugate descent directions from the gradient at each element reached in the descent sequence. Our purpose here is to describe this particular method of descent with a quadratic functional and to show that it is indeed a conjugate descent method. The method is then illustrated with an example.

Description of Conjugate Gradient Descent

The functional of interest here is the same quadratic functional considered in Section 3.2; that is,

$$F(x) = F_0 + \langle a, x \rangle + \tfrac{1}{2}\langle x, Ax \rangle \tag{3.15}$$

for x and a in Hilbert space $\mathscr{H}$ with A a positive definite, symmetric, linear operator. By Theorem 2.5 we know that the minimum x^* for this F exists in $\mathscr{H}$ and that the gradient at x^* is null.

With conjugate gradient descent, as with any descent method, the first element of the descent sequence x_0 is simply guessed. The remaining members of the sequence are then found as follows:

$$p_0 = -g_0 = -(a + Ax_0) \tag{3.16a}$$

$$x_{i+1} = x_i + \alpha_i p_i \tag{3.16b}$$

$$\alpha_i = \frac{\langle g_i, g_i \rangle}{\langle p_i, Ap_i \rangle} \tag{3.16c}$$

$$g_{i+1} = g_i + \alpha_i Ap_i \tag{3.16d}$$

$$p_{i+1} = -g_{i+1} + \beta_i p_i \tag{3.16e}$$

$$\beta_i = \frac{\langle g_{i+1}, g_{i+1} \rangle}{\langle g_i, g_i \rangle} \tag{3.16f}$$

where now g_i is the gradient at the ith element of the descent sequence x_i. It can be seen from (3.16c) that the sequence converges, that is, $\alpha_i = 0$, if the gradient g_i is null.

We now wish to show that the descent method given in (3.16) is indeed a conjugate descent method. To do this we need to show the following:

1. α_i is chosen at each step to minimize $F(x_i + \alpha_i p_i)$.
2. The set $\{p_i\}$ are conjugate w.r.t. the linear operator A.

To begin, we show two things needed in the proof. The first is that the gradient as given in (3.16a) and (3.16d) is indeed the gradient of the functional F of (3.15). To this end we note that F of (3.15) is the same F as in (3.1) for which the gradient at x_i is given by (3.9). Equation 3.16a follows directly from (3.9). To obtain (3.16d) we use (3.16b) to get

$$Ax_{i+1} = Ax_i + \alpha_i Ap_i$$
$$a + Ax_{i+1} = a + Ax_i + \alpha_i Ap_i$$
$$g_{i+1} = g_i + \alpha_i Ap_i$$

again by use of (3.9). This is (3.16d).

Also required is an expression for the descent direction at the ith step p_i in terms of the gradients. This can be found as follows starting with (3.16a):

$$p_0 = -g_0$$

$$p_1 = -g_1 + \beta_0 p_0$$

$$= -g_1 - \frac{\langle g_1, g_1 \rangle}{\langle g_0, g_0 \rangle} g_0$$

$$p_2 = -g_2 + \beta_1 p_1$$

$$= -g_2 + \frac{\langle g_2, g_2 \rangle}{\langle g_1, g_1 \rangle} \left(-g_1 - \frac{\langle g_1, g_1 \rangle}{\langle g_0, g_0 \rangle} g_0 \right)$$

$$= -g_2 - \frac{\langle g_2, g_2 \rangle}{\langle g_1, g_1 \rangle} g_1 - \frac{\langle g_2, g_2 \rangle}{\langle g_0, g_0 \rangle} g_0$$

$$p_3 = -g_3 - \frac{\langle g_3, g_3 \rangle}{\langle g_2, g_2 \rangle} g_2 - \frac{\langle g_3, g_3 \rangle}{\langle g_1, g_1 \rangle} g_1 - \frac{\langle g_3, g_3 \rangle}{\langle g_0, g_0 \rangle} g_0$$

from which we can see the recursion relationship

$$p_k = -\langle g_k, g_k \rangle \sum_{i=0}^{k} \frac{g_i}{\langle g_i, g_i \rangle} \tag{3.17}$$

which is the desired result.

We now show the following:

Lemma 3.1. α_i of (3.16c) minimizes $F(x_i + \alpha p_i)$ w.r.t. α.

The proof is by induction. For $i = 0$ we have

$$\frac{d}{d\alpha} F(x_0 + \alpha p_0) = F'(x_0 + \alpha p_0) p_0$$

$$= \langle g(x_0 + \alpha p_0), p_0 \rangle \tag{3.18}$$

from Theorem 2.1. From (3.9)

$$g(x_0 + \alpha p_0) = a + Ax_0 + \alpha Ap_0$$
$$= g_0 + \alpha Ap_0$$

Using this in (3.18) we get

$$\frac{d}{d\alpha} F(x_0 + \alpha p_0) = \langle g_0, p_0 \rangle + \alpha \langle p_0, Ap_0 \rangle \qquad (3.19)$$

but $p_0 = -g_0$ from (3.16a), so that for

$$\alpha = \frac{\langle g_0, g_0 \rangle}{\langle p_0, Ap_0 \rangle} \qquad (3.20)$$

$$\frac{d}{d\alpha} F(x_0 + \alpha p_0) = 0$$

We can see from (3.19) that

$$\frac{d^2}{d\alpha^2} F(x_0 + \alpha p_0) = \langle p_0, Ap_0 \rangle > 0$$

Since A is positive definite, α_0 as given by (3.20) minimizes $F(x_0 + \alpha p_0)$. Since $x_1 = x_0 + \alpha_0 p_0$ we also have $\langle g_1, p_0 \rangle = 0$. To complete the induction we assume that $\alpha = \alpha_i$ of (3.16c) minimizes $F(x_i + \alpha p_i)$ for $0 \le i \le j - 1$. We now show that α_i, also given by (3.16c), minimizes $F(x_i + \alpha p_i)$ for $i = j$. Thus we consider

$$\frac{d}{d\alpha} F(x_j + \alpha p_j) = F'(x_j + \alpha p_j) p_j$$

$$= \langle g(x_j + \alpha p_j), p_j \rangle$$

from Theorem 2.1. $g(x_j + \alpha p_j)$ as given by (3.9) gives

$$\frac{d}{d\alpha} F(x_j + \alpha p_j) = \langle a + Ax_j + \alpha Ap_j, p_j \rangle$$

$$= \langle g_j, p_j \rangle + \alpha \langle p_j, Ap_j \rangle \qquad (3.21)$$

But

$$\langle g_j, p_j \rangle = \langle g_j, -g_j + \beta_j p_{j-1} \rangle$$
$$= -\langle g_j, g_j \rangle + \beta_j \langle g_j, p_{j-1} \rangle \qquad (3.22)$$

But α_i for $i = j - 1$ minimizes $F(x_{j-1} + \alpha p_{j-1})$ and therefore

$$\frac{d}{d\alpha} F(x_{j-1} + \alpha p_{j-1}) \bigg|_{\alpha = \alpha_{j-1}} = \langle g_j, p_{j-1} \rangle = 0$$

Using this in (3.22) and the result in (3.21) gives

$$\frac{d}{d\alpha} F(x_j + \alpha p_j) = -\langle g_j, g_j \rangle + \alpha \langle p_j, A p_j \rangle$$

and

$$\alpha = \frac{\langle g_j, g_j \rangle}{\langle p_j, A p_j \rangle} = \alpha_j \qquad (3.23)$$

gives

$$\frac{d}{d\alpha} F(x_j + \alpha_j p_j) = 0$$

From (3.21)

$$\frac{d^2}{d\alpha^\alpha} F(x_j + \alpha p_j) = \langle p_j, A p_j \rangle > 0$$

since A is positive definite. Thus α_j of (3.23), which is (3.16c), minimizes $F(x_j + \alpha p_j)$ and the induction, and the proof of Lemma 3.1 is complete.

To complete the proof that conjugate gradient descent as described in (3.16) is a conjugate descent method, we need only show the following:

Lemma 3.2. The gradients $g_0, g_1, \ldots, g_{n-1}$ and the descent directions $p_0, p_1, \ldots, p_{n-1}$ as given by (3.16) satisfy

$$\langle g_i, g_j \rangle = 0 \qquad i \neq j \qquad (3.24)$$

(i.e., all gradients are orthogonal) and

$$\langle p_i, A p_j \rangle = 0 \qquad i \neq j \qquad (3.25)$$

(i.e., all descent directions are conjugate).

The proof is again by induction. We begin by showing g_0 and g_1 are orthogonal and p_0 and p_1 are conjugate w.r.t. A. Let us consider

$$\langle g_0, g_1 \rangle = \langle g_0, g_0 + \alpha_0 A p_0 \rangle$$

using (3.16d). Use of (3.16a) now gives

$$\langle g_0, g_1 \rangle = \langle g_0, g_0 \rangle - \alpha_0 \langle g_0, A g_0 \rangle \qquad (3.26)$$

Use of α_0 as determined by (3.16c) with $p_0 = -g_0$ in (3.26) gives

$$\langle g_0, g_1 \rangle = 0 \qquad (3.27)$$

which shows g_0 and g_1 orthogonal. Now let us consider

$$\langle p_0, A p_1 \rangle = \langle A p_0, p_1 \rangle$$
$$= \langle -A g_0, -g_1 - \beta_0 g_0 \rangle \qquad (3.28)$$

from (3.16a) and (3.16e). Now evaluation of β_0 by use of (3.16f) gives

$$\langle p_0, Ap_1 \rangle = \langle Ag_0, g_1 \rangle + \langle Ag_0, g_0 \rangle \frac{\langle g_1, g_1 \rangle}{\langle g_0, g_0 \rangle}$$

$$= \langle Ag_0, g_1 \rangle + \frac{1}{\alpha_0} \langle g_1, g_1 \rangle \tag{3.29}$$

by use of (3.16c) again. By (3.16d)

$$g_1 = g_0 + \alpha_0 Ap_0 = g_0 - \alpha_0 Ag_0$$

$$Ag_0 = \frac{g_0 - g_1}{\alpha_0} \tag{3.30}$$

Use of (3.30) in (3.29) gives

$$\langle p_0, Ap_1 \rangle = \frac{1}{\alpha_0} \langle g_0, g_1 \rangle$$

which by use of (3.27) gives

$$\langle p_0, Ap_1 \rangle = 0 \tag{3.31}$$

which shows p_0 and p_1 conjugate w.r.t. A.

We now assume that $g_0, g_1, \ldots, g_k$ are orthogonal and that $p_0, p_1, \ldots, p_{k-1}$ are conjugate w.r.t. A. To complete the proof of the lemma we need only show that g_{k+1} and p_k can be added to these orthogonal and conjugate sets, respectively. We begin by showing p_k conjugate to $p_0, p_1, \ldots, p_{k-1}$. We have

$$\langle g_i, g_j \rangle = 0 \quad i \neq j \quad 0 \leq i \leq k \quad 0 \leq j \leq k \tag{3.32a}$$

$$\langle p_i, Ap_j \rangle = 0 \quad i \neq j \quad 0 \leq i \leq k-1 \quad 0 \leq j \leq k-1 \tag{3.32b}$$

From (3.16d)

$$g_{i+1} = g_i + \alpha_i Ap_i$$

and hence

$$\langle g_{i+1}, p_k \rangle = \langle g_i, p_k \rangle + \alpha_i \langle p_k, Ap_i \rangle$$

Use of (3.17) gives

$$\left\langle g_{i+1}, -\langle g_k, g_k \rangle \sum_{j=0}^{k} \frac{g_j}{\langle g_j, g_j \rangle} \right\rangle = \left\langle g_i, -\langle g_k, g_k \rangle \sum_{j=0}^{k} \frac{g_j}{\langle g_j, g_j \rangle} \right\rangle + \alpha_i \langle p_k, Ap_i \rangle$$

By use of (3.32a) this becomes

$$-\langle g_k, g_k \rangle = -\langle g_k, g_k \rangle + \alpha_i \langle p_k, Ap_i \rangle \quad 0 \leq i \leq k-1$$

or

$$\alpha_i \langle p_k, A p_i \rangle = 0 \qquad 0 \le i \le k - 1 \qquad (3.33)$$

but

$$\alpha_i = \frac{\langle g_i, g_i \rangle}{\langle p_i, A p_i \rangle} \ne 0 \qquad 0 \le i \le k - 1$$

Therefore from (3.33)

$$\langle p_i, A p_k \rangle = \langle p_k, A p_i \rangle = 0 \qquad 0 \le i \le k - 1 \qquad (3.34)$$

and hence p_k is conjugate w.r.t. A to $p_0, p_1, \ldots, p_{k-1}$.

Now it only remains to show that g_{k+1} is orthogonal to $g_0, g_1, \ldots, g_k$. The assumption is that $g_0, g_1, \ldots, g_k$ are orthogonal and we want to show

$$\langle g_i, g_{k+1} \rangle = 0 \qquad 0 \le i \le k \qquad (3.35)$$

Thus using (3.16d),

$$\begin{aligned}
\langle g_i, g_{k+1} \rangle &= \langle g_i, g_k + \alpha_k A p_k \rangle \\
&= \langle g_i, g_k \rangle + \alpha_k \langle g_i, A p_k \rangle \qquad (3.36)
\end{aligned}$$

We consider two cases:

1. $i < k$
For this case (3.36) gives

$$\langle g_i, g_{k+1} \rangle = \alpha_k \langle g_i, A p_k \rangle \qquad (3.37)$$

since g_k is orthogonal to $g_0, g_1, \ldots, g_{k-1}$ by assumption. We have from (3.34)

$$\langle p_{i-1}, A p_k \rangle = 0 \qquad i < k$$

Thus we can write by use of (3.37) and (3.34)

$$\begin{aligned}
\langle g_i, g_{k+1} \rangle &= \alpha_k \langle g_i - \beta_{i-1} p_{i-1}, A p_k \rangle \\
&= -\alpha_k \langle p_i, A p_k \rangle \\
&= 0 \qquad i < k \qquad (3.38)
\end{aligned}$$

by the conjugacy of p_i and p_k for $i < k$

2. $i = k$
Here (3.36) gives

$$\begin{aligned}
\langle g_k, g_{k+1} \rangle &= \langle g_k, g_k \rangle + \alpha_k \langle g_k, A p_k \rangle \\
&= \langle g_k, g_k \rangle + \frac{\langle g_k, g_k \rangle}{\langle p_k, A p_k \rangle} \langle g_k, A p_k \rangle \qquad (3.39)
\end{aligned}$$

by using (3.16c). Now let us consider

$$\langle g_k, A p_k \rangle = \langle g_k - \beta_{k-1} p_{k-1}, A p_k \rangle \qquad (3.40)$$

since p_{k-1} and p_k are conjugate w.r.t. A by (3.34). Use of (3.16e) in (3.40) gives

$$\langle g_k, A p_k \rangle = -\langle p_k, A p_k \rangle \tag{3.41}$$

Using (3.41) in (3.39) we get

$$\langle g_k, g_{k+1} \rangle = 0 \tag{3.42}$$

Equations 3.38 and 3.42 give (3.35) which is the desired result. This completes the proof of Lemma 3.2.

Lemma 3.1 and Lemma 3.2 above gives us the following;

Theorem 3.2. The conjugate gradient descent method as defined in (3.16) is a conjugate descent method for the functional F of (3.15).

Theorem 3.1 therefore applies to the conjugate gradient descent method of (3.16). Thus conjugate gradient descent applied to a quadratic functional F as in (3.15) on an n-dimensional Hilbert space, with A positive definite, converges to the minimum of F in at most n steps.

Example 3.1.

We consider finding the minimum in $\mathscr{R}^2$ of

$$F(x) = 1 + x_1 + x_2 + \tfrac{1}{2} x_1^2 + x_1 x_2 + x_2^2$$

$$F(x) = 1 + [1 \ \ 1] \begin{bmatrix} x_1 \\ x_2 \end{bmatrix} + \tfrac{1}{2} [x_1 \ \ x_2] \begin{bmatrix} 1 & 1 \\ 1 & 2 \end{bmatrix} \begin{bmatrix} x_1 \\ x_2 \end{bmatrix}$$

$$= F_0 + \langle a, x \rangle + \tfrac{1}{2} \langle x, A x \rangle$$

For this functional Theorem 2.5 applies as the matrix A is positive definite. so that the minimum is

$$x^* = -A^{-1} a = - \begin{bmatrix} 1 & 1 \\ 1 & 2 \end{bmatrix}^{-1} \begin{bmatrix} 1 \\ 1 \end{bmatrix}$$

$$= - \begin{bmatrix} 2 & -1 \\ -1 & 1 \end{bmatrix} \begin{bmatrix} 1 \\ 1 \end{bmatrix}$$

$$= \begin{bmatrix} -1 \\ 0 \end{bmatrix}$$

Now let us use conjugate gradient descent to find this minimum. By Theorem 3.2 the sequence should converge on the minimum in at most two steps.

We choose

$$x_0 = \begin{bmatrix} 0 \\ 0 \end{bmatrix}$$

for which

$$g_0 = a + Ax_0 = \begin{bmatrix} 1 \\ 1 \end{bmatrix} + \begin{bmatrix} 1 & 1 \\ 1 & 2 \end{bmatrix} \begin{bmatrix} 0 \\ 0 \end{bmatrix}$$

$$= \begin{bmatrix} 1 \\ 1 \end{bmatrix}$$

and

$$p_0 = \begin{bmatrix} -1 \\ -1 \end{bmatrix}$$

$$x_1 = x_0 + \alpha_0 p_0 = \begin{bmatrix} 0 \\ 0 \end{bmatrix} + \frac{\langle g_0, g_0 \rangle}{\langle g_0, Ag_0 \rangle} \begin{bmatrix} -1 \\ -1 \end{bmatrix}$$

$$\alpha_0 = \frac{\langle g_0, g_0 \rangle}{\langle g_0, Ag_0 \rangle} = \frac{2}{5}$$

$$x_1 = \begin{bmatrix} -\frac{2}{5} \\ -\frac{2}{5} \end{bmatrix}$$

$$g_1 = g_0 + \alpha_0 Ap_0 = g_0 - \alpha_0 Ag_0$$

$$= \begin{bmatrix} 1 \\ 1 \end{bmatrix} - \frac{2}{5} \begin{bmatrix} 1 & 1 \\ 1 & 2 \end{bmatrix} \begin{bmatrix} 1 \\ 1 \end{bmatrix}$$

$$= \begin{bmatrix} \frac{1}{5} \\ -\frac{1}{5} \end{bmatrix}$$

$$\beta_0 = \frac{\langle g_1, g_1 \rangle}{\langle g_0, g_0 \rangle} = \frac{1}{25}$$

$$p_1 = -g_1 + \beta_0 p_0 = \begin{bmatrix} -\frac{1}{5} \\ \frac{1}{5} \end{bmatrix} + \frac{1}{25} \begin{bmatrix} -1 \\ -1 \end{bmatrix}$$

$$= \begin{bmatrix} -\frac{6}{25} \\ \frac{4}{25} \end{bmatrix}$$

$$\alpha_1 = \frac{\langle g_1, g_1 \rangle}{\langle p_1, Ap_1 \rangle} = \frac{5}{2}$$

$$x_2 = x_1 + \alpha_1 p_1$$

$$= \begin{bmatrix} -\frac{2}{5} \\ -\frac{2}{5} \end{bmatrix} + \frac{5}{2} \begin{bmatrix} -\frac{6}{25} \\ \frac{4}{25} \end{bmatrix} = \begin{bmatrix} -1 \\ 0 \end{bmatrix} = x^*$$

We leave it to the reader to check that g_0 and g_1 are orthogonal and p_0 and p_1 are conjugate w.r.t. A and that $g_2 = 0$.

Remarks

This example also illustrates the correspondence of the problem of finding a a solution to the equation

$$Ax^* = -a$$

(where A is a linear, symmetric, positive-definite operator on Hilbert space $\mathscr{H}$ to $\mathscr{H}$) to the problem of finding the minimum of

$$F(x) = F_0 + \langle a, x \rangle + \tfrac{1}{2}\langle x, Ax \rangle$$

which is an operator from $\mathscr{H}$ to $\mathscr{R}^1$. In fact, conjugate gradient descent was originally developed (see [1]) to find solutions to equations of the form

$$Ax = y$$

where A is a symmetric, positive definite, $n \times n$ matrix and x and y are in $\mathscr{R}^n$.

Convergence

Let us now consider the rate at which the quadratic functional of (3.15) decreases, that is, how fast the conjugate gradient descent algorithm converges. We also get the rate at which the norm of the gradient and $\|x_i - x^*\|$ decrease, where x^* is the minimum sought. We consider a functional as in (3.15) where the linear operator A is both positive definite and bounded, that is,

$$0 < m \le A \le M \tag{3.43}$$

If A is positive definite, $F(x)$ has a unique minimum by Theorem 2.5. We note that (3.43) means in general that

$$0 \le m\|x\|^2 \le \langle x, Ax \rangle \le M\|x\|^2 \tag{3.44}$$

for all $x \ne 0$.

To study convergence we here introduce the functional

$$E(x) \triangleq \tfrac{1}{2}\langle x - x^*, A(x - x^*) \rangle \tag{3.45}$$

where x^* is the minimum of $F(x)$ of (3.15), that is,

$$x^* = -A^{-1}a \tag{3.46}$$

Multiplying out (3.45) using (3.46) we get

$$E(x) = \langle a, x \rangle + \tfrac{1}{2}\langle x, Ax \rangle + \tfrac{1}{2}\langle x^*, Ax^* \rangle$$
$$= F(x) - F_0 + \tfrac{1}{2}\langle x^*, Ax^* \rangle \qquad (3.47)$$

Thus $E(x)$ is just $F(x)$ plus a constant, so any statement concerning the convergence of $E(x)$ applies as well to $F(x)$. Taking the gradient $g(x)$ of $F(x)$ of (3.15), we obtain

$$g(x) = a + Ax$$

and use of this with (3.45) and (3.46) gives

$$E(x) = \tfrac{1}{2}\langle x + A^{-1}a, Ax + a \rangle = \tfrac{1}{2}\langle A^{-1}(Ax + a), Ax + a \rangle$$
$$= \tfrac{1}{2}\langle g(x), A^{-1} \cdot g(x) \rangle \qquad (3.48)$$

Use of the bounds on A as given by (3.43) gives

$$\frac{\|g(x)\|^2}{2M} \leq E(x) \leq \frac{\|g(x)\|^2}{2m} \qquad (3.49)$$

which shows that $E(x)$ also bounds the gradient. We note from (3.49) that for M finite, $g(x^*) = 0$ for $E(x^*) = 0$.

Now we assume that a conjugate gradient descent sequence as given by (3.16) is constructed. We consider the decrease in the functional $E(x)$ at the ith iteration. Thus

$$E(x_i) - E(x_{i+1}) = \tfrac{1}{2}\langle x_i - x^*, A(x_i - x^*) \rangle - \tfrac{1}{2}\langle x_{i+1} - x^*, A(x_{i+1} - x_*) \rangle$$

and from (3.16) we have

$$E(x_i) - E(x_{i+1}) = -\alpha_i \langle p_i, A(x_i - x^*) \rangle - \tfrac{1}{2}\alpha_i^2 \langle p_i, Ap_i \rangle$$
$$= -\alpha_i \langle p_i, Ax_i + a \rangle - \tfrac{1}{2}\alpha_i^2 \langle p_i, Ap_i \rangle$$
$$= -\alpha_i \langle p_i, g_i \rangle - \tfrac{1}{2}\alpha_i \langle g_i, g_i \rangle \qquad (3.50)$$

Due to the orthogonality of g_i and p_{i-1}

$$\langle p_i, g_i \rangle = \langle -g_i + \beta_{i-1}p_{i-1}, g_i \rangle$$
$$= -\langle g_i, g_i \rangle \qquad (3.51)$$

Use of (3.51) in (3.50) with α_i and $E(x_i)$ as in (3.16c) and (3.48) gives

$$E(x_i) - E(x_{i+1}) = \frac{\langle g_i, g_i \rangle^2 E(x_i)}{\langle p_i, Ap_i \rangle \langle g_i, A^{-1}g_i \rangle} \qquad (3.52)$$

Using (3.16e) and the conjugacy of p_i and p_{i-1}, we get

$$\langle g_i, Ag_i \rangle = \langle \beta_{i-1}p_{i-1} - p_i, A(\beta_{i-1}p_{i-1} - p_i) \rangle$$
$$= \beta_{i-1}^2 \langle p_{i-1}, Ap_{i-1} \rangle + \langle p_i, Ap_i \rangle$$
$$\geq \langle p_i, Ap_i \rangle \qquad (3.53)$$

since A is assumed positive definite.

Equation 3.53 into (3.52) now gives

$$E(x_i) - E(x_{i+1}) \geq \frac{\langle g_i, g_i \rangle^2 E(x_i)}{\langle g_i, A g_i \rangle \langle g_i, A^{-1} g_i \rangle} \qquad (3.54)$$

The RHS of (3.54) is a form to which Kantorovich's inequality† may be applied to give

$$E(x_i) - E(x_{i+1}) \geq \frac{4mM}{(m + M)^2} E(x_i)$$

from which

$$E(x_{i+1}) \leq \left(\frac{1 - m/M}{1 + m/M} \right)^2 E(x_i) \qquad (3.55)$$

From (3.55) after n iterations

$$E(x_n) \leq \left(\frac{1 - m/M}{1 + m/M} \right)^{2n} E(x_0) \qquad (3.56)$$

which is the desired result. We may use (3.44) and (3.45) with (3.56) to get

$$\frac{m}{2} \|x_n - x^*\|^2 \leq E(x_n) = \tfrac{1}{2}\langle x_n - x^*, A(x_n - x^*) \rangle \leq \left(\frac{1 - m/M}{1 + m/M} \right)^{2n} E(x_0)$$

and hence

$$\|x_n - x^*\| \leq \sqrt{\frac{M}{m}} \left(\frac{1 - m/M}{1 + m/M} \right)^n \|x_0 - x^*\| \qquad (3.57)$$

Using (3.49) we have

$$\|g(x_n)\| \leq \sqrt{\frac{M}{m}} \left(\frac{1 - m/M}{1 + m/M} \right)^n \|g(x_0)\| \qquad (3.58)$$

Equations 3.56, 3.57, and 3.58 give the convergence rates for $E(x_n)$, $\|x_n - x^*\|$, and $\|g(x_n)\|$, respectively. We see that in all cases convergence is a function of the ratio m/M.

Remarks

1. It is interesting to note that in the two-dimensional case, that is, $x \in \mathcal{R}^2$, the ratio m/M is a measure of the eccentricity of the ellipses that form the contours of constant values of $F(x)$. For $m/M = 1$ the ellipses become circles

---

† From Luenberger [6] or Daniels [8] we have Kantorovich's inequality as

$$\frac{\langle x, A x \rangle \langle x, A^{-1} x \rangle}{\langle x, x \rangle^2} \leq \frac{(m + M)^2}{4mM}$$

for $0 < m \leq A \leq M$.

and our convergence formula (3.56) shows convergence in one step. This is obvious, for in the case of circular constant cost contours the negative gradient direction passes through the common center, which is the minimum.

2. The convergence rate as given in (3.56) also applies in the case of the steepest descent algorithm where the step size is chosen to minimize the cost functional in the direction of descent[†] (in steepest descent this is the negative gradient direction). Daniel[‡], using spectral analysis methods, has shown that the rate of convergence for conjugate gradient descent is faster than this. He obtains

$$E(x_n) \leq 4\left(\frac{1 - \sqrt{m/M}}{1 + \sqrt{m/M}}\right)^{2n} E(x_0) \tag{3.59}$$

which indicates a much faster rate of convergence for a given m/M. This is in accordance with experience, which shows that conjugate gradient descent does in general converge faster than steepest descent.

3.4. CONJUGATE GRADIENT DESCENT OF A SMOOTH FUNCTIONAL

We have considered conjugate gradient descent (CGD) of a quadratic functional on a Hilbert space in the previous section. Although there are a number of cases where a quadratic functional is practically important, such as the one in Example 2.6, the functionals one ordinarily encounters in minimization problems are not necessarily quadratic. This motivates the search for a descent method that works on a functional more general than a quadratic one. Our choice here is to simply extend the conjugate gradient method of the previous section. The extension is such that when the functional of interest is quadratic, the descent method reduces to the descent method of (3.16). Hence the quadratic convergence properties are retained if the functional turns out to be quadratic. This is desirable, for we can argue that if a functional is smooth (and we define this below) in the neighborhood of a minimum, it will be very nearly quadratic (see Section 2.5). Thus if we ever get to within a close neighborhood of the minimum we can expect good convergence to the minimum. This is a desirable characteristic in a descent method and one not exhibited by steepest descent.

We here define conjugate gradient descent for a general, smooth functional and show (1) that it is a descent sequence and (2) that if it converges to an element x^* then $g(x^*) = 0$ where g is the gradient of the functional.

† See [6] p. 309, problem 11.
‡ See [8] p. 121, proposition 5.4.2.

The Functional Considered

We now assume that the functional, for which a minimum is sought, in some open region that contains the minimum can be expanded into a Taylor series expansion as in (2.40) of the form

$$F(x + t) = F(x) + F'(x)t + o(t) \tag{3.60}$$

which, since $x, t \in \mathcal{H}$, a Hilbert space, can be written in the form of (2.57)

$$F(x + t) = F(x) + \langle g(x), t \rangle + o(t) \tag{3.61}$$

where $g(x)$ is the gradient of F at x. We assume $o(t)$ bounded for all x and t. Since by the mean value theorem

$$o(t) = \tfrac{1}{2}F''(x + \zeta t)t \cdot t \qquad 0 \le \zeta \le 1$$
$$= \tfrac{1}{2}\langle t, A(x + \zeta t)t \rangle$$

That $o(t)$ is bounded means that the second derivative operator A satisfies for all x in the region of $\mathcal{H}$ of interest.

$$m\|t\|^2 \le \langle t, A(x)t \rangle \le M\|t\|^2 \qquad |m|, |M| < \infty \tag{3.62}$$

Equation 3.62 defines what is meant by a smooth functional. We note that since the second derivative is assumed to exist and to be bounded in the region wherein we work, the functional F and the gradient g are both continuous there.

The Construction of the Conjugate Gradient Descent Sequence

As in the case of the quadratic functional, the first element in the descent sequence x_0 is simply guessed. In addition, we now assume that the *functional* F and the *gradient* g can be evaluated at x_0 and all subsequent values of x that are encountered. The descent sequence is then constructed as follows, (again we assume $g_i = g(x_i)$, the gradient at the ith step):

$$p_0 = -g(x_0) = -g_0 \tag{3.63a}$$

$$x_{i+1} = x_i + \alpha_i p_i \tag{3.63b}$$

where $\alpha_i > 0$ is chosen to minimize $F(x_i + \alpha p_i)$

$$p_{i+1} = -g_{i+1} + \beta_i p_i \tag{3.63c}$$

$$\beta_i = \frac{\langle g_{i+1}, g_{i+1} \rangle}{\langle g_i, g_i \rangle} \tag{3.63d}$$

Remarks

1. Note that the descent sequence as given by (3.63) is the same as the descent sequence of (3.16) if the functional F is quadratic as in (3.15). Equation 3.16 simply tells how to evaluate α_i and g_{i+1} [which (3.63) does not] for the case of a quadratic functional. For a quadratic functional, starting from the same x_0, the sequences constructed by (3.16) and (3.63) should be the same.

2. The length of the step taken at each iteration [see (3.63)], is determined by the constant α_i and this is assumed determined so as to minimize $F(x_i + \alpha p_i)$. This introduces the problem of minimizing a real-valued function of a single variable which is in general a tractable one. Some practical details of how one might go about this specifically are discussed in Appendix B. Since α_i is chosen to minimize $F(x_i + \alpha p_i)$, then

$$\frac{d}{d\alpha} F(x_i + \alpha p_i)\bigg|_{\alpha = \alpha_i} = \langle g(x_i + \alpha_i p_i), p_i \rangle$$

$$= \langle g_{i+1}, p_i \rangle = 0 \tag{3.64}$$

that is, the gradient at the $(i + 1)$st element in the descent sequence is orthogonal to the ith descent direction. This also holds for the case of descent of a quadratic functional as seen in (3.7) and Fig. 3.2.

3. It should be noted that the conjugate gradient descent method of (3.63) does not require explicitly any knowledge of the second derivative of the functional F upon which descent is being accomplished. Yet the sequence generated exhibits quadratic convergence. This is possibly the principle reason for considering this type of descent. In fact the method of (3.63) requires very little more computation than simple steepest descent, which is the same as the method described in (3.63) except $\beta_i = 0$ (and therefore $p_i = -g_i$ at all steps).

4. From (3.63) the sequence terminates if $g_i = 0$ for some i.

We now turn to showing that, under the assumptions made on the functional F, (3.63) does produce a descent sequence. We have the following theorem.

Theorem 3.3. For a smooth functional F on Hilbert space $\mathscr{H}$, the conjugate gradient descent sequence of (3.63) satisfies

$$F(x_{i+1}) < F(x_i) \tag{3.65}$$

unless $g_i = 0$.

Proof.† Consider $F(x_i + \alpha p_i)$ and assume no $\alpha > 0$ exists for which

$$F(x_i + \alpha p_i) < F(x_i) \tag{3.66}$$

† This proof is essentially as given in [6].

Therefore we must have

$$F(x_i + \alpha p_i) - F(x_i) \geq 0$$

for $\alpha > 0$, and therefore

$$\lim_{\substack{\alpha \to 0 \\ \alpha > 0}} \frac{F(x_i + \alpha p_i) - F(x_i)}{\alpha} = \frac{d}{d\alpha} F(x_i + \alpha p_i)\Big|_{\alpha=0} \geq 0 \qquad (3.67)$$

But

$$\frac{d}{d\alpha} F(x_i + \alpha p_i)\Big|_{\alpha=0} = \langle g(x_i), p_i \rangle$$

$$= \langle g_i, p_i \rangle$$
$$= \langle g_i, -g_i + \beta_i p_{i-1} \rangle$$
$$= -\langle g_i, g_i \rangle = -\|g_i\|^2 \qquad (3.68)$$

where we have used the expression for p_i as given by (3.63c) and the fact that g_i and p_{i-1} are orthogonal, (3.64). Now we note that (3.68) contradicts (3.67) unless $g_i = 0$. Thus if $g_i \neq 0$ our assumption that no $\alpha > 0$ exists for which (3.66) is satisfied is invalid, which proves the theorem. We note again (Remark 4 above), the sequence terminates if $g_i = 0$ for some i.

A Smooth Functional with Positive-Definite Second Derivative

A logical question here is: When does the conjugate gradient (CG) algorithm converge? The closest available answer is that convergence occurs when the second derivative is positive definite. This is the same result as in the case of quadratic functionals. We hence now consider a smooth functional $F(x)$ for which

$$0 < m \leq F''(x) \leq M < \infty \qquad (3.69)$$

for all $x \in \mathcal{H}$, the Hilbert space of interest. In this case we have the following theorem.

Theorem 3.4.† The sequence x_n generated by the conjugate gradient algorithm starting with arbitrary x_0 converges to the unique x^* minimizing F over $\mathcal{H}$. The error estimate

$$\|x_n - x^*\| \leq \frac{1}{m} \|g(x_n)\| \qquad (3.70)$$

is valid.

† This is Theorem 5.6.1 of [8]. The proof is essentially as given there.

Theorem 3.4 is as far as we shall go in considering convergence of the CG algorithm for a general smooth functional. Before going into the proof of the theorem we show the following lemma.

Lemma 3.3.   For a smooth functional that satisfies (3.69)

$$m\|x - y\|^2 \le \langle g(x) - g(y), \; x - y \rangle \le M\|x - y\|^2 \tag{3.71}$$

and for the CG algorithm of (3.63)

$$\|g_n\|^2 \le \|p_n\|^2 \le \frac{M}{m}\|g_n\|^2 \tag{3.72}$$

To show (3.71), we expand $F(x)$ about y in a Taylor series, which gives

$$F(x) = F(y) + F'(y)(x - y) + \tfrac{1}{2}F''(y)(x - y)\cdot(x - y) + o^2(x - y)$$
$$= F(y) + \langle g(y), x - y \rangle + \tfrac{1}{2}\langle x - y, A(y)(x - y) \rangle + o^2(x - y)$$

Taking the derivative of the preceding expression, we have

$$F'(x) = g(x) = g(y) + A(y)(x - y) + o^2(x - y)$$

and by the mean value theorem

$$g(x) = g(y) + A(y + \zeta(x - y))(x - y) \qquad 0 \le \zeta \le 1$$

and hence

$$\langle g(x) - g(y), x - y \rangle = \langle x - y, A(y + \zeta(x - y))(x - y) \rangle$$

which gives (3.71) by use of (3.69).

Now looking at (3.72), to show $\|g_n\|^2 \le \|p_n\|^2$, we use (3.63c) to get

$$\|p_n\|^2 = \langle -g_n + \beta_{n-1}p_{n-1}, \; -g_n + \beta_{n-1}p_{n-1} \rangle$$
$$= \langle g_n, g_n \rangle + \beta_{n-1}^2 \langle p_{n-1}, p_{n-1} \rangle$$
$$= \|g_n\|^2 + \beta_{n-1}^2 \|p_{n-1}\|^2 \tag{3.73}$$

which follows since $\langle g_n, p_{n-1} \rangle = 0$ from (3.64). The first inequality of (3.72) follows directly from (3.73). To show $\|p_n\|^2 \le (M/m)\|g_n\|^2$ we consider

$$\langle g_n, A(x_n)g_n \rangle = \langle -p_n + \beta_{n-1}p_{n-1}, \; A(x_n)(-p_n + \beta_{n-1}p_{n-1}) \rangle$$
$$= \langle p_n, A(x_n)p_n \rangle + \beta_{n-1}^2 \langle p_{n-1}, A(x_n)p_{n-1} \rangle \tag{3.74}$$

where $A(x_n)$ is the second derivative operator of F at x_n. Equation 3.74 follows since p_n and p_{n-1} are conjugate w.r.t. $A(x_n)$. Using (3.74) with (3.69) we get

$$m\|p_n\|^2 \le \langle p_n, A(x_n)p_n \rangle \le \langle g_n, A(x_n)g_n \rangle \le M\|g_n\|^2$$

from which the last inequality of (3.72) follows. We now begin the proof of Theorem 3.4 by showing that $g(x_n) \to 0$.

By definition
$$f(\alpha) = F(x_n + \alpha p_n)$$
then
$$f'(\alpha) = \langle g(x_n + \alpha p_n), p_n \rangle$$
and
$$m\|p_n\|^2 \le f''(\alpha) = \langle A(x_n + \alpha p_n)p_n, p_n \rangle \le M\|p_n\|^2 \qquad (3.75)$$

From (3.63c)
$$f'(0) = \langle g_n, p_n \rangle = -\|g_n\|^2 < 0 \qquad (3.76)$$

Using (3.75) with (3.76), we conclude that α_n, the α that minimizes $f(\alpha)$, must satisfy
$$\max_{0 \le \alpha \le \alpha_n} f''(\alpha) \cdot \alpha_n \ge \|g_n\|^2$$

and hence
$$\alpha_n \ge \frac{\|g_n\|^2}{M\|p_n\|^2}$$

and therefore
$$\alpha_n \ge \frac{m}{M^2} \qquad (3.77)$$

from (3.72). Now expanding $F(x)$ about x_n in a Taylor series, we have
$$F(x_n + \alpha p_n) = F(x_n) + \alpha \langle g_n, p_n \rangle + \frac{\alpha^2}{2} \langle A(x_n + \zeta \alpha p_n)p_n, p_n \rangle$$

$$= F(x_n) - \alpha\|g_n\|^2 + \frac{\alpha^2}{2} \langle A(x_n + \zeta \alpha p_n)p_n, p_n \rangle$$

for $0 \le \zeta \le 1$. From (3.69) and (3.72).
$$F(x_n + \alpha p_n) \le F(x_n) - \alpha\|g_n\|^2 + \frac{1}{2}\alpha^2 \frac{M^2}{m}\|g_n\|^2$$

Thus from (3.77)
$$F(x_n + \alpha_n p_n) = F(x_{n+1}) \le F\left(x_n + \frac{m}{M^2}p_n\right)$$

$$\le F(x_n) - \frac{m}{M^2}\|g_n\|^2 + \frac{1}{2}\frac{m}{M^2}\|g_n\|^2$$

$$F(x_{n+1}) \le F(x_n) - \frac{1}{2}\frac{m}{M^2}\|g_n\|^2 \qquad (3.78)$$

According to (3.78), if $F(x)$ is bounded below then $\|g_n\| \to 0$ and hence $g_n \to 0$.

We now show that the CG descent sequence is a cauchy sequence, which hence converges. Expanding F about x_0 we have

$$
\begin{aligned}
F(x) &= F(x_0) + \langle g(x_0), x - x_0 \rangle + \tfrac{1}{2}\langle x - x_0, A(t_0)(x - x_0) \rangle \\
&\geq F(x_0) - \|g(x_0)\|\,\|x - x_0\| + \tfrac{1}{2}m\|x - x_0\|^2
\end{aligned}
\tag{3.79}
$$

$$
t_0 = x_0(1 - \zeta) + \zeta x \qquad 0 \leq \zeta \leq 1
$$

We conclude from (3.79) that for

$$
\|x - x_0\| \geq \frac{2}{m}\|g(x_0)\|
$$

$F(x) \geq F(x_0)$, and hence the set of x for which $F(x) \leq F(x_0)$ is bounded. The whole CG descent sequence is within this set so $\|x_{n+k} - x_n\|$ is bounded. From (3.71)

$$
m\|x_{n+k} - x_n\|^2 \leq \langle g_{n+k} - g_n, x_{n+k} - x_n \rangle
$$

The RHS converges to zero since $g_n \to 0$ and hence

$$
\lim_{n \to \infty} \|x_{n+k} - x_n\| = 0
$$

which means the CG descent sequence is a cauchy sequence. Since our space $\mathcal{H}$ is assumed a Hilbert space and hence complete, the CG descent sequence approaches a limit $x^* \in \mathcal{H}$.

To show that x^* is unique, we assume that there is another CG descent sequence that has the limit y. We have from (3.71)

$$
m\|x^* - y\|^2 \leq \langle g(x^*) - g(y), x - y \rangle
$$

The RHS is zero since the limit of a CG sequence has null gradient. Hence $\|x^* - y\| = 0$ and hence $x^* = y$.

To obtain the error estimate in the theorem we again apply (3.71) to get

$$
m\|x_n - x^*\|^2 \leq \langle g(x_n) - g(x^*), x_n - x^* \rangle \leq \|g(x_n) - g(x^*)\|\,\|x_n - x^*\|
$$

from which the error estimate follows since $g(x^*) = 0$.

Remarks

1. The assumptions on F'' as given by (3.69) need not apply for all $x \in \mathcal{H}$, but only for those x where $F(x) \leq F(x_0)$ since the CG sequence always remains within this region.

2. Theorem 3.4 indicates no special value for the CG descent algorithm. The results apply equally well to simple steepest descent. CG descent is used in the case of quadratic functionals because it gives rapid convergence.

Near the minimum it may be expected that the quadratic terms should dominate for a general smooth functional so that, at least asymtotically, the same rapid convergence rates should apply. It is beyond the scope of this text to show it here; however Daniel [8] has shown that this is in fact the case. CG descent in this respect is an improvement, as it is well known that steepest descent has a tendency to bog down in the neighborhood of the minimum where the gradient is small.

3. In Section 3.3, (3.56) precisely, it is shown that the convergence rate for quadratic functionals is a function of the ratio m/M. Equation 3.72 gives an upper bound on this ratio for general CG descent as

$$\frac{m}{M} \leq \frac{\| g_n \|^2}{\| p_n \|^2} \tag{3.80}$$

In using CG descent the ratio on the RHS of (3.80) is easily found.

3.5. SCALED CONJUGATE GRADIENT DESCENT IN $\mathscr{R}^n$

The idea is well established that in doing a gradient descent of a function on $\mathscr{R}^n$, if the contours of equal cost are spheres, one steepest descent step taken in the direction of the negative gradient takes one to the minimum. This is shown for $\mathscr{R}^2$ in Fig. 3.3. Of course this delightful situation seldom applys in any practically useful case, as attested to by the fact that steepest descent is well recognized to have several disadvantages as a descent method. However it does serve to illustrate that rapid descent may be expected if somehow

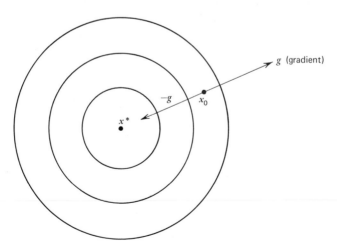

Figure 3.3   Steepest descent with spherical cost contours in $\mathscr{R}^2$.

the space in which the descent is taking place can be rescaled so that the cost contours are approximately spherical. In scaled conjugate gradient descent (SCGD) the object is to step through the space with a conjugate gradient descent cycle of n iterations. As the cycle progresses a scaling matrix is constructed that on the next cycle allows one to do a CGD cycle in a space where the cost contours are approximately spherical (for a quadratic cost function the contours will be spherical). One may thus expect swift convergence after the first cycle. With SCGD all operations are done in the original space, that is, without any change of coordinates in the space in which the operations are occurring. What happens is that a descent is accomplished that amounts to CGD in a space where the cost contours are spheres. The number of cycles may be extended indefinitely, since in each cycle the scaling matrix for the next cycle is being constructed.

The notion of rescaling to obtain spherical cost contours is of course not new. The Fletcher and Powell method [10] is one in which the eigenvalues of the second derivative of the cost function are one at a time set to unity as the iterations progress. This has the effect of rescaling one coordinate direction at a time so that after one cycle of n iterations the condition of spherical cost contours should be reached. A problem with this method, which has been pointed out by Luenberger [12], is that it may be expected to badly decondition the problem if one eigenvalue of the second derivative is set equal to unity and the remaining eigenvalues differ greatly in relative magnitude from unity. Luenberger's proposal to alleviate this problem is partial conjugate gradient descent, which is just restarting CGD after $s < n$ iterations, that is, without completing a full cycle. He shows this to have some real advantages in speeding up descent. Bertsekas [11] introduces the notion of scaling in using partial conjugate gradient descent and shows the proper scaling to get the desired increase in descent rate. With SCGD the approach is to complete a cycle of n iterations of CGD. Then using the information collected in the first cycle, a rescaling is done, which attempts to at once change all eigenvalues of the second derivative to unity. Subsequent cycles continually update the rescaling effort in the same manner, that is, an all-at-once rescaling after each cycle.

The order of progression here is to give the algorithm and then to give the theoretical justification for it. This is then followed by some simple examples of its use.

The Algorithm

In this section we make a problem statement and an introduction of notation and then state the specific steps in the algorithm. We seek to perform a descent on the functional F from $\mathscr{R}^n$ to $\mathscr{R}^1$; the argument is $x \in \mathscr{X} = \mathscr{R}^n$. The assumption is that F is a smooth functional for which a gradient $g(x)$ at x, can be found for all $x \in \mathscr{X}$. As in all descent processes, the initial argument x_0 is assumed given and the desire is to construct a sequence $x_0, x_1, \ldots$ such that

$$F(x_{k+1}) < F(x_k)$$

The scaling matrix here, denoted by S^i, is an $n \times n$ real, symmetric matrix where the superscript i denotes the particular cycle in the descent sequence. In each cycle there are n steps and the index on these is $k = 0, 1, 2, \ldots, n - 1$. In general the cycle index is indicated by a superscript while the particular step within a cycle is indicated by a subscript. Standard matrix notation† is assumed with superscript $+$ indicating transpose. For convenience $g_k = g(x_k)$ is used.

The algorithm in the ith cycle proceeds as follows:

$$p_0 = -S^i g_0, \qquad S^0 = I \tag{3.81a}$$

$$x_{k+1} = x_k + \alpha_k p_k \tag{3.81b}$$

$$\alpha_k = \alpha > 0 \quad \text{that minimizes} \quad F(x_k + \alpha p_k) \tag{3.81c}$$

$$p_{k+1} = -S^i g_{k+1} + \beta_k p_k \tag{3.81d}$$

$$\beta_k = \frac{g_{k+1}^+ S^i g_{k+1}}{g_k^+ S^i g_k} \tag{3.81e}$$

$$S_{k+1}^{i+1} = S_k^{i+1} + \eta_k p_k p_k^+, \qquad S_0^{i+1} = 0 \tag{3.81f}$$

$$\eta_k = \frac{\alpha_k}{g_k^+ S^i g_k} \tag{3.81g}$$

$$S^{i+1} = S_n^{i+1} \tag{3.81h}$$

$$x_0^{i+1} = x_n^i \tag{3.81j}$$

We note here one basic fact that arises from α_k minimizing $F(x_k + \alpha p_k)$. Thus

$$\frac{d}{d\alpha} F(x_k + \alpha p_k) \bigg|_{\alpha = \alpha_k} = g^+(x_k + \alpha_k p_k)p_k = g_{k+1}^+ p_k = 0 \tag{3.82}$$

Using p_{k+1} as defined by (3.81d) and (3.82), we then get

$$-g_{k+1}^+ p_{k+1} = g_{k+1}^+ S^i g_{k+1} - \beta_k g_{k+1}^+ p_k = g_{k+1}^+ S^i g_{k+1} \tag{3.83}$$

† Since all operations are in $\mathscr{R}^n$ in this section the scalar product for a given x and y is written $\langle x, y \rangle = x^+ y = \sum_{i=1}^{n} x_i y_i$.

It may be noted from (3.81) that the algorithm is straightforward CGD as in Fletcher and Reeves [5] and (3.63) in the initial cycle where $S^i = I =$ identity matrix. Also, the sequence terminates only if an x_k is reached where $g(x_k) = 0$. Storage requirements for the algorithm are n memory locations each for x_k, x_{k+1}, g_{k+1}, p_k, and p_{k+1} and n^2 locations each required to store S^i and S^{i+1}. This gives a total of $2n^2 + 5n$ locations in all. Some saving in this may be realized if advantage is taken of the fact that S^i and S^{i+1} are symmetric. For SCGD the algorithm requires

$$n^2 + \frac{n(n+1)}{2} = \frac{3n^2 + n}{2}$$

more multiplications and additions per iteration than ordinary conjugate gradient descent.

Theory: The Three Basic Spaces

Underlying the discussion of the SCGD algorithm are the three spaces as shown in Fig. 3.4. These are labeled $\mathcal{X}$, $\mathcal{Y}$, and $\mathcal{R}^1$. Here $\mathcal{X} = \mathcal{R}^n$, $\mathcal{Y} = \mathcal{R}^n$, and $\mathcal{R}^1$ is the one dimensional real space. The problem is to find $x^* \in \mathcal{X}$ such that $F(x) \geq F(x^*)$ for all x in some neighborhood of x^*. Here, as diagrammed in Fig. 3.4, F is the cost functional on $\mathcal{X}$ and to $\mathcal{R}^1$. The approach to finding this x^* is by descent from an initial guess x_0. We speak of $\mathcal{X}$ as the original space and $\mathcal{Y}$ as the secondary space.

In the original space $\mathcal{X}$ it is assumed that descent is difficult because of the unconditioned nature of the cost contours, that is, their nonspherical nature. So we seek a transformation of coordinates, called T in Fig. 3.4,

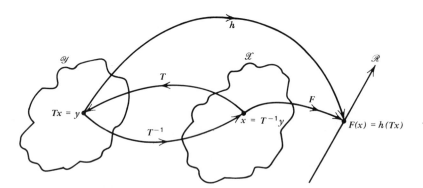

Figure 3.4   The three spaces involved in scaled conjugate gradient descent.

to the secondary space $\mathscr{Y}$ where T is such that in $\mathscr{Y}$ the cost contours are of a shape more conducive to rapid descent. For simplicity, T is assumed to be linear, and since the transformation from $\mathscr{R}^n$ to $\mathscr{R}^n$ is linear, it may be thought of as an $n \times n$, real matrix. If T is to be a meaningful change of coordinates then it may be assumed nonsingular, so that T^{-1} exists and hence one may also transform back from $\mathscr{Y}$ to $\mathscr{X}$.

Restriction to linear T restricts the class of functionals for which the cost contours can be brought to the desired spherical character in $\mathscr{Y}$. It is shown below that for $F(x)$ quadratic in x, a linear T can be found that produces the desired shape to the contours, that is, one that leads to one-step convergence of steepest descent in $\mathscr{Y}$. It is also shown below that SCGD in $\mathscr{X}$ corresponds to CGD in $\mathscr{Y}$ and that the scaling matrix S^{i+1} produced by the SCGD algorithm will be such that in the case of quadratic $F(x)$, the transformation produced will make the cost contours spherical in $\mathscr{Y}$.

The Form of the Underlying Quadratic Cost Function on $\mathscr{X}$

The functional upon which SCGD is based and for which convergence to the minimum x^* is obtained in one cycle is the quadratic of the form

$$F(x) = f_0 + a^+x + \tfrac{1}{2}x^+Ax \tag{3.84}$$

where now $f_0 \in \mathscr{R}^1$, $a \in \mathscr{R}^n$, and A is a real, symmetric, $n \times n$ matrix. In order to insure that this F has a unique minimum x^* we also assume that A is positive definite. Thus A is a real, symmetric, positive definite, $n \times n$ matrix.

For the $F(x)$ of (3.84) the gradient at a given $x \in \mathscr{X}$, $g_{\mathscr{X}}(x)$ is given by

$$g_{\mathscr{X}}(x) = \nabla_x F(x) = a + Ax \tag{3.85}$$

From which we see that the minimum x^* must be given by

$$x^* = -A^{-1}a \tag{3.86}$$

which, under the assumptions on A, is unique and well defined. Taking the derivative of $g_{\mathscr{X}}(x)$ in (3.85) w.r.t. x gives the second derivative of $F(x)$ as

$$D_x^2 F(x) = A \qquad \forall x \in \mathscr{X} \tag{3.87}$$

Again, since A is assumed positive definite and thus the second derivative is a positive-definite operator, (3.87) shows that the x^* of (3.86) is the global minimum in $\mathscr{X}$ of the F of (3.84).

The Transformation T Which Leads to Spherical Cost Contours in $\mathcal{Y}$

We now consider a linear transformation T from $\mathcal{X}$ to $\mathcal{Y}$, $y = Tx$, such that the cost contours in $\mathcal{Y}$ will cause steepest descent to converge in one step for a cost functional as in (3.84). We consider

$$T = A^{1/2} \tag{3.88}$$

where $A^{1/2}$ is the square root matrix of A such that

$$A^{1/2}A^{1/2} = A \tag{3.89}$$

The assumptions on A are already sufficient to insure that a real, symmetric, positive definite $A^{1/2}$ exists. And, since $A^{1/2}$ is positive definite, $A^{-1/2} = (A^{1/2})^{-1}$ exists and

$$\begin{aligned} A^{-1/2}A &= A^{1/2} \\ (A^{-1/2})^+ A &= A^{1/2} \\ AA^{-1/2} &= A^{1/2} \end{aligned} \tag{3.90}$$

Thus using

$$\begin{aligned} y &= A^{1/2}x \\ x &= A^{-1/2}y \end{aligned} \tag{3.91}$$

we take the functional F of (3.84) into a functional on $\mathcal{Y}$, $h(y)$, where

$$\begin{aligned} h(y) = F(A^{-1/2}y) &= f_0 + a^+ A^{-1/2}y + \tfrac{1}{2}y^+y \\ &= f_0 + (A^{-1/2}a)^+ y + \tfrac{1}{2}y^+y \end{aligned} \tag{3.92}$$

where use has been made of the fact that A and $A^{-1/2}$ are symmetrical. The gradient of h at a given $y \in \mathcal{Y}$, $g_{\mathcal{Y}}(y)$ is now

$$g_{\mathcal{Y}}(y) = \nabla_y h(y) = A^{-1/2}a + y \tag{3.93}$$

We immediately make the following observations from (3.93):

1. The minimizing element in $\mathcal{Y}$, y^*, is given by

$$y^* = -A^{-1/2}a \tag{3.94}$$

[It may be noted from (3.92) that the second derivative matrix of h is the unit matrix that is positive definite.]

2. Starting at an initial y_0,

$$y_1 = y_0 + -g_{\mathcal{Y}}(y_0) = -A^{-1/2}a = y^*$$

that is, one step in the negative gradient direction from any y_0 takes one to the minimizing element y^*. From (3.86) and (3.94) it can be seen that

$$x^* = A^{-1/2}y^*$$

which agrees with (3.91). Also, $h(y)$ of (3.92) may be factored into the form

$$
\begin{aligned}
h(y) &= \tfrac{1}{2}(y - y^*)^+(y - y^*) + f_0 - \tfrac{1}{2}y^{*+}y^* \\
&= \tfrac{1}{2}\rho^2(y, y^*) + \text{constant}
\end{aligned}
\tag{3.95}
$$

where

$$\rho(y, y^*) = \sqrt{(y - y^*)^+(y - y^*)}$$

which may be interpreted as the euclidean distance from y to y^*. That is, we see that cost at a given y is a function only of the distance of y from the minimizing element y^*. Thus the cost contours must be spheres. We conclude that $T = A^{1/2}$ is the proper coordinate transformation to achieve the properties desired in $\mathscr{Y}$.

Conjugate Gradient Descent in $\mathscr{Y}$

We show here that SCGD in $\mathscr{X}$ corresponds to conjugate gradient descent (CGD) in $\mathscr{Y}$.

We begin by considering CGD of h in $\mathscr{Y}$. CGD from (3.63) used on h, which is the algorithm of Fletcher and Reeves, from [5], gives

$$
\begin{aligned}
d_0 &= -g_{y_0} \\
y_{k+1} &= y_k + \alpha_k d_k \qquad y_0 \text{ given} \\
\alpha_k &= \alpha \qquad \text{which minimizes} \quad h(y_k + \alpha d_k) \\
d_{k+1} &= -g_{y_k} + \beta_k d_k \\
\beta_k &= \frac{g_{y_k}^+ g_{y_k}}{g_{y_{k+1}}^+ g_{y_{k+1}}}
\end{aligned}
\tag{3.96}
$$

where now

$$g_{y_k} = g_{\mathscr{Y}}(y_k) = \nabla_y h(y_k)$$

is the gradient of h at $y_k \in \mathscr{Y}$.

We now consider $\mathscr{X}$ and $\mathscr{Y}$ related through

$$
\begin{aligned}
y &= Tx \\
x &= T^{-1}x
\end{aligned}
\tag{3.97}
$$

and consider what the result of CGD in $\mathscr{Y}$, as in (3.96), means in $\mathscr{X}$. To see this we first need to consider the relationship of the gradients in $\mathscr{X}$ and $\mathscr{Y}$.

The starting point for this is the relationship

$$h(y) = F(x) = F(T^{-1}y)$$

from which

$$g_{\mathscr{Y}}(y) = \nabla_y h(y) = \nabla_y F(T^{-1}y)$$
$$= T^{-1+} \nabla_x F(x)|_{x=T^{-1}y}$$
$$= T^{-1+} g_{\mathscr{X}}(x) \tag{3.98}$$

By use of (3.98) and

$$T^{-1} d_k = p_k \tag{3.99}$$

CGD in $\mathscr{Y}$ of (3.96) transforms into

$$p_0 = -T^{-1}T^{-1+}g_{x_0}$$

$$x_{k+1} = x_k + \alpha_k p_k, \qquad x_0 \text{ given}$$

$$\alpha_k = \alpha \qquad \text{which minimizes} \quad F(x_k + \alpha p_k) \tag{3.100}$$

$$p_{k+1} = -T^{-1}T^{-1+}g_{x_k} + \beta_k p_k$$

$$\beta_k = \frac{g_{x_k}^+ T^{-1}T^{-1+}g_{x_k}}{g_{x_{k-1}}^+ T^{-1}T^{-1+}g_{x_{k-1}}}$$

in $\mathscr{X}$, where now

$$g_{x_k} = g_{\mathscr{X}}(x_k) = \nabla_x F(x_k)$$

has been used. Equation 3.100 may be recognized as (3.81a) through (3.81e) with

$$S^i = T^{-1}T^{-1+} \tag{3.101}$$

and

$$g_k = g_{x_k}$$

It was shown in (3.95) that if $T = A^{1/2}$ with T symmetric and with F quadratic in $\mathscr{X}$, then the cost contours in $\mathscr{Y}$ are spherical and steepest descent converges (again, for the quadratic cost case) in one step. It remains to be shown that if the cost functional F is quadratic in the form of (3.84), then indeed

$$S^{i+1} = A^{-1/2}A^{-1/2+} = A^{-1}$$

The Scaling Matrix S^{i+1} in the Case of a Quadratic Cost Functional

Using SCGD of (3.81), we show here that the scaling matrix constructed by the algorithm is the inverse of the second derivative matrix, that is,

$$S^{i+1} = A^{-1} \tag{3.102}$$

for

$$F(x) = f_0 + a^+ x + \tfrac{1}{2} x^+ A x \qquad (3.103)$$

The condition on this is that S^i and A be real, symmetric, and positive definite.

We first note that if, referring to Fig. 3.4 again, $\mathscr{X}$ and $\mathscr{Y}$ are related by the transformation

$$y = Tx$$

and the criterion in $\mathscr{Y}$ is

$$h(y) = F(T^{-1}y) = f_0 + (T^{-1}a)^+ y + \tfrac{1}{2} y^+ T^{-1+} A T^{-1} y$$

and if the set

$$\{d_k\} \qquad k = 0, 1, 2, \ldots, n - 1$$

is conjugate w.r.t. the second derivative matrix of $h(y)$, $T^{-1+} A T^{-1}$, then the set

$$\{p_k\} \qquad k = 0, 1, 2, \ldots, n - 1 \qquad (3.104)$$

is conjugate w.r.t. A if

$$d_k = T p_k$$

This can be seen by simply noting that if $d_k, k = 0, 1, \ldots, n - 1$, are conjugate w.r.t. $T^{-1+} A T^{-1}$, then

$$d_k^+ T^{-1+} A T^{-1} d_j = 0 \qquad k \neq j \qquad (3.105)$$

But if $d_k = T p_k$ then (3.105) gives

$$p_k^+ A p_j = 0 \qquad k \neq j \qquad (3.106)$$

which shows the p_k of (3.104) conjugate w.r.t. A. If A is positive definite (as assumed), then also

$$p_k^+ A p_k > 0 \qquad \text{if} \quad p_k \neq 0 \qquad (3.107)$$

It has been shown that SCGD in $\mathscr{X}$, (3.100), corresponds to conjugate gradient descent in $\mathscr{Y}$, (3.96). It is shown in Section 3.3 that the CGD algorithm produces a set of descent directions that are conjugate w.r.t. the second derivative matrix of the cost functional when it is quadratic. Thus, with the quadratic cost functional of (3.103), the descent directions in $\mathscr{Y}$, $d_k, k = 0, 1, \ldots, n - 1$, generated in one cycle of SCGD are conjugate w.r.t. the second derivative matrix in $\mathscr{Y}$ and hence the set $p_k, k = 0, 1, \ldots, n - 1$, in $\mathscr{X}$ is conjugate w.r.t. A, the second derivative in $\mathscr{X}$. SCGD is thus a conjugate direction method.

The next fact required in showing that $S^{i+1} = A^{-1}$ is the identity

$$p_k^+ A p_k = \frac{g_k^+ S^i g_k}{\alpha_k} \tag{3.108}$$

where p_k is the kth descent direction, g_k the gradient at x_k, α_k the step-size constant, and S^i the scaling matrix. To see this let us consider the gradient of $F(x)$ of (3.103) at a given x_k which is

$$g_{\mathscr{X}}(x_k) = g_k = a + A x_k$$

and

$$g_{\mathscr{X}}(x_{k+1}) = g_{k+1} = a + A x_{k+1}$$

Thus

$$\begin{aligned} g_{k+1} - g_k &= A(x_{k+1} - x_k) \\ &= \alpha_k A p_k \end{aligned} \tag{3.109}$$

by use of (3.81b). From (3.109)

$$p_k^+ A p_k = \frac{p_k^+ (g_{k+1} - g_k)}{\alpha_k} = -\frac{p_k^+ g_k}{\alpha_k} \tag{3.110}$$

which arises because α_k is chosen to minimize $F(x_k + \alpha p_k)$ and thus g_{k+1} and p_k must be orthogonal, as given by (3.82). Now using the expression for p_k in SCGD from (3.81d) in (3.110), we obtain

$$p_k^+ A p_k = \frac{g_k^+ S^i g_k - \beta_k p_{k-1}^+ g_k}{\alpha_k} \tag{3.111}$$

But again p_{k-1} and g_k are orthogonal by the same arguments by which p_k and g_{k+1} were found orthogonal, that is, (3.82). Thus the second term in the numerator on the right-hand side of (3.111) vanishes, which gives (3.108), the desired result.

We now show that $S^{i+1} = A^{-1}$ as constructed by SCGD of (3.81) if $F(x)$ is quadratic of the form of (3.103). To begin we define the matrix

$$P \triangleq [p_0, p_1, \ldots, p_{n-1}]$$

that is, P is the matrix whose columns are the descent directions obtained in one cycle of SCGD. As we have seen above in this section, if the cost functional $F(x)$ is quadratic as in (3.103), then the descent directions $\{p_k\}$, $k = 0, 1, \ldots,$ $n - 1$, are conjugate w.r.t. A, the second derivative matrix. Thus by (3.107)

$$P^+ A P = \Lambda \tag{3.112}$$

where Λ is a diagonal matrix, that is,

$$\Lambda = \text{diag}\,[p_0^+ A p_0,\, p_1^+ A p_1,\, \ldots,\, p_{n-1}^+ A p_{n-1}] \tag{3.113}$$

Since A is assumed positive definite, the set $\{p_k\}$, $k = 0, 1, \ldots, n-1$, is linearly independent and hence P has an inverse. Thus (3.112) gives

$$A = (P^+)^{-1} \Lambda P^{-1}$$

from which

$$A^{-1} = P \Lambda^{-1} P^+ \tag{3.114}$$

Using the fact that Λ is diagonal as given by (3.113), we may write (3.114) as

$$A^{-1} = \sum_{k=0}^{n-1} \frac{p_k p_k^+}{p_k^+ A p_k}$$

which using (3.108) becomes

$$A^{-1} = \sum_{k=0}^{n-1} \frac{\alpha_k p_k p_k^+}{g_k^+ S^i g_k} \tag{3.115}$$

We now simply note that $S_n^{i+1} = S^{i+1}$ as realized by SCGD in (3.81f), (3.81g), and (3.81h) is the right-hand side of (3.115) and thus

$$S^{i+1} = A^{-1} \tag{3.116}$$

if the cost functional is quadratic of the form

$$F(x) = f_0 + a^+ x + \tfrac{1}{2} x^+ A x$$

which is the result desired.

Summary

Our discussion of the theory of the three basic spaces up to this point is summarized below. (Terminology here is that of Fig. 3.4 and (3.81). All statements are in reference to the quadratic cost functional $F(x) = f_0 + a^+ x + \tfrac{1}{2} x^+ A x$.)

1. Above (3.95) it is shown that the transformation T from $\mathcal{X}$ to $\mathcal{Y}$ that leads to spherical cost contours in $\mathcal{Y}$ is $T = A^{1/2}$.

2. Above (3.101) it is shown that SCGD in $\mathcal{X}$ corresponds to CGD in $\mathcal{Y}$ with $S^i = T^{-1+} T^{-1} = T^{-2}$ when S^i is symmetrical [which it is when it is constructed as in the algorithm, (3.81)].

3. Above (3.116) it is shown that $S^{i+1} = A^{-1}$ if A and S^i are symmetric and positive definite.

We thus conclude that SCGD in $\mathcal{X} = \mathcal{R}^n$ implies CGD in $\mathcal{Y} = \mathcal{R}^n$ where $x \in \mathcal{X}$ and $y \in \mathcal{Y}$ are related by $y = Tx$, $T^{-2} = S^i$. If the cost functional is quadratic, the cost contours in $\mathcal{Y}$ are spherical after the first cycle of SCGD.

Remarks

Positive Definiteness of the Scaling Matrix S^{i+1}. Let us consider the scaling matrix S^{i+1} as constructed by the SCGD algorithm. From (3.115), (3.116), and (3.81h) we have

$$S^{i+1} = \sum_{k=0}^{n-1} \frac{\alpha_k}{g_k^+ S^i g_k} p_k p_k^+ \tag{3.117}$$

Considering the quadratic form associated with this $n \times n$ matrix, we see

$$x^+ S^{i+1} x = \sum_{k=0}^{n-1} \frac{\alpha_k}{g_k^+ S^i g_k} x^+ p_k p_k^+ x$$

$$= \sum_{k=0}^{n-1} \frac{\alpha_k}{g_k^+ S^i g_k} (p_k^+ x)^2 \tag{3.118}$$

It is seen from (3.118), that the RHS is positive if

1. $\alpha_k > 0$
2. S^i is positive definite
3. $p_k^+ x \neq 0$ for all k

Since the step-size search in the algorithm is only for $\alpha > 0$, $\alpha_k > 0$. The p_k generated by the algorithm is conjugate w.r.t. the second derivative of the cost function and if this is positive definite (as it must be if we are to have a meaningful minimization problem), the p_k are linearly independent. Hence $x_k^+ p_k = 0$ for all k does not occur for any $x \neq 0$. Thus in doing a descent, S^{i+1} is positive definite if S^i is positive definite. Since at the start $S^0 = I$, the identity matrix, which is positive definite, subsequent S^i are positive definite.

From (3.118) one may see how the SCGD algorithm may be expected to terminate. The iterations will continue until either an iteration for which $g_k = 0$, which is the optimum sought, will have been found, or through error (roundoff or whatever) some p_k will be reached for which no $\alpha_k > 0$ can be found that produces $F(x_k + \alpha_k p_k) < F(x_k)$.

The Step-Size Constant α_k. An interesting feature about the SCGD algorithm is that when it is descending on a quadratic cost functional, after the first cycle, and the algorithm has constructed a scaling matrix that is the inverse of the second derivative matrix, thus the second derivative matrix in $\mathcal{Y}$ is the identity matrix, then

$$\alpha_k = 1$$

for all iterations.† This is very helpful in accomplishing the search [in (3.81c)]

---

† This may be seen by use of the fact that the second derivative matrix in $\mathcal{Y}$ is the identity matrix and then evaluating α_k by (3.16c).

to find the α that minimizes $F(x_k + \alpha p_k)$, for it immediately gives the right order of magnitude for α at which to begin the search. Also, as the iterations progress, the departure of α_k from unity gives an indication of how well the scaling is being accomplished.

Solution to Sets of Linear Simultaneous Equations. SCGD is also useful (as is CGD) in finding the solutions to

$$Ax = -a \tag{3.119}$$

for A real, symmetric, and positive definite. Use of

$$f(x) = a^+ x + \tfrac{1}{2} x^+ A x \tag{3.120}$$

for one cycle of SCGD produces

$$x^* = -A^{-1}a$$

which is the desired solution of (3.119). Subsequent iterations may be run to improve the accuracy to whatever degree is required. Also, the scaling matrix S^{i+1} obtained after the first and subsequent cycles gives an approximation to A^{-1}. The $\{p_k\}$ $k = 0, 1, \ldots, n - 1$ for any cycle gives a set of vectors conjugate w.r.t. A, if such is desired. If one wishes a solution to

$$Bx = c$$

where B is nonsymmetric and not necessarily positive definite, but nonsingular, a solution may be found by letting

$$A = B^+ B$$

and

$$a = -B^+ c$$

in the quadratic cost function of (3.120). The result in the SCGD algorithm produces

$$x^* = -A^{-1}a = B^{-1}c$$

To find the approximation for the inverse of B we use

$$S^{i+1}B^+ = A^{-1}B^+ = B^{-1}$$

In general if the SCGD algorithm is used to find the inverse of a matrix, in the manner shown above, because of the way the S^{i+1} (the scaling matrix) is constructed, the accuracy of the inverse obtained in the first cycle may be expected to be roughly as good as the obtained solution to the set of linear equations. As S^{i+1} is reconstructed from the null matrix in each cycle, subsequent cycles will however not necessarily improve the accuracy of the approximation.

Convergence. Let us consider convergence of SCGD in a slightly more quantitative manner. We consider convergence in $\mathcal{Y}$ (see Fig. 3.4) since it is for CGD that convergence results are available. To this end let us assume we are descending on a quadratic criterion $h(y)$ such that the eigenvalues of the second derivative matrix of h lie in the interval $[m, M]$. To have a meaningful descent problem, $0 < m \leq M$ may be assumed to apply. Using the result of (3.55) here, we get as a measure of the descent rate the result

$$\frac{h(y^{k+1}) - h(y^*)}{h(y^k) - h(y^*)} \leq \left(\frac{M - m}{M + m}\right)^2 \qquad (3.121)$$

where y^k is the point reached at the kth conjugate gradient descent iteration and y^* is the minimizing element. But with SCGD the scaling matrix after the first cycle is such that the second derivative matrix of h is the unit matrix in $\mathcal{Y}$. For the unit matrix the eigenvalues are all unity and thus we have $m = M = 1$, which results in the RHS of (3.121) going to zero. We have seen this result before in the fact that for a quadratic cost functional, the scaling constructed by the SCGD algorithm is such that the minimizing element is reached in one steepest descent iteration, and the first iteration in a CGD cycle is always a steepest descent step. This is what is termed *superlinear convergence* by Luenberger [12]. Thus SCGD exhibits superlinear convergence after the first cycle.

An Initial Guess for the Scaling Matrix S^0. The SCGD algorithm as given in (3.81) uses the initial guess for the scaling matrix $S^0 = I$, the identity matrix. There is of course no need for starting with the identity matrix. This is done for simplicity and convenience only. If for a given cost functional one has, or at least has an estimate for, the second derivative matrix (A let us call it) in the region where the descent is begun, then faster initial descent may be expected if the initial scaling matrix $S^0 = A^{-1}$ is used.

Example 3.2

As a first example of the use of SCGD on a cost function let us consider the function $\mathcal{R}^2$ as in Example 3.1.

$$F(x) = 1 + x_1 + x_2 + \tfrac{1}{2}x_1^2 + x_1x_2 + x_2^2$$

$$= 1 + [1 \quad 1]\begin{bmatrix} x_1 \\ x_2 \end{bmatrix} + \tfrac{1}{2}[x_1 \quad x_2]\begin{bmatrix} 1 & 1 \\ 1 & 2 \end{bmatrix}\begin{bmatrix} x_1 \\ x_2 \end{bmatrix}$$

$$= f_0 + a^+ \quad x \quad + \tfrac{1}{2} \quad x^+ \quad A \quad x \qquad (3.122)$$

The sequence is started, as in Example 3.1, at $x_0 = 0$. We have from (3.86) and Example 3.1 that $x^* = -A^{-1}a$, which gives here

$$x^* = \begin{bmatrix} -1 \\ 0 \end{bmatrix} \tag{3.123}$$

For the first attempt here at the use of SCGD let us choose the initial guess scaling matrix $S_0 = I$, the identity matrix as prescribed in (3.81a). So for the first cycle of two iterations here, the gradients, the descent directions, the elements in the descent sequence, and so on are the same as for conjugate gradient descent, which was done in Example 3.1. Thus we shall here use the gradients, descent directions, and so on from that example and we show only how SCGD uses these elements to construct the scaling matrix for the next cycle S^1. Thus using $S^0 = I$ and results from Example 3.1, we have

$$x_0 = [0 \quad 0]^+$$
$$g_0 = [1 \quad 1]^+$$
$$p_0 = [-1 \quad -1]^+$$
$$\alpha_0 = \tfrac{2}{5}$$
$$x_1 = x_0 + \alpha_0 p_0 = [-\tfrac{2}{5} \quad -\tfrac{2}{5}]^+$$

From (3.81f)

$$S_1^1 = S_0^1 + \eta_0 p_0 p_0^+ \qquad S_0^1 = 0$$

$$\eta_0 = \frac{\alpha_0}{g_0^+ S^0 g_0} = \frac{\tfrac{2}{5}}{2} = \frac{1}{5}$$

$$S_1^1 = \tfrac{1}{5}\begin{bmatrix} -1 \\ -1 \end{bmatrix}[-1 \quad -1] = \begin{bmatrix} \tfrac{1}{5} & \tfrac{1}{5} \\ \tfrac{1}{5} & \tfrac{1}{5} \end{bmatrix}$$

which completes the first iteration.

For the second iteration, again using the results from Example 3.1, we get

$$x_1 = [-\tfrac{2}{5} \quad -\tfrac{2}{5}]^+$$
$$g_1 = [\tfrac{1}{5} \quad \tfrac{1}{5}]^+$$
$$p_1 = [-\tfrac{6}{25} \quad \tfrac{4}{25}]^+$$
$$\alpha_1 = \tfrac{5}{2}$$
$$x_2 = [-1 \quad 0]^+ = x^* \tag{3.123}$$

Continuing the construction of S^1 using (3.81), we obtain

$$S_2^1 = S_1^1 + \eta_1 p_1 p_1^+$$

$$\eta_1 = \frac{\alpha_1}{g_1^+ S^0 g_1} = \frac{\frac{5}{2}}{\frac{2}{25}} = \frac{125}{4}$$

$$S_2^1 = \begin{bmatrix} \frac{1}{5} & \frac{1}{5} \\ \frac{1}{5} & \frac{1}{5} \end{bmatrix} + \frac{125}{4} \begin{bmatrix} -\frac{6}{25} \\ \frac{4}{25} \end{bmatrix} \begin{bmatrix} -\frac{6}{25} & \frac{4}{25} \end{bmatrix}$$

$$= \begin{bmatrix} 2 & -1 \\ -1 & 1 \end{bmatrix} = S^1 \qquad\qquad (3.124)$$

It may thus be seen that

$$S^1 = A^{-1}$$

where A is the second derivative matrix of the function of (3.122) which confirms (3.116). We have from (3.123) that the sequence has converged to the minimum of the function under consideration. Thus SCGD has converged after the first cycle, as did the CGD sequence. This was of course as expected, since the function under consideration was quadratic. As both descent methods were done in full precision, convergence was precisely to the correct value for the minimum. However by SCGD we now have the scaling matrix of (3.124), which is the inverse of the second derivative matrix. To see how SCGD might offer some advantage for descent, even in this very simple case, let us do the descent for this function once again starting at the same initial point, that is, $x_0 = \mathbf{0}$. However this time we let the initial guess for the scaling matrix S^0 be

$$S^0 = \begin{bmatrix} 2 & -1 \\ -1 & 1 \end{bmatrix} \qquad\qquad (3.125)$$

which we know to be the inverse of the second derivative matrix. From just above we have $g_0 = \begin{bmatrix} 1 & 1 \end{bmatrix}^+$ and use of this in (3.81a) gives

$$p_0 = -S^0 g_0 \begin{bmatrix} 2 & -1 \\ -1 & 1 \end{bmatrix} \begin{bmatrix} 1 \\ 1 \end{bmatrix} = \begin{bmatrix} -1 \\ 0 \end{bmatrix}$$

Now use of (3.81b) gives

$$x_1 = x_0 + \alpha_0 p_0$$

$$= \begin{bmatrix} 0 \\ 0 \end{bmatrix} + \alpha_0 \begin{bmatrix} -1 \\ 0 \end{bmatrix}$$

and we note that for $\alpha_0 = 1$ we have

$$x_1 = \begin{bmatrix} -1 \\ 0 \end{bmatrix} = x^*$$

that is, SCGD here has converged to the minimum in one iteration. It may be restarted from any initial state, that is, x_0, and if we use S^0 as given in (3.125) it will always converge to the minimum in one step with $\alpha_0 = 1$.

Example 3.3

Another quadratic cost functional

For an example of the use of the algorithm with the computer, the algorithm was tested with the simple quadratic criterion

$$F(x) = \tfrac{1}{2} x^+ A x \tag{3.126}$$

where A is the diagonal, positive-definite matrix

$$A = \text{diag} \; [0.01, 0.1, 1.0, 1.0, 10.0, 100.0] \tag{3.127}$$

The idea here was to use a cost criterion for which the minimizing element was known, the step size $[\alpha_k$ of (3.81c)$]$ could be determined precisely, and the SCGD descent properties were well understood. A, the second derivative matrix of (3.127), was chosen so as to have a wide range in the magnitude of its eigenvalues. For this case since the matrix is diagonal it can easily be seen that

$$\frac{\lambda_{\max}}{\lambda_{\min}} = \frac{100.0}{0.01} = 10^4 \tag{3.128}$$

which gives eigenvalues that are both small and large w.r.t. unity.

The iterations were started at

$$x_0^+ = [10, 10, 10, 10, 10, 10] \tag{3.129}$$

and run with both CGD and SCGD to see if the scaling properties of SCGD actually gave any real advantage. The results are shown in Table 3.1 for both descent algorithms for five cycles. The cost function values are the same for both descent methods through the first cycle since for the first cycle the two descent methods are identical. Descent was dramatically faster for SCGD after the first cycle, which was as expected. The final state reached by the SCGD algorithm after the five cycles was

$$x^* = [-1.04E - 41, 1.8E - 43, 3.19E - 44,$$
$$3.19E - 44, 3.91E - 44, -5.78E - 45] \tag{3.130}$$

**Table 3.1   Descent on Quadratic Criterion
with Conjugate Gradient Descent and Scaled
Conjugate Gradient Descent**

	Cost Functional Value	
Cycle	CGD	SCGD
0	5605.3	5605.3
1	$3.936E - 01$	$3.936E - 01$
2	$2.871E - 06$	$1.511E - 14$
3	$3.021E - 11$	$9.365E - 42$
4	$2.107E - 15$	$4.374E - 59$
5	$1.601E - 19$	$< 1.0E - 79$

$$x_0^+ = \lceil 10, 10, 10, 10, 10, 10 \rceil$$
$$\text{SCGD } x_{\text{cycle 5}}^+ = [-1.04E - 41,$$
$$1.8E - 43, 3.19E - 44,$$
$$3.19E - 44, 3.91E - 44,$$
$$-5.78E - 45]$$

which is also given in Table 3.1. We note the following:

1. Considering the largest and smallest components of x^*, we can write

$$\frac{|x_i|_{\max}}{|x_i|_{\min}} = \frac{1.04E - 41}{5.78E - 45} \cong 10^4$$

which is approximately the same ratio as the ratio of largest to smallest magnitudes of eigenvalues in the second derivative matrix A as seen in (3.128). This ratio of largest to smallest magnitude of components was established at the end of the first cycle and maintained thereafter. The ordering of the magnitudes of the components of x^*, again as could be expected, was in inverse order to the magnitude of the eigenvalues to which the component (of x^*) corresponded. As a matter of interest, the ratio of magnitudes of components of the solution obtained by CGD after five cycles was approximately 10^6.

2. The cost functional minimizing argument [x^* of (3.130)] is seen to be accurate to a minimum of 40 significant figures. SCGD here shows itself to be a powerful tool for finding to very high accuracy the minima of quadratic functionals. This capability may be translated to the equivalent problem of finding solutions to the related system of linear, simultaneous equations (i.e., $Ax = -a$ for the quadratic functional of (3.84).

3. Convergence after the first cycle was very rapid with SCGD. The criterion was reduced by a factor of about 100 on each iteration. One iteration reduced the criterion by a factor of 10^9.

To test the algorithms sensitivity to error in step size α_k [of (3.81c)], the descent in the preceding case was run with a fixed 1% error in the determination of α_k. The correct value of α_k was calculated at each iteration and the resulting α_k was then multiplied by 1.01. The descent was again run using both SCGD and CGD to see how the two compared. The values of the cost function for this example for five cycles are shown in Table 3.2. It is seen from the

Table 3.2   Descent on a Quadratic Criterion with CGD and SCGD with 1% Error in Step-Size Determination

	Cost Functional Value	
Cycle	CGD	SCGD
0	5605.3	5605.3
1	4.418	4.418
2	$3.863E - 01$	$3.955E - 01$
3	$7.718E - 02$	$3.954E - 01$
4	$1.347E - 02$	$3.953E - 01$
5	$4.162E - 03$	$1.620E - 05$

table that CGD had a faster descent rate (in fact it appears as though SCGD had about converged in iteration 2, 3, and 4) until the fifth cycle. At that cycle SCGD made a dramatic improvement and passed where CGD was at that point. This happened because it was not until at the end of the fourth cycle that SCGD was able to construct a good approximation to A^{-1} in the scaling matrix S^i [of (3.81)]. A point to be made here is that although the SCGD algorithm was slowed down in its construction of a descent rate improving scaling matrix by the error in step size, it did eventually manage to do so and descent was speedy thereafter.

A nonquadratic example

To see the performance of the algorithm in a nonquadratic case that is known to be ill-conditioned and to give convergence difficulties for standard descent methods, the algorithm was tried on an example from Fletcher and Reeves [5] as discussed below.

Rosenbrock's Banana-Shaped Valley Function. This is a two dimensional problem where the criterion is

$$J = f(x_1, x_2) = 100.0(x_2 - x_1^2)^2 + (1.0 - x_1)^2$$

and as the name implies is from Rosenbrock [13]. This is a fourth order criterion with a banana-shaped valley with minimum at

$$x^* = [1.0, 1.0]^+$$

Following Fletcher and Reeves the initial point for the descent was taken at $x_0 = [-1.2, 1.0]^+$. The performance of SCGD here was a straightforward steady descent with no difficulties. The limits of the machine were reached in 11 cycles, giving $J < 10^{-79}$ and x^* to the maximum significance possible. CGD was also run with this example by simply setting the scaling matrix S^i to the unit matrix for all cycles. The result was steady descent to $J = 1.3 \times 10^{-2}$ in 11 cycles, bottoming out at $J = 4.7 \times 10^{-12}$ in 16 cycles, and then sticking there. The convergence obtained was somewhat slower than that reported by Fletcher and Reeves [5]. The difference can be attributed to the different method used for finding the α_k that minimized $F(x_k + \alpha p_k)$ in (3.81c).

Some practical details

Convergence could be expected to depend critically on the method in which the step-size constant α_k [which minimized $F(x_k + \alpha p_k)$ in (3.81c)] was determined. For the quadratic criterion of the form of (3.84), $J = F(x_k) = f_0 + a^+ x_k + \frac{1}{2} x_k^+ A x_k$ this could be determined exactly as

$$\alpha_k = \frac{-a^+ p_k - p_k^+ A x_k}{p_k^+ A p_k}$$

This was used in the quadratic criteria examples.

In the nonquadratic criteria cases, an α_k was determined as discussed in Appendix B.

Fletcher and Reeves [5] suggest a cycle of $n + 1$ iterations as the best for restarting CGD. The notion of running SCGD with a cycle of $n + 1$ iterations was also tried with the quadratic criterion used in Example 3.3. The best results were obtained when the last n iterations were used to construct the scaling matrix for the next cycle. In all examples tried with both SCGD and CGD, (and confirming Fletcher and Reeves) better cost improvement per iteration was obtained.

All calculations with SCGD in this section were done single precision on the IBM 360 System at NASA/Ames Research Center.

PROBLEMS

1. (a) Let A be a positive-definite, symmetric $n \times n$ matrix and let $(d_0, d_1, \ldots, d_{n-1})$ be a set of linearly independent vectors. Show that the set $(p_0, p_1, \ldots, p_{n-1})$ constructed recursively by the Gram–Schmidt procedure

$$p_0 = d_0$$

$$p_{k+1} = d_{k+1} - \sum_{i=0}^{k} \frac{d_{k+1}^+ A\, d_i}{d_i^+ A\, d_i} d_i$$

is conjugate w.r.t. A.

(b) Give a procedure for constructing a set of orthogonal, unit norm vectors from the set $(d_0, d_1, \ldots, d_{n-1})$.

(c) For

$$A = \begin{bmatrix} 1 & 2 & 0 \\ 2 & 6 & 1 \\ 0 & 1 & 1 \end{bmatrix}$$

and $d_0 = [1, 0, 0]^+, d_1 = [0, 1, 0]^+, d_2 = [0, 0, 1]^+$, construct the conjugate w.r.t. A set by the procedure of part (a).

(d) Using the conjugate w.r.t. A set of vectors found in part (c), do a cycle of three iterations of conjugate descent, starting at $x_0 = 0$, on

$$F(x) = a^+ x + \tfrac{1}{2} x^+ A x$$

for $a = [-6, -2, -6]^+$ with A as in part (c).

2. Let A be a real, symmetric matrix with distinct eigenvalues. Show that the eigenvectors form a conjugate w.r.t. A set.

3. Let A be an $n \times n$ symmetric matrix with the set $(p_0, p_1, \ldots, p_{n-1})$ conjugate w.r.t. A. Find a matrix P such that $P^+ A P$ is diagonal.

4. Do conjugate gradient descent on

$$F(x) = 1 + x_1 + x_2 + x_3 + x_1^2 + 2x_2^2 + 4x_3^2 - 2x_1 x_2$$

starting at $x_0 = 0$ and continuing until it converges to the minimum.

5. Find the solution of

$$\begin{bmatrix} 1 & 2 & 0 \\ 2 & 6 & 1 \\ 0 & 1 & 1 \end{bmatrix} \begin{bmatrix} x_1 \\ x_2 \\ x_3 \end{bmatrix} = \begin{bmatrix} 6 \\ 2 \\ 6 \end{bmatrix}$$

$$A \qquad\quad x \;=\; b$$

using one cycle of conjugate gradient descent.

6. Do three cycles (of three iterations each) on Rosenbrock's banana-shaped valley function

$$F(x) = 100.0(x_2 - x_1^2)^2 + (1.0 - x_1)^2$$

starting at $x_0 = [-1.2, 1]^+$.

7. Do one cycle of SCGD on

$$F(x) = 1 + x_1 + x_2 + x_3 + x_1^2 + 2x_2^2 + 4x_3^2 - 2x_1x_2$$

starting at $x_0 = 0$.

8. Restart SCGD at $x_0 = [1, -1, 1]^+$ with the $F(x)$ of problem 7 and with $S^0 = S^1$ as found in doing the cycle of SCGD in problem 7.

9. Show that for SCGD as given in (3.81)

$$-p_k^+ g_k = g_k^+ S^i g_k$$

10. Consider doing SCGD on a quadratic functional $F(x) = f_0 + a^+ x + \frac{1}{2}x^+ Ax$. Show that $\alpha_k = 1$ [α_k of (3.81c)] if $S^i = A^{-1}$.

11. For the matrix A of problem 5, find A^{-1} using one cycle of SCGD.

12. Do three cycles (of three iterations each) of SCGD on Rosenbrock's function of problem 6 starting at $x_0 = [-1.2, 1]^+$ and each of the following:

   (a) Starting with $S^0 = I$
   (b) Starting with $S^0 = [F''(x_0)]^{-1}$

13. Show the convergence rates for $\|x_n - x^*\|$ and $\|g(x_n)\|$ as implied by

$$E(x_n) \le 4\left(\frac{1 - \sqrt{m/M}}{1 + \sqrt{m/M}}\right)^{2n} E(x_0)$$

where

$$E(x) = \frac{1}{2}\langle x - x^*, A(x - x^*)\rangle$$

and

$$m\|x\|^2 \le \langle x, Ax\rangle \le M\|x\|^2$$

REFERENCES

[1] Hestenes, M. R., and E. Stiefel, "Method of Conjugate Gradients for Solving Linear Systems," *J. Res. NBS*, **49**, 409 (1952).

[2] Lasdon, L. S., S. K. Mitter, and A. D. Warren, "The Method of Conjugate Gradients for

Optimal Control Problems," *IEEE Trans. Autom. Control*, **AC-12**, No. 2, 132 (April 1967).

[3] Antosiewicz, H. A., and W. C. Rheinboldt, "Numerical Analysis and Functional Analysis," Chapter 14 of *Survey of Numerical Analysis*, J. Todd, Ed., McGraw-Hill, 1962.

[4] Halmos, P. R., *Introduction to Hilbert Space*, 2nd ed., Chelsea, 1957.

[5] Fletcher, R., and C. M. Reeves, "Function Minimization by Conjugate Gradients," *Br. Comput. J.*, **7**, 149 (July 1964).

[6] Luenberger, D. G., *Optimization by Vector Space Methods*, Chapter 10, Wiley, 1969.

[7] Willoughby, J. K., "Adaptations of the Conjugate Gradient Method to Optimal Control Problems with Terminal State Constraints," Engineering Research Institute, Technical Report ERI-62500, Iowa State University.

[8] Daniels, J. W., Chapter 5, *The Approximate Minimization of Functionals*, Prentice-Hall, 1971.

[9] Ortega, J. M., and W. C. Rheinboldt, *Iterative Solution of Nonlinear Equations in Several Variables*, Academic Press, 1970.

[10] Fletcher, R., and M. J. D. Powell, "A Rapidly Convergent Descent Method for Minimization," *Comput. J.*, **6**, 163 (1963).

[11] Berksekas, D. P., "Partial Conjugate Gradient Methods for a Class of Optimal Control Problem," *IEEE Trans. Autom. Control*, **AC-19**, No. 3, 209–216 (June 1974).

[12] Luenberger, D. G., *Introduction to Linear and Nonlinear Programming*, Addison-Wesley, 1973.

[13] Rosenbrock, H. H., "An Automatic Method for Finding the Greatest or Least Value of a Function," *Comput. J.*, **3**, 175 (1960).

PART TWO

Chapter 4

The Gradient of the Cost Functional for Some Common Cases of Interest in Control Systems

---

4.1. A GENERAL METHOD FOR FINDING THE GRADIENT OF A FUNCTIONAL

In the preceding two chapters we have developed some mathematical tools and concepts. We now turn to the use of these tools and concepts in the general problem of finding inputs to control systems that minimize a cost functional on the operation of the control system. Our main tool here for finding these inputs is conjugate gradient descent as described in Section 3.4. This requires, among other things, that we be able to evaluate the functional itself and the gradient of the functional of interest for any element in the region wherein the minimum is sought. It is generally safe to assume that the functional can be evaluated for any given argument of the functional. However this still leaves the task of finding the gradient. This may or may not be a problem depending on what the particular functional is. In the control problem of interest, how to find the gradient is not that obvious, so we here develop a general method to do this. The applicability of this method extends far beyond the control problem considered here, so we shall discuss this method of finding the gradient first—even before the cost functional of the control systems is defined.

Finding the Gradient of a Functional

We now consider a functional F from Hilbert space $\mathcal{H}$ to $\mathcal{R}^1$ as shown in Fig. 1.1. F is assumed differentiable at a given x_0, so from (2.30) for $t \in \mathcal{H}$

$$\lim_{t \to 0} \frac{\|F(x_0 + t) - F(x_0) - F'(x_0)t\|}{\|t\|} = 0 \tag{4.1}$$

and $F'(x_0)$ is related to the gradient at x_0, $g(x_0)$, by (2.33), which is

$$F'(x_0)t = \langle g(x_0), t \rangle \tag{4.2}$$

To find $g(x_0)$ we consider a t of the form

$$t = \varepsilon z$$

where $\|z\| = 1$ and ε is a scalar parameter. Using this form of t in (4.1) and the linearity of $F'(x_0)$ we get

$$\lim_{\substack{\varepsilon \to 0 \\ \varepsilon > 0}} \left\| \frac{F(x_0 + \varepsilon z) - F(x_0)}{\varepsilon} - F'(x_0)z \right\| = 0$$

from which we have by the definition of limit

$$\lim_{\substack{\varepsilon \to 0 \\ \varepsilon > 0}} \frac{F(x_0 + \varepsilon z) - F(x_0)}{\varepsilon} = F'(x_0)z$$

$$= \langle g(x_0), z \rangle \tag{4.3}$$

where (4.3) is obtained by use of Theorem 2.1 and (2.33). $g(x_0)$ is the gradient at x_0 that is sought. Equation (4.3) can be put into a slightly more convenient form by recognizing that

$$\lim_{\varepsilon \to 0} \frac{F(x_0 + \varepsilon z) - F(x_0)}{\varepsilon} = \frac{d}{d\varepsilon} F(x_0 + \varepsilon z) \bigg|_{\varepsilon = 0}$$

which used in (4.3) gives

$$\frac{d}{d\varepsilon} F(x_0 + \varepsilon z) \bigg|_{\varepsilon = 0} = \langle g(x_0), z \rangle \tag{4.4}$$

which is the desired result. It is the basic method by which all gradients are computed here.

Equation 4.4 can be obtained directly by letting $t = \varepsilon z$ in the Taylor Series expansion of (2.57) and performing the operations as indicated on the LHS of (4.4) on this series. This also illustrates that (4.4) holds for z for which

$\|z\| \neq 1$. We may also note while considering the Taylor series of (2.57) with $t = \varepsilon z$ that

$$\frac{d^2}{d\varepsilon^2} F(x_0 + \varepsilon z)\bigg|_{\varepsilon=0} = \langle z, A(x_0)z \rangle \qquad (4.5)$$

where $A(x_0)$ is the second derivative operator at x_0.

The quantity computed in (4.4), in the case where F is a general differentiable operator (i.e., not necessarily a functional), is called the Gateaux differential in the literature. This differential plays a prominent role in optimization theory. It is basic in the calculus of variation where it is used to obtain necessary conditions for a minimum. It can be seen that if x_0 minimizes F, then necessarily

$$\frac{d}{d\varepsilon} F(x_0 + \varepsilon z)\bigg|_{\varepsilon=0} = \langle g(x_0), z \rangle = 0 \qquad (4.6)$$

for all $z \in \mathcal{H}$. Our use of (4.4) here is, however, not to find conditions that the minimum must satisfy, but to find the gradient $g(x_0)$ for arbitrary x_0. Our approach to finding the gradient is to perform the operations on the LHS of (4.4) for arbitrary x_0 and z in a space with a scalar product. Through knowledge of the scalar product in the space of interest and the value of z, the gradient $g(x_0)$ can in general be identified from the RHS of (4.4). This method works when the functional is defined in such a way that the operation on the LHS can be accomplished.

To see how (4.4) may be used to find a gradient of a functional, we consider a real-valued function ϕ on $\mathcal{R}^n$. Let us find the gradient at a given x_0. We have an x of the form

$$x = [x_1, x_2, \ldots, x_n]^+$$

and so

$$z = [z_1, z_2, \ldots, z_n]^+$$

and

$$\phi(x) = \phi(x_1, x_2, \ldots, x_n)$$

$$\phi(x_0 + \varepsilon z) = \phi(x_{1_0} + \varepsilon z_1, x_{2_0} + \varepsilon z_2, \ldots, x_{n_0} + \varepsilon z_n)$$

$$\frac{d}{d\varepsilon} \phi(x_0 + \varepsilon z) = \sum_{i=1}^{n} \frac{\partial}{\partial x_i} \phi(x_0 + \varepsilon z) \cdot z_i$$

$$\frac{d}{d\varepsilon} \phi(x_0 + \varepsilon z)\bigg|_{\varepsilon=0} = \sum_{i=1}^{n} \frac{\partial \phi(x_0)}{\partial x_1} \cdot z_i = \langle g(x_0), z \rangle \qquad (4.7)$$

Recognizing the scalar product in $\mathscr{R}^n$ in (4.7), we have

$$g(x_0) = \nabla_x \phi(x_0) = \left[\frac{\partial \phi(x_0)}{\partial x_1} \frac{\partial \phi(x_0)}{\partial x_2} \cdots \frac{\partial \phi(x_0)}{\partial x_n} \right]^+ \quad (4.8)$$

which is the gradient of a function of n variables as it is usually defined in the calculus.

4.2. THE COST FUNCTIONAL OF INTEREST IN CONTROL SYSTEM DESIGN

We have heretofore considered the minimization of a general functional on a Hilbert space. We now turn to a specific case and define the functional that is of interest in the remainder of the text. Our object here is the design of control systems, so we begin by defining the system first. The system of interest here is one whose dynamics† are given by a differential equation of the form

$$\dot{x} = f(x, u) \colon x(t_0) = c \quad (4.9)$$

where now $x \in \mathscr{R}^n$ and $u \in \mathscr{U}$, a Hilbert space. $f(\cdot, \cdot)$ is a mapping from $\mathscr{R}^n \times \mathscr{U}$ to $\mathscr{R}^n$. $x(t_0)$, the state at the initial time, t_0, is assumed given as the fixed vector c. x is called the state of the system and u the control input.

The space $\mathscr{U}$ is the domain space of the cost functional we wish to define. The elements of this space are left open for the moment. However, to give an idea of what these might be, some typical examples are an input control function, a set of parameters, the initial condition c, and some combination of these.

For the mapping $f(\cdot, \cdot)$, we assume that for a given u, $f(x, u)$ has bounded second partial derivatives w.r.t. components of x for $\|x\|$ bounded. Also for a given $\dot{x}$, $f(x, u)$ has a bounded second derivative w.r.t. $u \in \mathscr{U}$ for u bounded. It is assumed that f is in general a smooth operator on $\mathscr{R}^n \times \mathscr{U}$ and is such that for a given u, (4.9) has a unique solution over the time interval of interest which is $[t_0, t_f]$ with $t_f > t_0$. The tacit assumption is also made that f is well enough behaved to permit the integration of (4.9) by numerical means since implementation of the optimization method will be by digital computer.

Given the time interval $[t_0, t_f]$ and a given $u \in \mathscr{U}$, under the assumption of uniqueness of solution of (4.9) the final state, that is, the state x at time t_f, which we shall call $x(t_f, u)$, is unique for each given control input u. To each final state, and correspondingly to each control input u, a cost of

---

† In the next chapter we briefly consider some systems whose dynamics vary somewhat from this form.

operation of the system is assigned of the form

$$\text{cost} = J[u] = \phi(x(t_f, u)) \tag{4.10}$$

where ϕ is a smooth functional from $\mathscr{R}^n$ to $\mathscr{R}^1$. $J[u]$ is the cost functional of interest on the space of control inputs. To evaluate $J[u]$ for a given u we apply u to the system of (4.9), which gives a corresponding $x(t_f, u)$. $J[u]$ is then evaluated by (4.10). $J[u]$ is thus seen to be a composite operator, from $\mathscr{U}$ to the space of final states, which is $\mathscr{R}^n$ here, and then the function ϕ from $\mathscr{R}^n$ to $\mathscr{R}^1$. This is shown in Fig. 4.1.

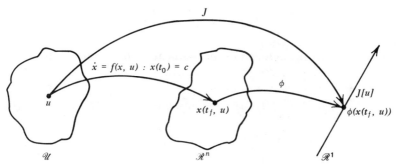

Figure 4.1   The cost functional $J[u]$ as a composite operator.

The general control problem of interest here is as follows:

Find $u^* \in \mathscr{U}$ that minimizes J

Our tool for finding this minimum is the conjugate gradient descent method of Section 3.4. In general we know from Theorem 3.3 and 3.4 that this takes us to a u for which the gradient is null. It is then assumed that given such a u we have means to determine whether or not this is the minimum u^* that we seek. In control system applications this is most often done simply by observing how the system responds for the so-found u.

To apply conjugate gradient descent we must know, for a given u, how to evaluate the functional and its gradient. Given a system of the form of (4.9) we assume that the equations can be integrated to get $x(t_f, u)$ for a given u. If we have ϕ of (4.10), $J[u]$ can be evaluated. This leaves the problem of finding the gradient that we call $g(u)$, and this $g(u)$ is the subject of the remainder of this chapter and the next.

Our main tool in finding this gradient is (4.4). In general to find the gradient $g(u)$ it is necessary to be more explicit as to the nature of u and the space $\mathscr{U}$. But we get one step closer to the desired gradient by applying (4.4) with the assumptions as they are now. Equation 4.4 applied to $J[u]$ gives

$$\frac{d}{d\varepsilon} J[u + \varepsilon z]\bigg|_{\varepsilon=0} = \langle g(u), z \rangle \qquad (4.11)$$

where $u, z, g(u) \in \mathcal{U}$. Using (4.10) we get

$$\frac{d}{d\varepsilon} J[u + \varepsilon z]\bigg|_{\varepsilon=0} = \frac{d}{d\varepsilon} \phi(x(t_f, u + \varepsilon z))\bigg|_{\varepsilon=0}$$

$$= \langle \nabla_x \phi(x(t_f, u + \varepsilon z)), \frac{d}{d\varepsilon} x(t_f, u + \varepsilon z) \rangle\bigg|_{\varepsilon=0}$$

$$- \left\langle \nabla_x \phi(x(t_f, u)), \frac{dx(t_f, u)}{d\varepsilon} \right\rangle \qquad (4.12)$$

where now $\nabla_x \phi$ is the gradient of the gradient of the function ϕ from $\mathcal{R}^n$ to $\mathcal{R}^1$. This has been evaluated in (4.8). In (4.12)

$$\frac{d}{d\varepsilon} x(t_f, u) = \frac{d}{d\varepsilon} x(t_f, u + \varepsilon z)\bigg|_{\varepsilon=0} \qquad (4.13)$$

Equation 4.12 used with (4.11) now gives

$$\frac{d}{d\varepsilon} J[u + \varepsilon z]\bigg|_{\varepsilon=0} = \langle g(u), z \rangle$$

$$= \left\langle \nabla_x \phi(x(t_f, u)), \frac{d}{d\varepsilon} x(t_f, u) \right\rangle \qquad (4.14)$$

which is the result desired. Equation 4.14 reduces the problem of finding the gradient to simply evaluating $dx/d\varepsilon$ as in (4.13). However additional assumptions on u are required before this evaluation can be made. This is done in subsequent sections.

As a last note here, (4.12) illustrates the composite nature of the functional J. $dx/d\varepsilon$ in (4.12) is the derivative of the operator from $\mathcal{U}$ to $\mathcal{R}^n$, (see Fig. 4.1) and $\nabla_x \phi$ is the derivative of the operator from $\mathcal{R}^n$ to $\mathcal{R}^1$. Equation 4.12 is an example of a composite derivative as derived previously in (2.42).

4.3. THE GRADIENT FOR THE CASES OF A CONTINUOUS FUNCTION INPUT

We now make the specific assumption that $\mathcal{U}$, the space in which the minimum of the cost functional is sought, is the space of continuous functions over the time interval $[t_0, t_f]$. We have then

$$u = u(t) \qquad t \in [t_0, t_f] \qquad (4.15)$$

where $u(t)$ is continuous over $[t_0, t_f]$. We now seek the gradient of the cost functional in such a space of functions. Our approach is by (4.14), which requires the evaluation of $dx/d\varepsilon$. To this end we consider

$$x(t, u) = x(t_0) + \int_{t_0}^t f(x, u) \, d\tau \tag{4.16}$$

which we get by integrating the system d.e.† of (4.9). We look in turn at the final state for an input $u + \varepsilon z$ where now z is the same form as u of (4.15), that is,

$$z = z(t) \qquad t \in [t_0, t_f]$$

Thus again from (4.9)

$$x(t_f, u + \varepsilon z) = x(t_0) + \int_{t_0}^{t_f} f(x, u + \varepsilon z) \, dt \tag{4.17}$$

Differentiating this w.r.t. ε, we have

$$\frac{d}{d\varepsilon} x(t_f, u + \varepsilon z) \Big|_{\varepsilon=0} = \frac{d}{d\varepsilon} x(t_0) \Big|_{\varepsilon=0} + \int_{t_0}^{t_f} f_x(x, u) \frac{d}{d\varepsilon} x(t, u) + f_u(x, u) z(t) \, dt \Big|_{\varepsilon=0} \tag{4.18}$$

Here now $x(t, u)$ is as given by (4.16) and f_x and f_u are a matrix and vector, respectively, whose elements are given by

$$\left(f_x(x, u) \right)_{ij} = \frac{\partial f_i (x, u)}{\partial x_j} \qquad i, j = 1, 2, \ldots, n \tag{4.19a}$$

$$\left(f_u(x, u) \right)_i = \frac{\partial f_i (x, u)}{\partial u} \qquad i = 1, 2, \ldots, n \tag{4.19b}$$

The arguments x and u, of f here, are functions of time given by (4.16) and (4.15), respectively. f_i is the ith component of the vector-valued function f. Elimination of some of the arguments in (4.18) gives the more tractable expression

$$\frac{d}{d\varepsilon} x(t_f, u) = \frac{d}{d\varepsilon} x(t_0) + \int_{t_0}^{t_f} f_x \frac{d}{d\varepsilon} x(t, u) + f_u z(t) \, dt \tag{4.20}$$

We see that $dx/d\varepsilon$, which is needed to evaluate the gradient by (4.14), is the solution to the integral equation of (4.20). In seeking the solution to this equation, we note that (4.20) must hold for arbitrary $t_f > t_0$ since t_f has been

---

† Here d.e. = differential equation.

unspecified so far. Thus by letting $t_f = t$ in (4.20) and differentiating w.r.t. t we get the d.e.

$$\frac{d}{dt}\frac{d}{d\varepsilon}x(t, u) = f_x \frac{d}{d\varepsilon}x(t, u) + f_u z(t) \qquad (4.21)$$

which $dx/d\varepsilon$ must satisfy. This is a standard linear, time-varying d.e. of the form

$$\dot{x} = A(t)x + B(t)u \qquad (4.22)$$

for which the solution is considered in Appendix C. The solution to (4.22) as given in Appendix C, and applied to (4.21) gives

$$\frac{d}{d\varepsilon}x(t, u) = \Phi(t, t_0)\frac{d}{d\varepsilon}x(t_0) + \int_{t_0}^{t}\Phi(t, \tau)f_u z(\tau)\,d\tau \qquad (4.23)$$

where now Φ is the matrix function of t and t_0 that satisfies

$$\frac{d}{dt}\Phi(t, t_0) = f_x \Phi(t, t_0): \Phi(t_0, t_0) = I \qquad (4.24)$$

where I is the $n \times n$ identity matrix.

We now need only to substitute (4.23) into (4.14) to evaluate the desired gradient. Note that for the case here $x(t_0) = c$, a constant, hence

$$\frac{d}{d\varepsilon}x(t_0) = 0$$

and hence

$$\frac{d}{d\varepsilon}J[u + \varepsilon z]\bigg|_{\varepsilon=0} = \langle g(u), z\rangle = \left\langle \nabla_x \phi(x(t_f, u), \int_{t_0}^{t_f}\Phi(t_f, \tau)f_u z(\tau)\,d\tau \right\rangle$$

And with a few obvious manipulations†

$$\langle g(u), z\rangle = \int_{t_0}^{t_f}\left\langle f_u^+ \Phi^+(t_f, \tau)\nabla_x \phi(x(t_f, u)), z(\tau)\right\rangle d\tau \qquad (4.25)$$

Equation 4.25 can be simplified further by letting

$$\lambda(t) = \Phi^+(t_f, t)\nabla_x \phi(x(t_f, u)) \qquad (4.26)$$

and noting that $z(\tau)$ is a scalar-valued function so that (4.25) becomes

$$\langle g(u), z\rangle = \int_{t_0}^{t_f} f_u^+ \lambda(\tau)z(\tau)\,d\tau \qquad (4.27)$$

† We here make use of the relationship

$$\langle x, Ay\rangle = \langle A^+ x, y\rangle$$

for $x \in \mathscr{R}^n$, $y \in \mathscr{R}^m$ and A an $n \times m$ matrix. Superscript $+$ indicates transpose.

The integral on the RHS of (4.27), which is the scalar product on the space of functions under consideration, shows the gradient of the cost functional for this case to be

$$g(u(t)) = f_u^+ \lambda(t) \qquad t \in [t_0, t_f] \tag{4.28}$$

which is the desired result. Equation 4.28 is the gradient required to do conjugate gradient descent of the cost functional in the space of input control functions considered here.

Computation of the gradient as in (4.28) can be greatly simplified by recognizing that λ as given by (4.26) satisfies

$$\dot{\lambda} = -f_x^+ \lambda : \lambda(t_f) = \nabla_x \phi(x(t_f, u)) \tag{4.29}$$

This is shown in Appendix D. The system of differential equations in (4.29) is called the adjoint system to the system of (4.9).

Computation of the Gradient in the Space of Input Control Functions

The computation of the gradient of the cost functional as given by (4.28) may be outlined briefly as follows. We assume the input control function $u(t)$, $t \in [t_0, t_f]$ is given and we seek the gradient of the cost functional at this given u. To accomplish this the following steps must be taken:

1. Integrate the system equations, using the given u, forward in time from t_0 to t_f, that is, integrate

$$\dot{x} = f(x, u) : x(t_0) = c \tag{4.9}$$

to get $x_{[t_0, t_f]}$

2. Having $x(t_f)$, evaluate $\lambda(t_f) = \nabla_x \phi(x(t_f))$ and integrate the adjoint system

$$\dot{\lambda} = -f_x^+ \lambda : \lambda(t_f) = \nabla_x \phi(x(t_f)) \tag{4.29}$$

backwards in time from t_f to t_0 to get $\lambda_{[t_0, t_f]}$. f_x is given by (4.19a)

3. Construct

$$g(u(t)) = f_u^+ \lambda(t) \qquad t \in [t_0, t_f] \tag{4.28}$$

where f_u is as given by (4.19b).

Example 4.1

As an example of the use of the above described method of finding the gradient of the cost functional and its use with the conjugate gradient descent method to obtain an approximately optimal control, let us consider the field-controlled DC motor as shown in Fig. 4.2. Values of the pertinent parameters for a motor of approximately 5 hp are shown in the figure. We define state variables by

$$x_1 = \theta$$
$$x_2 = \dot\theta \qquad\qquad (4.30)$$
$$x_3 = i_f$$

The system differential equations for this choice of state variables are

$$\dot x_1 = x_2$$
$$\dot x_2 = -\left(\frac{B}{J}\right)x_2 + \left(\frac{K_T}{J}\right)x_3 \qquad\qquad (4.31)$$
$$\dot x_3 = -\left(\frac{R_f}{L_f}\right)x_3 + \frac{u}{L_f}$$

where $u = e_f$ = field voltage is the control input.

Let us consider the problem of finding the input e_f so as to approximate a step change in the output shaft's position. To make the problem fit the formulation used in Section 4.2 we take a step change of 10 rad as the desired output, and let the cost criterion be the integral square of the error between the desired step and the actual shaft position with an integral term added to limit control power and a final term added to insure the proper final state.

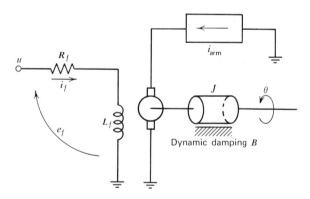

Armature torque = $K_T i_f$

Figure 4.2 A field-controlled DC motor. $R_f = 10$ ohms; $L_f = 10$ h; $J = 2$ kg m^2; $B = 0.66$ kg m^2/sec; $K_T = 10$ newton-m/A.

Thus we consider a criterion of the form

$$J = \int_{t_0}^{t_f} [(\theta - 10)^2 + R(e_f)^2] \, dt + W_1(\theta(t_f) - 10)^2 + W_2(\dot{\theta}(t_f))^2 + W_3(i_f(t_f))^2$$

$$= \int_{t_0}^{t_f} [(x_1 - 10)^2 + Re_f^2] \, dt + [W_1(x_1 - 10)^2 + W_2 x_2^2 + W_3 x_3^2]\Big|_{t=t_f}$$

$$(4.32)$$

The $R(e_f)^2$ term has been added under the integral to limit the energy applied to the input (the field) of the motor. The constant R is chosen to limit the energy as desired. The final value terms are chosen to insure that $\theta(t_f) = 10$, $\dot{\theta}(t_f) = 0$, and $i_f(t_f) = 0$.

To handle a criterion of the form of (4.32), the system differential equations are augmented by an additional equation by defining a new state variable x_4, which satisfies

$$\dot{x}_4 = (x_1 - 10)^2 + Ru^2 : x_4(0) = 0 \qquad (4.33)$$

For x_4 defined in this manner

$$J = [x_4 + W_1(x_1 - 10)^2 + W_2 x_2^2 + W_3 x_3^2]|_{t=t_f} = \phi(x(t_f)) \quad (4.34)$$

which is the form of the criterion defined in (4.10). Using (4.33) to augment the equations of (4.31) and using the values of the parameters as given in Fig. 4.2, we obtain

$$\dot{x}_1 = x_2$$

$$\dot{x}_2 = -\frac{x_2}{3} + 5x_3$$

$$(4.35)$$

$$\dot{x}_3 = -x_3 + 0.1u$$

$$\dot{x}_4 = (x_1 - 10)^2 + Ru^2$$

Under the assumption of quiescence at $t_0 = 0$ and with the initial condition on x_4 as given in (4.33), the initial conditions on the state vector are

$$x(0) = c = 0 \qquad (4.36)$$

Equations 4.35 and 4.36 give f and c as in (4.9). The adjoint system, (4.29), requires f_x and $\nabla \phi$. f_x is found by applying (4.19) to f in (4.35). The result is

$$f_x = \begin{bmatrix} 0 & 1 & 0 & 0 \\ 0 & -\frac{1}{3} & 5 & 0 \\ 0 & 0 & -1 & 0 \\ 2(x_1 - 10) & 0 & 0 & 0 \end{bmatrix} \qquad (4.37)$$

$\nabla_x \phi$, which is required to get the terminal condition for the adjoint system, (4.29), is found by taking the gradient of ϕ as given by (4.34), which is

$$\nabla_x \phi = [2W_1(x_1 - 10) \quad 2W_2 x_2 \quad 2W_3 x_3 \quad 1]^+ \qquad (4.38)$$

To construct the gradient of the cost functional, which for the case here, a continuous function input, is given by (4.28), f_u as given in (4.19b) is required. Using f we get

$$f_u^+ = [0 \quad 0 \quad 0.1 \quad 2Ru] \qquad (4.39)$$

Using (4.39) in (4.28) we may now write the gradient in the space of input control functions (field voltage as a function of time) as

$$g(u(t)) = 0.1[\lambda_3(t)] + 2Ru(t)[\lambda_4(t)] \qquad t \in [t_0, t_f] \qquad (4.40)$$

where now λ_3 and λ_4 are solutions to the adjoint system of (4.29), which in this case is

$$\frac{d}{dt}\begin{bmatrix} \lambda_1 \\ \lambda_2 \\ \lambda_3 \\ \lambda_4 \end{bmatrix} = -\begin{bmatrix} 0 & 0 & 0 & 2(x_1 - 10) \\ 1 & -\frac{1}{3} & 0 & 0 \\ 0 & 5 & -1 & 0 \\ 0 & 0 & 0 & 0 \end{bmatrix}\begin{bmatrix} \lambda_1 \\ \lambda_2 \\ \lambda_3 \\ \lambda_4 \end{bmatrix} \qquad (4.41)$$

using f_x from (4.37). The adjoint system must be evaluated with terminal condition $\lambda(t_f) = \nabla_x \phi$ with the $\nabla_x \phi$ of (4.38) evaluated at $t = t_f$.

The system of interest here, (4.35), was programmed for the computer with $R = 5$. The adjoint system of (4.41) was also programmed to be solved with the terminal condition as given by (4.38). The constants in (4.38) were chosen as

$$W_1 = W_2 = W_3 = 10,000$$

and these same values were used in the criterion of (4.33) and (4.34). Using the gradient as determined in (4.40) over

$$[t_0, t_f] = [0, 5 \text{ sec}]$$

conjugate gradient descent was accomplished with the program as described in Appendix G. The initial guess was simply $u(t) = 0$, $t \in [t_0, t_f]$. After 10 iterations the output response as shown in Fig. 4.3 was obtained. The input field voltage is shown in Fig. 4.4. The norm of the gradient squared that was obtained at each step in the conjugate gradient descent is shown in Table 4.1. The table shows the results for the eleventh iteration while the figure give the results for the tenth and eleventh iteration. The eleventh iteration step is included in the table to show that the sequence had converged. The table shows that although the value of the criterion decreases mono-tonically, the norm of the gradient does not. This is characteristic of the conjugate gradient descent method.

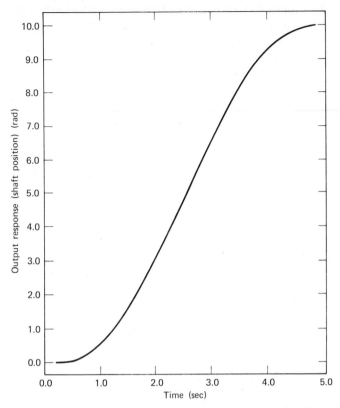

Figure 4.3   Response of field-controlled DC motor after 10 conjugate gradient descent iterations.

Table 4.1   Conjugate Gradient Descent to a Minimizing Control Function Input

Iteration	Norm Square Gradient	Criterion
1	$8.54E + 10$	$1.00E + 06$
2	$2.45E + 08$	$7.00E + 04$
3	$6.06E + 06$	$9.09E + 03$
4	$3.34E + 05$	$1.85E + 03$
5	$2.14E + 05$	$1.85E + 03$
6	$2.22E + 06$	$1.65E + 03$
7	$5.96E + 06$	$1.63E + 03$
8	$1.34E + 07$	$1.18E + 03$
9	$2.69E + 04$	$9.84E + 02$
10	$5.08E + 03$	$9.84E + 02$
11	$1.7\ E + 01$	$9.84E + 02$

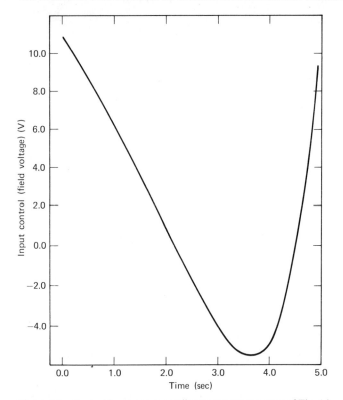

Figure 4.4   Control input corresponding to output response of Fig. 4.3.

Remarks

1. The gradient as seen in (4.28) illustrates the composite structure of the cost functional as shown in Fig. 4.1. Comparing (4.28) with the form of the composite derivative as seen in (2.42), we see that, at a given time t, $\lambda(t)$ is the gradient of the cost functional in $\mathscr{R}^n$, (see Fig. 4.1) at $x(t)$. f_u^+ is in turn the derivative of the mapping from $\mathscr{U}$ to $\mathscr{R}^n$ at $u(t)$.

2. Let us consider $g(u(t))$ in (4.28) and the space in which the gradient has been found. To see that, this is the space of continuous functions; let us consider u a continuous function over $[t_0, t_f]$. We note that $\lambda(t), t \in [t_0, t_f]$, is also continuous since it is the solution to the d.e. of (4.29). Under the assumption of smoothness on the mapping $f(\cdot, \cdot)$, f_u is also continuous [note $x(t)$, $t \in [t_0, t_f]$ is also continuous since it must satisfy (4.9)], and so $g(u(t))$ as given by (4.28) is also a continuous function. Thus, if we start in the space of continuous functions, the gradient we obtain is in the space of continuous functions.

3. A theoretical and practical difficulty arises when one seeks to apply the gradient as found in (4.28) to find a criterion-minimizing element in the space of continuous functions over a finite time interval. This difficulty arises, as pointed out in Section 2.1, because this space is not complete under the scalar product norm. Experience shows that in general if the criterion-minimizing control input is a continuous function, use of gradient descent with the gradient of (4.28) converges to it if the initial guess is close enough. The practical problem arises because quite often one does not know beforehand if the criterion-minimizing control input is continuous or not. If gradient descent is used with the gradient as in (4.28), what one would hope for is convergence to a continuous function that is a good approximation to the discontinuous optimal control. And here a good approximation is one in which the criterion for the computed continuous control is near the criterion value for the optimal discontinuous control. In general this is the case, though examples may be found where this does not hold. This difficulty is the motivation for Section 5.2 where the gradient is considered in the space of piecewise continuous control inputs. The reader is referred to that section for a slightly deeper analysis of the problem with this type of control input.

4.4. THE GRADIENT IN THE SPACE OF INPUT CONTROL PARAMETERS

A special case that is fairly trivial mathematically, but important practically, is the case of input parameters. Here the space $\mathscr{U}$ in which the minimum is sought is $\mathscr{R}^m$ and a typical element is

$$u = [u_1, u_2, \ldots, u_m]^+ \qquad (4.42)$$

where $u_1, u_2, \ldots, u_m$ are a set of parameters.

Our system d.e.'s are assumed again of the form

$$\dot{x} = f(x, u) \qquad x(t_0) = c \qquad (4.43)$$

where now f is assumed explicitly a function of the m parameters $u_1, u_2, \ldots, u_m$, that is, the components of u. f is assumed smooth w.r.t. x and u, so all partials with respect to any component of u exist and the second partials of f are bounded for bounded x and u.

The gradient of the cost functional, which we still assume to be of the form given in (4.10), can be found directly by observing that if u_1 is a control parameter, it can be considered to be an input control function that just happens to be a constant. And a constant happens to be a nice continuous function over $[t_0, t_f]$, so the derivation of the gradient as found in the previous section should apply. An exception to this derivation of the gradient is a variation about some input control u of the form $u + \varepsilon z$; z is of the form

$$z = [z_1, z_2, \ldots, z_m]^+ \tag{4.44}$$

where all components of z are constant over $[t_0, t_f]$. Thus in the expression for $\langle g(u), z \rangle$ in (4.25) we have

$$\langle g(u), z \rangle = \int_{t_0}^{t_f} \langle f_u^+ \Phi^+(t_f, \tau) \nabla_x \phi(x(t_f, u)), z \rangle \, d\tau$$

$$= \left\langle \int_{t_0}^{t_f} f_u^+ \Phi^+(t_f, \tau) \nabla_x \phi(x(t_f, u)) \, d\tau, z \right\rangle$$

where again letting

$$\lambda(t) = \Phi^+(t_f, t) \nabla_x \phi(x(t_f, u))$$

we have

$$\langle g(u), z \rangle = \left\langle \int_{t_0}^{t_f} f_u^+ \lambda(\tau) \, d\tau, z \right\rangle \tag{4.45}$$

where now the scalar product is on $\mathcal{U} = \mathcal{R}^m$. From (4.45) we identify

$$g(u) = \int_{t_0}^{t_f} f_u^+ \lambda(\tau) \, d\tau \tag{4.46}$$

In this case u is an m-vector, that is, in $\mathcal{R}^m$, so that f_u is an $n \times m$ matrix whose ijth element is given by

$$f_u(x, u)_{ij} = \frac{\partial f_i(x, u)}{\partial u_j} \qquad \begin{matrix} i = 1, 2, \ldots, n \\ j = 1, 2, \ldots, m \end{matrix} \tag{4.47}$$

λ in (4.46), as in the case of a continuous function input, satisfies the adjoint system given in (4.29).

Remarks

1. Computation of the gradient as in (4.46) for a given $u \in \mathcal{U} = \mathcal{R}^m$ goes as described in steps 1 and 2 under Computation of Gradient in Section 4.3. For step 3 the gradient is constructed as in (4.46).

2. In this case $\mathcal{R}^m$, the space in which we are seeking a minimum, is a Hilbert space, hence there is no difficulty with the gradient as in the case of a continuous function input. Since $\mathcal{R}^m$ is a Hilbert space it is hence complete and if we find a convergent sequence in this space, we are assured that the limit will also be in $\mathcal{R}^m$.

To illustrate the practical utility of the gradient found in (4.46) let us consider the following example.

Example 4.2.

We consider what might typically be a DC motor with transfer function

$$G(s) = \frac{34.2}{s(s + 2.23)(s + 5)} \tag{4.48}$$

where s is the Laplace transform variable, which is to be used as the plant in a unity-feedback position control system as shown in Fig. 4.5. As seen in the figure, in series with the plant is a compensator, which is chosen to improve the response of the overall system. The desire here is to have a tracking system, that is, have the output track the input.

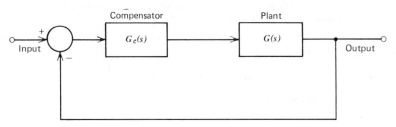

Figure 4.5   A unity-feedback control system with forward path compensation.

Negative feedback will accomplish this if the system is stable. From classical compensation theory it is known that a lead compensator speeds up the response of a system as in Fig. 4.5, so let us choose a simple lead compensator of the form

$$\frac{A(s + z)}{1 + s/p} \tag{4.49}$$

which is a compensator with a zero at $s = -z$ and pole at $s = -p$. To have a lead compensator then $z < p$ must hold. Also from classical compensation theory the pole at $-p$ is chosen far in the LHP relative to the poles of the plant, that is, p is large. With this assumption we make the approximation

$$G_c(s) \equiv A(s + z) \tag{4.50}$$

that is, that the compensator is a simple zero. With the approximation of (4.50) we have the forward path transfer function

$$G_c(s)G(s) = \frac{34.2A(s + z)}{s(s + 2.23)(s + 5)} \tag{4.51}$$

Figure 4.6 shows a simulation diagram that realizes the forward transfer function of (4.51) in a unity-feedback system of the form shown in Fig. 4.5. In the simulation diagram of Fig. 4.6, $\triangleright$ indicates an integrator (transfer function $1/s$), a rectangular block indicates multiplication by a constant, and a circle indicates an adder. Recognizing that the input of an integrator is the derivative of the output, we can write the differential equations of the system simulated in Fig. 4.6 as

$$
\begin{aligned}
\dot{x}_1 &= x_2 \\
\dot{x}_2 &= -34.2A{\cdot}x_1 - 2.23{\cdot}x_2 + 34.2A{\cdot}x_3 + 34.2A{\cdot}r \\
\dot{x}_3 &= -(z-5){\cdot}x_1 - 5{\cdot}x_3 + (z-5){\cdot}r
\end{aligned} \tag{4.52}
$$

Equation 4.52 is a set of d.e.'s of the form of (4.43). Our problem is now to specify the parameters A and z so as to achieve a response that makes the system a good overall tracking system. We seek a criterion such that when A and z are optimized w.r.t. this criterion, good tracking performance will be obtained. To this end, for the system of Fig. 4.6 where x_1 is the output and r the input, we define error as

$$
\text{error} = e = r - x_1 \tag{4.53}
$$

A logical criterion for our system then is

$$
J = \int_{t_0}^{t_f} e^2 \, dt = \int_{t_0}^{t_f} (r - x_1)^2 \, dt \tag{4.54}
$$

If A and z, the two free parameters, are chosen to minimize this criterion a good criterion tracking system should result.

The criterion of (4.54) is good, except that the input function $r(t)$ over $[t_0, t_f]$ has not been specified. Here again classical compensation theory is helpful in that it tells us, in general, that if a linear system, such as the one in

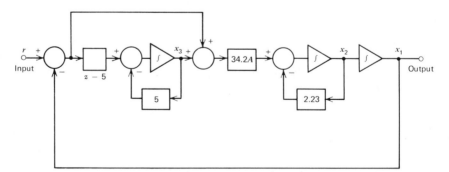

Figure 4.6   Simulation diagram for the system of Fig. 4.5.

Fig. 4.5, shows good tracking response to a step input, then it can be expected to show good response to any input. Thus for our purposes we choose

$$r(t) = 1(t) = 1 \quad t \geq 0$$
$$= 0 \quad t < 0 \qquad (4.55)$$

In addition, to use the criterion of (4.54), t_0 and t_f must be specified. We may choose $t_0 = 0$, since the system is time invariant. t_f must simply be chosen large enough to insure that the system will have reached steady state, that is, the transient portion is finished by time t_f. For our plant, (4.42), the principle pole is at $s = -2.23$, which corresponds to a time constant of 0.45 sec. Thus it is reasonable to assume that by $t_f = 2$ sec, which is more than four time constants, the system should have reached steady state. Thus we choose

$$t_f = 2 \qquad (4.56)$$

To insure that the output response will have reached steady state, we may add terminal, penalty function terms to the criterion, as was done for the criterion of Example 4.1, (4.34). At time t_f we want $x_1(t_f) = 1$ and $\dot{x}_1(t_f) = x_2(t_f) = 0$ for a unit-step input as in (4.55). Thus we consider the criterion

$$J = \int_0^2 (1 - x_1)^2 \, dt + W_1(1 - x_1(2))^2 + W_2(x_2(2))^2 \qquad (4.57)$$

If A and z are chosen so as to minimize this criterion, the system should exhibit good transient characteristics due to the integral term and good steady-state characteristics due to the terminal terms.

To make the criterion of the form of (4.10), as in Example 4.1, we define a new state variable x_4 that satisfies

$$\dot{x}_4 = (1 - x_1)^2 : x_4(0) \qquad (4.58)$$

and the criterion then becomes

$$J = \phi(x(t_f)) = [x_4 + W_1(1 - x_1)^2 + W_2(x_2^2)]|_{t=2} \qquad (4.59)$$

which is of the form of (4.10). This completes formulation of the problem.

To specifically define the terms required to compute the gradient as in (4.46), we augment the system of equations in (4.52) with (4.58) and use the input r as given in (4.55) to get

$$\dot{x}_1 = x_2$$
$$\dot{x}_2 = -34.2A{\cdot}x_1 - 2.23{\cdot}x_2 + 34.2A{\cdot}x_3 + 34.2A$$
$$\dot{x}_3 = -(z - 5){\cdot}x_1 - 5{\cdot}x_3 + (z - 5) \qquad (4.60)$$
$$\dot{x}_4 = (1 - x_1)^2$$

which gives f of (4.43). We assume the system quiescent before the step input which combined with the initial condition of (4.58) gives

$$x(0) = c = \boldsymbol{0} \qquad (4.61)$$

the required initial condition. The control input for which we seek the minimum is

$$u = \begin{bmatrix} A \\ z \end{bmatrix} \qquad (4.62)$$

To solve for λ required in (4.46) we evaluate f_x by (4.19a) for f as in (4.60) and get

$$f_x(x, u) = \begin{bmatrix} 0 & 1 & 0 & 0 \\ -34.2A & -2.23 & 34.2A & 0 \\ 5 - z & 0 & -5 & 0 \\ 2(x_1 - 1) & 0 & 0 & 0 \end{bmatrix} \qquad (4.63)$$

This f_x used in the adjoint system of (4.29) with the terminal condition

$$\lambda(t_f) = \nabla_x \phi(x(t_f, u)) = [2W_1(x_1 - 1) \quad 2W_2 x_2 \quad 0 \quad 1]|_{t=2} \qquad (4.64)$$

which we get by taking the gradient w.r.t. x of ϕ in (4.59), gives $\lambda_{[0, 2]}$. To finally find the gradient by use of (4.46) we evaluate, using (4.47) on f of (4.60),

$$f_u(x, u) = \begin{bmatrix} 0 & 0 \\ [34.2(x_3 - x_1 + 1)] & 0 \\ 0 & (1 - x_1) \\ 0 & 0 \end{bmatrix} \qquad (4.65)$$

The gradient in the space of control parameters as given by (4.46) is then

$$g\begin{bmatrix} A \\ z \end{bmatrix} = \begin{bmatrix} \int_0^2 \{34.2[x_3(t) - x_1(t) + 1]\lambda_2(t)\} \, dt \\ \int_0^2 \{[1 - x_1(t)]\lambda_3(t)\} \, dt \end{bmatrix} \qquad (4.66)$$

which is the desired result.

This problem was programmed for the conjugate gradient descent program described in Appendix G. To find the initial guess for A and z, the two parameters being optimized, use was made of classical compensation theory [11], which for this problem says that the pole at -2.23 should be cancelled with the compensator zero. Also, if the gain constant A is adjusted to give a pair of dominant closed-loop poles with a damping of 0.7, a satisfactory step response with overshoot of approximately 6% should be obtained.

With this in mind

$$u^0 = \begin{bmatrix} A^0 \\ z^0 \end{bmatrix} = \begin{bmatrix} 0.365 \\ 2.23 \end{bmatrix} \tag{4.67}$$

was chosen. The initial step response with these values of the two parameters is shown in Fig. 4.7.

Using the criterion of (4.59) with

$$W_1 = W_2 = 1000 \tag{4.68}$$

conjugate gradient descent was accomplished for five iterations; the result is shown in Fig. 4.7. We see in this figure that the response is somewhat faster

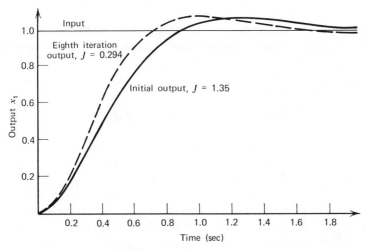

Figure 4.7 Initial and eighth iteration step response for the system of Fig. 4.6.

$$J = \int_0^2 (1 - x_1)^2 \, dt + 1000(1 - x_1(2))^2 + 1000 \, x_2^2(2).$$

with slightly more overshoot (6.3% compared with an initial 4.3%) but it is not substantially different from the response obtained with classical compensation theory. The parameters after eight iterations were found to be

$$u^8 = \begin{bmatrix} A^8 \\ z^8 \end{bmatrix} = \begin{bmatrix} 0.464 \\ 2.12 \end{bmatrix} \tag{4.69}$$

which are not too far from the initial value of (4.67). Table 4.2 shows the values of norm-square of the gradient and criterion at each iteration for this example.

Table 4.2   Conjugate Gradient Descent to a Minimizing Set of Parameters

Iteration	Norm-Square Gradient	Criterion
1	$1.35E - 02$	$1.37E - 00$
2	$2.23E - 01$	$2.96E - 01$
3	$2.47E - 03$	$2.95E - 01$
4	$1.22E - 01$	$2.95E - 01$
5	$3.95E - 03$	$2.94E - 01$
6	$1.29E - 04$	$2.94E - 01$
7	$6.46E - 05$	$2.94E - 01$
8	$6.59E - 05$	$2.94E - 01$

To illustrate the importance of the terminal terms in the criterion of (4.57), the problem was rerun with the same initial values as in (6.67) but with

$$W_1 = W_2 = 0.0$$

The criterion was then simply

$$J = \int_0^2 e^2 \, dt = \int_0^2 (1 - x_1)^2 \, dt \tag{4.70}$$

The results obtained after five conjugate gradient iterations are shown in Fig. 4.8. We see a dramatically different type of response. The response rises much more quickly than in the case shown in Fig. 4.7. The overshoot has increased significantly; there is considerable oscillation before the response settles down to a steady state value, which is slightly below the unity value required if a tracking system is desired. The value for the parameters optimized, found after five iterations, is

$$u = \begin{bmatrix} A \\ z \end{bmatrix} = \begin{bmatrix} 8.77 \\ -0.0171 \end{bmatrix} \tag{4.71}$$

The gain A has been increased greatly over the initial case and the zero of the compensator has essentially cancelled out the plant pole [see (4.48)] at $s = 0$. The criterion, (4.70), for the response of Fig. 4.8 had the value $J = 0.0792$ as compared to a value for the criterion, (4.57) ($W_1 = W_2 = 1000$), of $J = 0.294$ for the eighth iteration response of Fig. 4.7. In this case the integral square error may be determined analytically by classical Wiener filter theory as expounded in [7] of Chapter 2. Doing this and straightforwardly solving for A and z to minimize J we can show that

$$A \to \infty$$

$$z = 0$$

$$J = 0$$

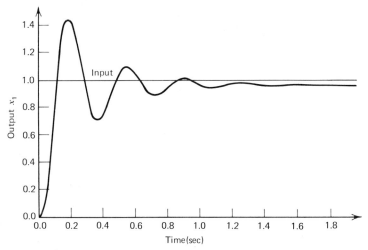

Figure 4.8 Output step response after five iterations with an integral square criterion without terminal terms.

$$J = \int_0^2 (1 - x_1)^2 \, dt = 0.0792.$$

The sequence, with the result as given in (4.71) for the fifth iteration, was obviously converging to this minimum.

4.5. THE CASE OF A SAMPLED INPUT

A case of some practical interest in control systems is the sampled input. A sampled input here means an input that changes only at regularly spaced sampling instants. A typical sampled input is shown in Fig. 4.9. The assumption in the figure is that the input starts at $t = t_0$ and changes at the sampling instance $t_0 + kT, k = 0, 1, \ldots, N - 1$ and $t_f = t_0 + NT$. The

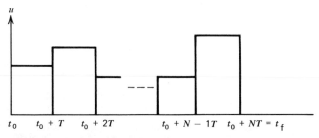

Figure 4.9 A sampled input.

sampling interval is thus T and the input is constant in between sampling instances. Let us consider finding the gradient of the cost functional of Section 4.2 for such an input.

To this end we consider the fact that the input of the form shown in Fig. 4.9 may be written as

$$u(t) = \sum_{k=0}^{N-1} u_k [1(t - t_0 - kT) - 1(t - t_0 - \overline{k+1}T)] \qquad t \in [t_0, t_f]$$

(4.72)

where $1(t)$ is the unit step function. A variation in such an input of the form $u + \varepsilon z$ in turn has

$$z(t) = \sum_{k=0}^{N-1} z_k [1(t - t_0 - kT) - 1(t - t_0 - \overline{k+1}T)] \qquad t \in [t_0, t_f]$$

(4.73)

and both u of (4.72) and z of (4.73) are completely specified by the N values $u_0, u_1, \ldots, u_{N-1}$ and $z_0, z_1, \ldots, z_{N-1}$, respectively. We may thus consider the input as

$$u = [u_0, u_2, \ldots, u_{N-1}]^+$$

(4.74)

and look for the gradient in the space of such elements, that is, $\mathscr{R}^N$.

To find the gradient, we consider $u(t)$ of (4.72). This is a function that is continuous except at the sampling instances. The discontinuities are finite in number, $N - 1$, and fixed in time of occurrence, $t_0 + T, t_0 + 2T, \ldots$. For this case the derivation of the gradient as found in Section 4.3 may be used. Thus by putting $z(t)$ of (4.73) into (4.27), we obtain

$$\langle g(u), z \rangle = \int_{t_0}^{t_f} f_u^+ \lambda(t) \sum_{t=0}^{N-1} z_k [1(t - t_0 - kT) - 1(t - t_0 - \overline{k+1}T)] \, dt$$

$$= \sum_{k=0}^{N-1} z_k \int_{t_0}^{t_f} f_u^+ \lambda(t) [1(t - t_0 - kT) - 1(t - T_0 - \overline{k+1}T)] \, dt$$

$$= \sum_{k=0}^{N-1} \int_{t_0+kT}^{t_0+\overline{k+1}T} f_u^+ \lambda(t) \, dt \cdot z_k$$

(4.75)

Recognizing the scalar product in $\mathscr{R}^N$ on the RHS of (4.75), we immediately get the gradient as

$$g(u) = [g_0 \ g_1 \cdots g_{N-1}]^+$$

where

$$g_k = \int_{t_0+kT}^{t_0+\overline{k+1}T} f_u^+ \lambda(t) \, dt$$

(4.76)

and f_u is as given in (4.19b) and $\lambda(t)$ is as given by (4.26) and (4.29). Equation 4.76 is the desired result, the gradient in the space of sampled inputs.

Remarks

1. To compute the gradient in the space of sampled inputs, the procedure as outlined in Computation of the Gradient in Section 4.3 may be followed up to step 3. In step 3 the gradient as given by (4.76) is used.

2. $\mathcal{R}^N$ is a Hilbert space, so there is no problem with the convergence of the sequence constructed in the space of sampled inputs with gradient as in (4.76).

Example 4.3.

As an example of the use of the gradient as given in (4.76), let us consider controlling the DC motor of Example 4.1 with a sampled input rather than with a continuous function input. We consider the same problem as in that example, that is, finding the input control that will make a 10 rad change in the motor shaft position. The system dynamic equations are given in (4.35) and the criterion J is given by (4.34). f_x and $\nabla\phi$ as required for the adjoint system are given in (4.37) and (4.38). Using (4.39) in the gradient as in (4.76), we get

$$ g_k = \int_{t_0+kT}^{t_0+\overline{k+1}T} [0.1 \cdot \lambda_3(t) + 2Ru_k \cdot \lambda_4(t)] \, dt \tag{4.77} $$

The conjugate gradient descent program as described in Appendix G was programmed to construct the gradient as in (4.76). The program was run with

$$ W_1 = W_2 = W_3 = 1000 $$

in the criterion of (4.34) and $\nabla\phi$ in (4.38), starting with an initial guess $u = 0$, for 12 iterations. The output shaft position and the corresponding control input found are shown in Figs. 4.10 and 4.11, respectively. The progress of the gradient and the criterion in the descent sequence are shown in Table 4.3.

Table 4.3   Norm-Square of the Gradient and
The Criterion for Input in Example 4.3

Iteration	Criterion	$\|g\|^2$
0	$1.008E + 03$	$2.692E + 09$
1	$2.268E + 03$	$1.107E + 06$
2	$7.417E + 02$	$6.222E + 06$
3	$4.739E + 02$	$6.753E + 02$
4	$4.726E + 02$	$3.320E + 04$
5	$4.509E + 02$	$4.116E + 03$
6	$4.507E + 02$	$5.412E + 02$
7	$4.501E + 02$	$4.122E + 03$
12	$4.494E + 02$	$3.163E + 01$

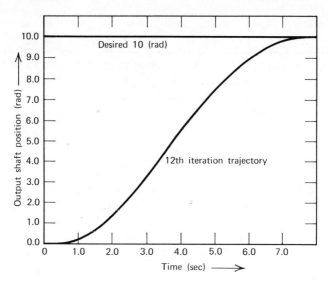

Figure 4.10 Output shaft position versus time for DC motor with sampled input.

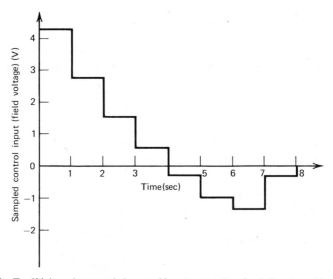

Figure 4.11 Twelfth iteration sampled control input versus time for DC motor of Example 4.3.

The initial guess for the control input was identically zero and the corresponding output shaft position was hence also zero over all time in the interval of interest.

4.6. SUMMARY

The results of the previous three sections may be concisely summarized by the introduction of the Hamiltonian defined by

$$H(x, u, \lambda) = \lambda^+ f(x, u)$$
$$= f^+(x, u)\lambda \qquad (4.78)$$

where now λ is the solution to the adjoint system (4.29) and $f(x, u)$ is the RHS of system dynamic equations in (4.9),

$$\dot{x} = f(x, u): x(t_0) = c \qquad (4.79)$$

Using H of (4.78), we may write the system and adjoint system dynamic equations (4.79) and (4.29) as

$$\dot{x} = \nabla_\lambda H(x, u, \lambda): x(t_0) = c$$
$$\dot{\lambda} = -\nabla_x H(x, u, \lambda): \lambda(t_f) = \nabla_x \phi(x(t_f, u)) \qquad (4.80)$$

where now ∇_λ and ∇_x indicate the gradient w.r.t. the n-vectors λ and x, respectively. Let us now consider the gradient in the cases considered in the above three sections in terms of the Hamiltonian H of (4.78).

The Case of a Continuous Function Input

For the case of a continuous function input the gradient of the cost functional is given in (4.28) as

$$g(u(t)) = f_u^+ \lambda(t) \qquad t \in [t_0, t_f] \qquad (4.81)$$

Using H of (4.78), we see that

$$g(u(t)) = \frac{\partial}{\partial u} H(x, u, \lambda) \qquad t \in [t_0, t_f] \qquad (4.82)$$

that is, the gradient of the cost functional evaluated at some $t \in [t_0, t_f]$ is the partial derivative of the Hamiltonian H w.r.t. the control input u, evaluated at the same time. Further, if u^* minimizes the cost functional $J[u(t)]$, then $g(u(t)) = 0$ for $t \in [t_0, t_f]$ and by (4.82)

$$\frac{\partial}{\partial u} H(x, u, \lambda) = 0$$

for $t \in [t_0, t_f]$, and H is in turn minimized. We hence have the following minimum principle

**If u^* minimizes the cost functional J of (4.10) then
H of (4.78) is in turn minimized w.r.t. u for all $t \in [t_0, t_f]$.** (4.83)

It may be noted that this minimum principle is simply Pontryagin's maximum principle (see [12]) stated as a minimum principle. Pontryagin considers maximizing a criterion and so obtains a maximum principle. The gradient as given in (4.81) and (4.82) is for the case of a continuous function input, and one might hence conclude that the minimum principle derived from it in (4.83) is only valid if the minimizing control input is a continuous function. Pontryagin et al. [12] show that the maximum principle holds for arbitrary piecewise continuous control inputs.

The Case of Input Control Parameters

In the space of input control parameters, for m parameters this is $\mathscr{R}^m$, the gradient is given by (4.46) as

$$g(u) = \int_{t_0}^{t_f} f_u^+ \lambda(t)\, dt \tag{4.84}$$

where f_u is given by (4.47) and λ is the adjoint system state vector. Using H of (4.78), we see that the gradient of (4.84) may be written as

$$g(u) = \nabla_u \int_{t_0}^{t_f} H(x, u, \lambda)\, dt \tag{4.85}$$

where now since $u \in \mathscr{R}^m$, ∇_u indicates the gradient in $\mathscr{R}^m$ w.r.t. u. We note now that if we minimize the criterion J of (4.10) using the gradient as in (4.84), we at the same time minimize $\int_{t_0}^{t_f} H(x, u, \lambda)\, dt$. We have the following minimum principle:

**If $u^* \in \mathscr{R}^m$, a set of input parameters, minimizes
the criterion J of (4.10), then u^* also minimizes**

$$\int_{t_0}^{t_f} H(x, u, \lambda)\, dt \tag{4.86}$$

where H is given in (4.78).

The Case of a Sampled Input

For a sampled input as considered in Section 4.5 and shown in Fig. 4.9, the input space here is $\mathscr{R}^N$ with typical element $u = [u_0 \, u_1 \dots u_{N-1}]^+$ where u_k is the value of the input over the time interval $t_0 + kT \leq t \leq t_0 + \overline{k+1}T$, and T is the sampling interval. The gradient in this case is of the form $g(u) = [g_0 \, g_1 \dots g_{n-1}]$ where g_k is given by (4.75) as

$$g_k = \int_{t_0+kT}^{t_0+\overline{k+1}T} f_u^+ \lambda(t) \, dt \tag{4.87}$$

where f_u is given by (4.19b).

Using H of (4.78), we have that g_k may be written as

$$g_k = \frac{\partial}{\partial u_k} \int_{t_0+kT}^{t_0+\overline{k+1}T} H(x, u_k, \lambda) \, dt \tag{4.88}$$

where we note that $u(t) = u_k$ in the time interval of the integral. Here again, if the gradient as given by (4.87) and (4.88) is used to minimize the cost criterion J of (4.10), then

$$\int_{t_0+kT}^{t_0+\overline{k+1}T} H(x, u_k, \lambda) \, dt$$

is simultaneously minimized. We here have the minimum principle:

If u_k^*, the value of the control input over the kth sampling instant which minimizes the criterion J of (4.10), then u_k^* also minimizes

$$\int_{t_0+kT}^{t_0+\overline{k+1}T} H(x, u_k, \lambda) \, dt \tag{4.89}$$

where H is given by (4.78).

PROBLEMS

1. For a means of identifying the second derivative operator of a functional at x_0 show that

$$\frac{d^2}{d\varepsilon^2} F(x_0 + \varepsilon z) \bigg|_{\varepsilon=0} = \langle z, F''(x_0)z \rangle$$

This is a useful result if one is seeking to confirm the positive definiteness of the second derivative of a functional at an x_0 where the gradient is null to assure that x_0 is a minimizing element.

2. Using the result of problem 1, find the second derivative at x_0 of:

(a) $F(x) = F_0 + a^+x + \frac{1}{2}x^+Ax$ where x, $a \in \mathcal{R}^n$, and A is an $n \times n$, real, symmetric matrix.

(b) $\phi(x)$ where $x \in \mathcal{R}^n$ and ϕ is a real-valued function.

(c) $F(x_1, x_2) = (x_1 + 1)^3 + 2(x_2 + 2)^3$

(d) $F(x) = \int_a^b x(t) \, dt \int_a^b k(t, s)x(s) \, ds$, $x \in \mathcal{L}^2_{[a, b]}$

3. Given the system

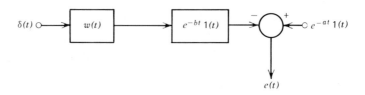

$\delta(t)$ $w(t)$ $e^{-bt} 1(t)$ $e^{-at} 1(t)$

$e(t)$

Here $e(t)$ is an error function. Given a plant with impulse response $e^{-bt}1(t)$. By adding a series compensator, alter the impulse response of the series combination to be $e^{-at}1(t)$. To make the problem nontrivial and feasible assume $a \neq b$ and $a, b > 0$.

(a) By conjugate gradient descent in the space spanned by $\delta(t)$ and $e^{-at}1(t)$, that is, looking for a $w(t)$ of the form

$$w(t) = c\delta(t) + d \, e^{-at}1(t)$$

find the $w(t)$ that produces minimum $\int_{-\infty}^{\infty} e^2(t) \, dt$.

(b) What is the minimum value of $\int_{-\infty}^{\infty} e^2(t) \, dt$ using the compensator $w(t)$ found in (a).

(c) Can a $w(t)$ from a more general space than the one in which we chose to search in (a) give a lower value of $\int_{-\infty}^{\infty} e^2(t) \, dt$?

4. Given the discrete time system

$$x_{k+1} = f(x_k, u_k) \qquad x_0 = c$$
$$x_k \in \mathcal{R}^n \qquad k = 0, 1, \ldots, N$$

cost criterion

$$J = \phi(x_N)$$

Find the gradient of the cost criterion in the space of control inputs where

(a) $u_k \in \mathcal{R}^m$, $k = 0, 1, 2, \ldots, N - 1$, that is, the control is an m-vector input that changes at each discrete time step or sampling instant.

(b) $u_k = u \in \mathcal{R}^m$, that is, a set of m constant parameters.

(c) $u_k = u_p \in \mathcal{R}^m$; $k = (p - 1)M, (p - 1)M + 1, \ldots, pM - 1$; $M > 1$; $p = 1, 2, \ldots, p_{max}$; $N = p_{max} M$. This is a discrete time input that changes only at every Mth sampling instant.

(d)   Find the gradient of the cost criterion in the space of initial conditions, that is, in $\mathcal{X}_0$ where $x_0 \in \mathcal{X}_0$. Hint: Follow the approach used for continuous time control inputs in Sections 4.3, 4.4, and 4.5 using the solution to the discrete time linear system as given in Appendix F. The adjoint system for the discrete time case is also given in Appendix F.

5.   Given the system with dynamics

$$\dot{x} = f(x) \qquad x \in \mathcal{R}^n \qquad x(t_0) = x_0$$

and cost criterion

$$J = \phi(x_0, x(t_f))$$

For $t_0 < t_f$, $t_0 \in \mathcal{T}_0$, $t_f \in \mathcal{T}_f$, $x \in \mathcal{X}_0$, $\mathcal{T}_0 = \mathcal{R}^1$, $\mathcal{T}_f = \mathcal{R}^1$, $\mathcal{X}_0 = \mathcal{R}^n$, find the gradient of the cost criterion J in $\mathcal{T}_0 \times \mathcal{T}_f \times \mathcal{X}_0$.

REFERENCES

[1]   Desoer, C. A., Lecture in Dept. of Electrical Engineering, University of California, Berkeley, August 17, 1963.

[2]   Luenberger, D. G., *Optimization by Vector Space Methods*, Chapter 7, Wiley, 1969.

[3]   Hasdorff, L., "The Gradient of the Cost Functional for Several Common Types of Control Inputs," *Proc. SWIEEECO, Dallas*, April 1970.

[4]   Bryson, A. E., W. F. Denham, F. J. Carrol, and K. Mikami, "Determination of Lift or Drag Programs to Minimize Re-Entry Heating," *J. Aero-Space Sci.*, **29**, No. 4 (April 1962).

[5]   Kelley, H. J., "Gradient Theory of Optimal Flight Paths," *ARS J.*, **30**, No. 10, 947–953, (Oct. 1960).

[6]   Lasdon, L. S., S. K. Mitter, and A. D. Warren, "The Method of Conjugate Gradients for Optimal Control Problems," *IEEE Trans. Autom. Control*, **AC-12**, No. 2, 132, (April 1967).

[7]   Zadeh, L. A., and C. A. Desoer, *Linear System Theory*, Chapter 6, McGraw-Hill, 1963.

[8]   Hasdorff, L., and S. C. Gupta, "An Iterative Procedure for Optimal Control of a System by Sampled Input," *J. Elec. Control*, **16**, No. 2 (Feb. 1964).

[9]   Reid, G. F., Private communication.

[10]   Joyner, L. L., Private communication.

[11]   Gupta, S. C., and L. Hasdorff, *Fundamentals of Automatic Control*, Chapter 8, Wiley, 1970.

[12]   Pontryagin, L. S., V. G. Boltyanskii, R. V. Gamkrelidze, and E. F. Mishchenko, *The Mathematical Theory of Optimal Processes*, Chapter I, Wiley-Interscience, 1962.

Chapter 5

The Gradient of the Cost Functional in Some Special Cases of Interest in Control Systems

---

5.1. SOME MOTIVATING CONSIDERATIONS

We here turn to finding the gradient in a few special cases which are of interest because of their usefulness in control system design and their illumination of some important details and problems that must be considered when one uses a gradient approach to solution for optimal controls. The gradient in the space of piecewise continuous control inputs is considered first, since as mentioned under Remarks in Section 4.3, the space of continuous function inputs is not complete under the Hilbert space (scalar product) norm. As a matter of fact, the space of piecewise continuous functions, for any finite number of pieces, is also not complete under the scalar product norm. However this space contains a larger proportion of those control inputs of interest in applications. Special cases of piecewise continuous controls considered are bang-bang controls which arise when one has magnitude constraints on the control input. Here the control is always on the magnitude limits and only changes when it switches instantaneously from one magnitude limit to another. The last special case of piecewise continuous control inputs considered is that of the pulse-width modulated controls. The input here is a series of unit magnitude pulses whose width and sign may be chosen.

From piecewise continuous control inputs we turn to the practically important problem of the gradient in the space of initial conditions on the system state vector. Lastly we consider a case that is growing in practical importance (and hence also in interest)—the case of systems with delay.

5.2. PIECEWISE CONTINUOUS CONTROL INPUTS

We consider again the system and criteria of Chapter 4, that is,

$$\dot{x} = f(x, u): x(t_0) = c \qquad (5.1)$$

with criterion of the performance of the system

$$J \triangleq \phi(x(t_f)) \qquad (5.2)$$

and where $f(\cdot, \cdot)$ and $\phi(\cdot)$ are assumed to have partial derivatives w.r.t. components of all arguments.

Here u is considered to be a piecewise continuous function over the time interval $[t_0, t_f]$ of the form given in Fig. 5.1. The control input is assumed to have discontinuities (jumps) at $t_1, t_2, \ldots, t_M$ and to be otherwise a smooth curve in between these jumps. M, the number of jumps, is assumed finite. Our approach here is to take as variables the magnitude of the jump and the times at which the jumps occur, which are assumed free to be chosen.

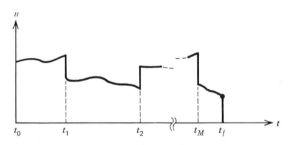

Figure 5.1 A piecewise continuous control input.

To do this we consider a piecewise continuous input function as the sum of a continuous function and a piecewise constant function with jumps at $t_1, t_2, \ldots, t_M$, as shown in Fig. 5.2. We see from the figure that $u(t)$ may be expressed as

$$u(t) = c(t) + \sum_{i=0}^{M} h_i \{1(t - t_i) - 1(t - t_{i+1})\} \qquad (5.3)$$

where now $c(t)$ is the continuous function, h_i is the height of the piecewise constant part of the input function in the interval $t_i < t < t_{i+1}$, and $1(t)$ is the unit step function.

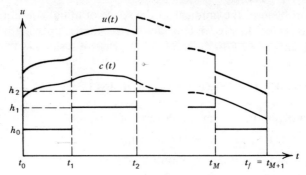

Figure 5.2   A piecewise continuous control input as the sum of a continuous and a piecewise constant function.

If u is an element from the space of piecewise continuous functions over the interval $[t_0, t_f]$ with M discontinuities, which we designate $\mathscr{PC}^M_{[t_0, t_f]}$, then (5.3) may be looked upon as a mapping from $\mathscr{C}_{[t_0, t_f]} \times \mathscr{R}^M \times \mathscr{R}^{M+1}$ to $\mathscr{PC}^M_{[t_0, t_f]}$. Here $\mathscr{C}_{[t_0, t_f]}$ is the space of continuous functions on $[t_0, t_f]$. To see the mapping more clearly we note that

$$c(t) \in \mathscr{C}_{[t_0, t_f]} \tag{5.4a}$$

$$t = \begin{bmatrix} t_1 \\ t_2 \\ \vdots \\ t_M \end{bmatrix} \in \mathscr{R}^M \tag{5.4b}$$

and

$$h = \begin{bmatrix} h_0 \\ h_1 \\ \vdots \\ h_M \end{bmatrix} \in \mathscr{R}^{M+1} \tag{5.4c}$$

Thus given an element $(c, t, h) \in \mathscr{C}_{[t_0, t_f]} \times \mathscr{R}^M \times \mathscr{R}^{M+1}$ and using (5.3), we can define a unique element $u \in \mathscr{PC}^M_{[t_0, t_f]}$. Our approach now is to look for the gradient of the cost functional of (5.2) in the space $\mathscr{C}_{[t_0, t_f]} \times \mathscr{R}^M \times \mathscr{R}^{M+1}$.

As before, we seek the gradient using (4.14). We note here, in order to use (4.14) to determine a gradient in $\mathscr{C}_{[t_0, t_f]} \times \mathscr{R}^M \times \mathscr{R}^{M+1}$, that the scalar product between two elements, (c^1, t^1, h^1) and (c^2, t^2, h^2), of this space is given by

$$\langle (c^1, t^1, h^1), (c^2, t^2, h^2) \rangle = \int_{t_0}^{t_f} c^1(t) c^2(t)\, dt + \sum_{i=1}^{M} t_i^1 t_i^2 + \sum_{i=0}^{M} h_i^1 h_i^2 \tag{5.5}$$

where c^1 and c^2, t^1 and t^2, and h^1 and h^2 are as given in (5.4).

To use (4.14), we seek $x(t_f, u + \varepsilon z)$ and $dx/d\varepsilon$. Integrating (5.1) with a u as given by (5.3), we obtain

$$x(t_f, u) = x(t_0) + \sum_{i=0}^{M} \int_{t_i}^{t_{i+1}} f(x, c(t) + h_i)\, dt \qquad t_{M+1} = t_f \qquad (5.6)$$

We now consider a variation of u by εz where z is in $\mathscr{PC}_{[t_0, t_f]}^M$. Corresponding to z in $\mathscr{C}_{[t_0, t_f]} \times \mathscr{R}^M \times \mathscr{R}^{M+1}$,

$$z \leftrightarrow (v, s, w)$$

by (5.3). Using $u + \varepsilon z$ in (5.6), we have

$$x(t_f, u + \varepsilon z) = x(t_0) + \sum_{i=0}^{M} \int_{t_i + \varepsilon s_i}^{t_{i+1} + \varepsilon s_{i+1}} f(x, c(t) + \varepsilon v(t) + h_i + \varepsilon w_i)\, dt$$

where now $s_0 = s_{M+1} = 0$ and $t_{M+1} = t_f$. Differentiating w.r.t. ε and letting $\varepsilon \to 0$, we get

$$\left. \frac{d}{d\varepsilon} x(t_f, u + \varepsilon z) \right|_{\varepsilon = 0} = \int_{t_0}^{t_f} f_x(x, u)\, \frac{d}{d\varepsilon} x(t, u) + f_u(x, u) v(t)\, dt$$

$$+ \sum_{i=0}^{M} \int_{t_i}^{t_{i+1}} f_u(x, u)\, dt \cdot w_i + \sum_{i=1}^{M} \left\{ \left. f(x, u) \right|_{t_i-} - \left. f(x, u) \right|_{t_i+} \right\} s_i$$

which may be written

$$\frac{d}{d\varepsilon} x(t_f, u) = \int_{t_0}^{t_f} \left[f_x(x, u)\, \frac{d}{d\varepsilon} x(t, u) + f_u(x, u) v(t) \right.$$

$$+ \sum_{i=0}^{M} f_u(x, u) \{1(t - t_i) - 1(t - t_{i+1})\} w_i$$

$$+ \left. \sum_{i=1}^{M} \left\{ \left. f(x, u) \right|_{t_i-} - \left. f(x, u) \right|_{t_i+} \right\} s_i\, \delta(t - t_i) \right] dt \qquad (5.7)$$

where now f_x and f_u are given by (4.19), $1(t)$ is the unit step, and $\delta(t)$ is the delta function. Equation (5.7) now is an integral equation in $dx/d\varepsilon$ of the same form as seen before in (4.20). The solution has been given in (4.23), which applies here to (5.7) with the assumption that $dx(t_0)/d\varepsilon = 0$ is

$$\frac{d}{d\varepsilon} x(t_f, u) = \int_{t_0}^{t_f} \Phi(t_f, t) f_u(x, u) v(t) \, dt$$

$$+ \sum_{i=1}^{M} \Phi(t_f, t_i) \left\{ f(x, u) \Big|_{t_{i-}} - f(x, u) \Big|_{t_{i+}} \right\} s_i$$

$$+ \sum_{i=0}^{M} \int_{t_i}^{t_{i+1}} \Phi(t_f, t) f_u(x, u) \, dt \, w_i \qquad (5.8)$$

where $\Phi(t_f, t)$ is the solution of (4.24). Equation 5.8 used in (4.14) gives

$$\frac{d}{d\varepsilon} J[u + \varepsilon z] \Big|_{\varepsilon=0} = \langle g(u), z \rangle$$

$$= \left\langle \nabla_x \phi(x(t_f, u)), \left[\int_{t_0}^{t_f} \Phi(t_f, t) f_u(x, u) v(t) \, dt \right. \right.$$

$$+ \sum_{i=1}^{M} \Phi(t_f, t_i) \left\{ f(x, u) \Big|_{t_{i-}} - f(x, u) \Big|_{t_{i+}} \right\} s_i$$

$$+ \left. \left. \sum_{i=0}^{M} \int_{t_i}^{t_{i+1}} \Phi(t_f, t) f_u(x, u) \, dt \, w_i \right] \right\rangle$$

which with some obvious manipulations gives

$$\langle g(u), z \rangle = \int_{t_0}^{t_f} f_u^+ \Phi^+(t_f, t) \nabla_x \phi v(t) \, dt$$

$$+ \sum_{i=1}^{M} \left\{ f \Big|_{t_{i-}} - f \Big|_{t_{i+}} \right\}^+ \Phi^+(t_f, t_i) \nabla_x \phi s_i$$

$$+ \sum_{i=0}^{M} \int_{t_i}^{t_{i+1}} f_u^+ \Phi^+(t_f, t) \nabla_x \phi \, dt \, w_i$$

$$= \int_{t_0}^{t_f} f_u^+ \lambda(t) v(t) \, dt$$

$$+ \sum_{i=1}^{M} \left\{ f \Big|_{t_{i-}} - f \Big|_{t_{i+}} \right\}^+ \lambda(t_i) s_i$$

$$+ \sum_{i=0}^{M} \int_{t_i}^{t_{i+1}} f_u^+ \lambda(t) \, dt \, w_i \qquad (5.9)$$

where the arguments of f and ϕ have been omitted and where we have set

$$\lambda(t) = \Phi^+(t_f, t) \nabla_x \phi(x(t_f, u)) \qquad (5.10)$$

From (5.9) we may identify the gradient in $\mathscr{C}_{[t_0, t_f]} \times \mathscr{R}^M \times \mathscr{R}^{M+1}$, noting the scalar product in this space is as given in (5.5)

$$[f_u^+ \lambda(t), t \in [t_0, t_f]] \in \mathscr{C}_{[t_0, t_f]}$$

$$g(c, t, h) = \begin{bmatrix} \begin{bmatrix} \left\{ f \Big|_{t_1} - \cdot f \Big|_{t_1+} \right\}^+ \lambda(t_1) \\ \vdots \\ \left\{ f \Big|_{t_M-} - f \Big|_{t_M+} \right\}^+ \lambda(t_M) \end{bmatrix} \in \mathscr{R}^M \\ \begin{bmatrix} \int_{t_0}^{t_1} f_u^+ \lambda(t) \, dt \\ \vdots \\ \int_{t_M}^{t_f} f_u^+ \lambda(t) \, dt \end{bmatrix} \in \mathscr{R}^{M+1} \end{bmatrix} \qquad (5.11)$$

Again we note from Appendix D that $\lambda(t)$ satisfies

$$\dot{\lambda} = -f_x^+(x, u)\lambda(t): \qquad \lambda(t_f) = \nabla_x \phi(x(t_f, u)) \qquad (5.12)$$

Equation 5.11 gives the gradient of the cost functional J of (5.2) in the space $\mathscr{C}_{[t_0, t_f]} \times \mathscr{R}^M \times \mathscr{R}^{M+1}$ which has been sought. This gradient may be used to seek the minimum in $\mathscr{C}_{[t_0, t_f]} \times \mathscr{R}^M \times \mathscr{R}^{M+1}$ and, by use of (5.3), the corresponding minimum in $\mathscr{P}\mathscr{C}_{[t_0, t_f]}^M$. We now turn to some examples of its use.

Example 5.1.

We consider first an example for which the exact solution is known so as to determine how close the approximate solution computed by gradient methods is to the true optimal solution. The example is from Sage, [2] and is interesting in that it is a case where the optimal trajectory has a singular arc when the solution is approached by standard techniques of calculus of variations.

The system is simple second order with dynamics

$$\dot{x}_1 = x_2 + u$$
$$\dot{x}_2 = -u$$
$$(5.13)$$

The object is to take the system from the origin in state space $x(t_0) = [0 \quad 0]^+$ to the state $x(t_f) = [1 \quad 0]^+$ while minimizing the criterion

$$J = \int_{t_0}^{t_f} (x_1 - 1)^2 \, dt \tag{5.14}$$

For our case, let us choose $t_0 = 0$, $t_f = 2$. The solution from Sage [2] is the control

$$u(t) = -1.04\delta(t) + 2.04 \cosh t - 1.04e^t + 0.275\delta(t - 2) \qquad 0 \le t \le 2 \tag{5.15}$$

where $\delta(t)$ is the dirac-delta function. For this control input the criterion is given by

$$J = \int_0^2 (x_1 - 1)^2 \, dt = 2 \tag{5.16}$$

The optimal trajectory resulting from the application of u of (5.15) is shown in the (x_1, x_2)-plane in Fig. 5.4.

The control as seen in (5.15) is not an element of the space of piecewise continuous control inputs $\mathscr{PC}^M_{[t_0, t_f]}$; such a space does not contain δ-functions. For our purposes the δ-function can be well approximated by a

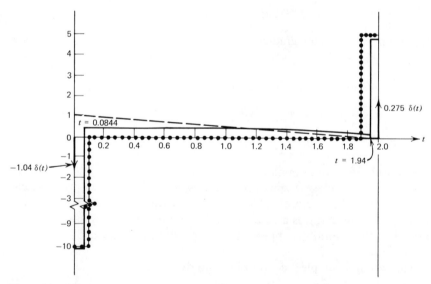

Figure 5.3 Input control functions for Example 5.1. (⋯⋯) Initial guess, (———) twenty-sixth iteration, (----) optimal control. Optimal $u(t) = -1.04\delta(t) - 0.02e^t + 1.02e^{-t} + 0.275\delta(t - 2)$.

short pulse of narrow width whose height may be adjusted to give an area under the pulse that is the same as the power of the δ-function being approximated. The solution to the problem as found by our gradient methods should hence be, looking at (5.15), a narrow negative pulse initially, followed by a continuous portion until just before the final time, $t_f = 2$, when a short positive pulse will occur. This is the form of input we seek and it is indeed in $\mathscr{PC}^M_{[t_0, t_f]}$.

The problem as given above by (5.13) and (5.14) requires reformulation to fit the format used in arriving at the gradient as given by (5.11). To this end, obtaining a criterion of the form of (5.2), we define a new state variable x_0, which satisfies

$$\dot{x}_0 = (x_1 - 1)^2 : x_0(t_0) = 0 \tag{5.17}$$

so that the criterion of (5.14) becomes

$$J = x_0(t_f) = x_0(2) \tag{5.18}$$

We require a final state $x(t_f) = [1 \quad 0]^+$; to satisfy this we add penalty function terms to the criterion of (5.18) to get

$$J = \phi(x(t_f)) = [x_0 + W_1(x_1 - 1)^2 + W_2(x_2)^2]|_{t=t_f} \tag{5.19}$$

which is in the form of (5.2). Use of (5.13) and (5.17) gives

$$\begin{aligned} \dot{x}_0 &= (x_1 - 1)^2 \\ \dot{x}_1 &= x_2 + u \\ \dot{x}_2 &= -u \end{aligned} \tag{5.20}$$

and the initial condition is

$$x(0) = [0 \quad 0 \quad 0]^+ \tag{5.21}$$

For the system (5.20) the adjoint system is

$$\frac{d}{dt} \begin{bmatrix} \lambda_0 \\ \lambda_1 \\ \lambda_2 \end{bmatrix} = - \begin{bmatrix} 0 & 0 & 0 \\ 2(x_1 - 1) & 0 & 0 \\ 0 & 1 & 0 \end{bmatrix} \begin{bmatrix} \lambda_0 \\ \lambda_1 \\ \lambda_2 \end{bmatrix} \tag{5.22a}$$

for which the terminal condition is given by

$$\lambda(t_f) = \nabla_x \phi(x(t_f)) = \begin{bmatrix} 1 \\ \tfrac{1}{2}W_1(x_1 - 1) \\ \tfrac{1}{2}W_2(x_2) \end{bmatrix}_{t=t_f} \tag{5.22b}$$

The solution to (5.22) gives λ as used in the gradient of (5.11).

For an initial guess for u we assume an input of the form plotted in Fig. 5.3, which is an initial spike of height -10 and width 0.1, followed by an input of zero and then a spike of height 5 and width 0.1. In $\mathscr{C}_{[t_0, t_f]} \times \mathscr{R}^M \times \mathscr{R}^{M+1}$ this is represented by the element (c, t, h) where

$$c = 0 \quad t \in [0, 2]$$

$$t = \begin{bmatrix} 0.1 \\ 1.9 \end{bmatrix} = \begin{bmatrix} t_1 \\ t_2 \end{bmatrix}$$

$$h = \begin{bmatrix} -10 \\ 0 \\ 5 \end{bmatrix} = \begin{bmatrix} h_0 \\ h_1 \\ h_2 \end{bmatrix}$$

(5.23)

The gradient at a typical element (c, t, h) by use of (5.11) and f as in (5.20) is then

$$g(c) = [\lambda_1(t) - \lambda_2(t) \quad t \in [0, 2]] \in \mathscr{C}_{[t_0, t_f]}$$

$$g(t) = \begin{bmatrix} [u(t_1-) - u(t_1+)][\lambda_1(t_1) - \lambda_2(t_1)] \\ [u(t_2-) - u(t_2+)][\lambda_1(t_2) - \lambda_2(t_1)] \end{bmatrix} \in \mathscr{R}^2$$

$$g(h) = \begin{bmatrix} \int_0^{t_1} \lambda_1(t) - \lambda_2(t) \, dt \\ \int_{t_1}^{t_2} \lambda_1(t) - \lambda_2(t) \, dt \\ \int_{t_2}^{2} \lambda_1(t) - \lambda_2(t) \, dt \end{bmatrix} \in \mathscr{R}^3$$

(5.24)

Using the gradient as given in (5.24) with an initial guess for a control input as given by (5.23) and the system and adjoint system as given in (5.20) and (5.22), respectively, we obtained the results shown in Fig. 5.4. The final value of the criterion, at the twenty-sixth iteration was $J = 2.08$ as compared to $J = 2$ for the optimal trajectory value. The optimal trajectory is also shown in the Fig. 5.4.

Remarks

1. The trajectory, as seen in Fig. 5.4, obtained by iterative, gradient computation falls right on top of the optimal trajectory and fits it with what appears roughly to be a minimum mean square error fit. Though the gradient-computed trajectory may not appear to be that close to the optimal trajectory, the value of the criterion, $J = 2.08$, is reasonably close to the optimal value $J = 2.0$. The error may be attributed to the following causes:

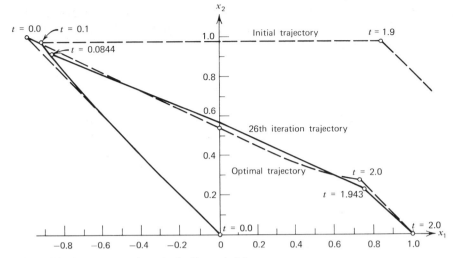

Figure 5.4 State space trajectories for Example 5.1.

(a) The approximation of the δ-function by finite width pulses.

(b) The numerical error in the integration of the differential equations and the construction of the gradient as given by (5.24).

The first error could possibly be reduced by choosing a narrower, higher pulse to approximate the δ-function. The second error could possibly be reduced by choosing a smaller integration step size. The results shown in Fig. 5.4 were obtained by use of 200 integration steps with fourth order Runge–Kutta integration.

2. The penalty function approach to the terminal constraints, used in the criterion of (5.19), worked very well here. The desired final state $x(2) = [1 \quad 0]^+$ was approached to within three significant figures in both components using $W_1 = W_2 = 100$. The penalty function terms gave a very negligible contribution ($< 10^{-4}$) to the $J = 2.08$ for the final trajectory.

3. The fact that the problem is a singular one when approached by the calculus of variations, or the maximum principle, never becomes evident in the approach via the iterative gradient method. It is handled straightforwardly and in the same manner as in the case of a nonsingular problem.

Bang-Bang Control Inputs

A bang-bang control input arises when one tries to control a system in optimal fashion, with the control input magnitude limited. These have been the subject of a great deal of investigation since the discovery of the maximum principle which showed clearly that the optimal control input for large classes of practical systems is of the bang-bang type. A bang-bang control, as we shall define it here, is simply a piecewise constant control input of the form shown in Fig. 5.5. The control input is constant except at the switching times when the value of the input jumps instantaneously from one constant value to another constant value. Typically if the input has magnitude limits, the jump is from one magnitude limit to another. We hence assume that the value of the input in between switching times is known. Analysis using the maximum principle is usually helpful in showing the constant values in between switchings. Thus the quantities required to specify the control input are the switching times. We here label these as in Fig. 5.5, $t_1, t_2, \ldots, t_M$.

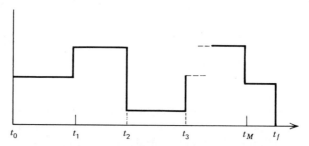

Figure 5.5   A bang-bang control input.

The control input is characterized by an element of $\mathcal{R}^M$ which we designate τ where

$$\tau = [t_1, t_2, \ldots, t_M]^+ \tag{5.25}$$

To find an optimum bang-bang control we now seek that element $\tau \in \mathcal{R}^M$ for which the corresponding bang-bang control minimizes the criterion of (5.2). The gradient of the criterion functional at a given $\tau \in \mathcal{R}^M$ may be found by recognizing that a bang-bang control of the type considered here is just a special case of a piecewise continuous control input with M discontinuities as considered earlier in this section. The difference is that a bang-bang control is fixed in between switching times and thus no variation of the value of input in between switchings is possible. Only the switching times can be changed. The gradient of the cost functional in the space of piecewise continuous control inputs is given in (5.11). For bang-bang control we ignore the portion of the gradient corresponding to times in between the switching times, (5.11), and take the gradient in the space of switching times ($\mathcal{R}^M$) from (5.11) to get the ith component as

$$[g(\tau)]_i = \lambda^+(t_i)[f(x, u)|_{t_i -} - f(x, u)|_{t_i +}] \qquad i = 1, 2, \ldots, M \tag{5.26}$$

We recall that $\lambda(t)$ is the adjoint system solution vector

$$\lambda(t) = \Phi^+(t_f, t)\nabla_x \phi(x(t_f, u)) \qquad (5.27)$$

which satisfies the adjoint systems of (4.29). Equation 5.26 is what is required for descent on the cost functional in the space of bang-bang control inputs.

Here again the question arises as to what the value of M should be, that is, how many switchings to consider. As mentioned above, application of the maximum principle here is helpful (see [1]). If the control input has the usual magnitude limits an approach to this problem is to simply treat the control input as a continuous function input, as discussed in Section 4.3, and to then solve for the criterion-minimizing control input under this assumption. The result is an approximation to the discontinuous bang-bang control input sought. From this approximation one can in general expect to see the number of switching times required and to be able to venture a good initial guess for what these switching times should be.

Example 5.2

As an example of the determination of a bang-bang control input by use of the gradient of (5.26), let us now consider the problem of Example 4.1. The problem there was changing the shaft position of a DC motor, shown in Fig. 4.2, by 10 rad with a resulting criterion as given in (4.32). In Example 4.1 it was assumed that the control input, e_f the field voltage, was unconstrained in magnitude. The $(e_f)^2$ term was added under the integral in the criterion of (4.32) so that the control input would not become unbounded. Here let us assume that there is a magnitude constraint on the control input, field voltage e_f, and that at every instant of time

$$e_f \leq 10 \qquad (5.28)$$

must be satisfied. We know from the maximum principle that to move the state of the system in minimum time bang-bang control, which is always at the magnitude bound, is required. Furthermore, since the system is third order, three independent switching times are required. Hence to change the state of the DC motor let us postulate a control input $u = e_f$ of the form shown in Fig. 5.6. There are three switchings, so the vector τ of (5.25) is

$$\tau = \begin{bmatrix} t_1 \\ t_2 \\ t_3 \end{bmatrix} \qquad (5.29)$$

The objective in this example is to change the shaft position by $+10$ rad and to then have the system quiescent. Hence the initial control input is

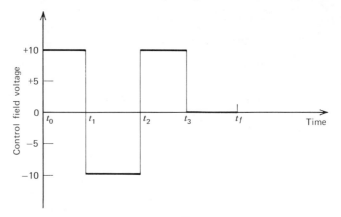

Figure 5.6   Typical control input for Example 5.2.

positive (see Fig. 5.6), and after the last switching t_3, the control input is brought to zero and held there.

The system differential equations and criterion from Example 4.2, as seen in (4.35) and (4.32), respectively, were used. Since the magnitude of the control input is bounded by hypothesis here, there is no longer any need to weight the control input in the criterion. Hence R, [see (4.32)] was assumed zero. With $R = 0$, f, f_x, ϕ, and $\nabla_x \phi$ are then as given in (4.35), (4.37), (4.34), and (4.38), respectively. The initial condition vector is as given in (4.36). The gradient at the ith switching time t_i as given by (5.26) is for this example

$$[g(\tau)]_i = -0.1\lambda_3(t_i)[u(t_{i^-}) - u(t_{i^+})] \tag{5.30}$$

where λ_3 is the third component of λ, the solution to the adjoint system, (4.29).

Figure 4.4 was consulted for an initial guess for the switching times to be used, t_1, t_2, and t_3 of Fig. 5.6. Figure 4.4 gives the control input found in Example 4.1. The control is seen to cross the axis at $t = 2.0$ and $t = 4.5$. The output reached the desired state (see Fig. 4.3) by $t = 5.0$. The initial guess was hence

$$\tau = \begin{bmatrix} t_1^0 \\ t_2^0 \\ t_3^0 \end{bmatrix} = \begin{bmatrix} 2.0 \\ 4.5 \\ 5.0 \end{bmatrix}$$

The resulting initial control input is shown in Fig. 5.7.

The problem was run for 18 conjugate gradient descent iterations with the gradient as given in (5.30). The resulting control is shown in Fig. 5.7. A smooth, no overshoot response was achieved with a bang-bang input. The

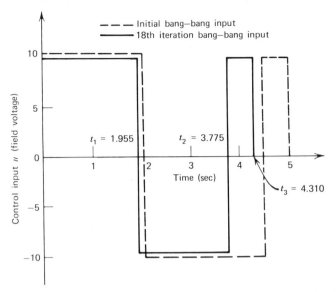

Figure 5.7 Bang-bang control inputs for the DC motor of Example 5.2. (---) Initial bang-bang input, (——) eighteenth iteration bang-bang input.

switching time vector τ, achieved after 18 iterations, was to four significant figures

$$\tau = \begin{bmatrix} 1.955 \\ 3.775 \\ 4.310 \end{bmatrix}$$

The program used $W_1 = W_2 = W_3 = 100.0$, which gave terminal constraint satisfaction to three significant figures. The final run involved 150 integration steps in a fourth order Runge–Kutta integration of the differential equations. Figure 5.8 shows the output shaft time response.

Piecewise Constant Control Inputs

Another type of control input that can be handled easily with the theory developed in this section and one that has some practical utility because of its simplicity is the piecewise constant input. A piecewise constant input is one of the form seen in Fig. 5.5. The input is constant until a switching time is reached, at which point the value changes instantaneously to another constant value, which is held until the next switching time. The input may be expressed in closed form as

$$u(t) = \sum_{i=0}^{M} h_i[1(t - t_i) - 1(t - t_{i+1})] \qquad t_{M+1} = t_f \qquad (5.31)$$

from which it is seen that the control input is completely defined by the vector of switching times

$$\tau = \begin{bmatrix} t_1 \\ t_2 \\ \vdots \\ t_M \end{bmatrix} \in \mathscr{R}^M \qquad (5.32)$$

and the vector of input values

$$h = \begin{bmatrix} h_0 \\ h_1 \\ \vdots \\ h_M \end{bmatrix} \in \mathscr{R}^{M+1} \qquad (5.33)$$

We may thus consider the input as an element of $\mathscr{R}^M \times \mathscr{R}^{M+1}$, and the cost criterion of (5.2), which we seek to minimize, as a mapping from $\mathscr{R}^M \times \mathscr{R}^{M+1}$ to $\mathscr{R}^1$. The gradient of this criterion $g(\tau, h) \in \mathscr{R}^M \times \mathscr{R}^{M+1}$ for a given control input (i.e., given τ and h) may be found from the gradient in the space of piecewise continuous control inputs as seen in (5.11) by ignoring that portion of $g(c, t, h)$ in $\mathscr{C}_{[t_0, t_f]}$. We thus have as the gradient

$$g(\tau, h) = \begin{bmatrix} \begin{bmatrix} \lambda^+(t_1)\left[f(x, u)\Big|_{t_1+} - f(x, u)\Big|_{t_1+} \right] \\ \vdots \\ \lambda^+(t_M)\left[f(x, u)\Big|_{t_M-} f(x, u)\Big|_{t_M+} \right] \end{bmatrix} \in \mathscr{R}^M \\ \begin{bmatrix} \int_{t_0}^{t_1} f_u^+(x, u)\lambda(t)\, dt \\ \vdots \\ \int_{t_M}^{t_f} f_u^+(x, u)\lambda(t)\, dt \end{bmatrix} \in \mathscr{R}^{M+1} \end{bmatrix} \qquad (5.34)$$

where again $\lambda(t)$ is the adjoint vector given by (5.27) and which must satisfy (4.29), and f_u is as given by (4.19b). Using (5.31) we have

$$
\begin{aligned}
u(t) &= h_i \qquad t_i < t < t_{i+1} \\
u(t_i-) &= h_{i-1} \\
u(t_i+) &= h_i
\end{aligned}
\tag{5.35}
$$

which used in (5.34) gives

$$
g(\tau, h) =
\begin{bmatrix}
\begin{bmatrix}
\lambda^+(t_1)[f(x(t_1), h_0) - f(x(t_1), h_1)] \\
\lambda^+(t_2)[f(x(t_2), h_1) - f(x(t_2), h_2)] \\
\vdots \\
\lambda^+(t_M)[f(x(t_M), h_{M-1}) - f(x(t_M), h_M)]
\end{bmatrix} \\[2em]
\displaystyle\int_{t_0}^{t_1} f_u^+(x, h_0)\lambda(t)\, dt \\[1.5em]
\displaystyle\int_{t_1}^{t_2} f_u^+(x, h_1)\lambda(t)\, dt \\[1.5em]
\vdots \\[1em]
\displaystyle\int_{t_M}^{t_f} f_u^+(x, h_M)\lambda(t)\, dt
\end{bmatrix}
\tag{5.36}
$$

Equation 5.36 is required to do descent on the criterion of (5.2) with the system of (5.1), where the input control is constrained to be a piecewise constant function of time.

Example 5.3

As an example of the use of a piecewise constant control input let us consider the same system and problem as in Example 5.2. Here the problem is to move the shaft of a field-controlled DC motor 10 rad from rest to rest. In Example 5.2 the input (field voltage e_f as seen in Fig. 4.2) was constrained to be a bang-bang control input with

$$
|e_f| = 10
$$

Here we have the same form of control input except the constraint on the magnitude is lifted. The basic form of the control input is assumed to be as in Fig. 5.6 in that three switchings are assumed, that is, $M = 3$ in (5.31) and (5.36). The switching time vector τ is as given in (5.29). The input values between switching are given by the vector

$$h = \begin{bmatrix} h_0 \\ h_1 \\ h_2 \\ h_3 \end{bmatrix} \tag{5.37}$$

and the value of the input $u(t)$ for any t may be evaluated using (5.29) and (5.37) in (5.31) or equivalently in (5.35).

The dynamics of the DC motor and the criterion function ϕ are given in Example 4.1 in (4.35) and (4.32), respectively. In this case, as in Example 5.2, $R = 0$ was chosen and with this value for R, f, f_x, f_u, ϕ and $\nabla_x \phi$ are given by (4.35), (4.37), (4.39), (4.34), and (4.38), respectively. The initial condition vector on the state is again the null vector as given in (4.36).

The gradient for this case, as calculated from (5.36), may be written in detail as

$$g(\tau, h) = \begin{bmatrix} \begin{bmatrix} 0.1\lambda_3(t_1)[h_0 - h_1] \\ 0.1\lambda_3(t_2)[h_1 - h_2] \\ 0.1\lambda_3(t_3)[h_2 - h_3] \end{bmatrix} \in \mathcal{R}^3 \\[2em] \begin{bmatrix} \int_0^{t_1} 0.1\lambda_3(t)\, dt \\[1em] \int_{t_1}^{t_2} 0.1\lambda_3(t)\, dt \\[1em] \int_{t_1}^{t_3} 0.1\lambda_3(t)\, dt \\[1em] \int_{t_3}^{t_f} 0.1\lambda_3(t)\, dt \end{bmatrix} \in \mathcal{R}^4 \end{bmatrix} \tag{5.38}$$

The problem was submitted to the computer for conjugate gradient descent using as an initial guess for the input the final bang-bang control input found in Example 5.2. This gave as the initial guess for the switching time vector

$$\tau^0 = \begin{bmatrix} 1.955 \\ 3.775 \\ 4.310 \end{bmatrix} \tag{5.39}$$

and for the input function values vector

$$\boldsymbol{h}^0 = \begin{bmatrix} 10 \\ -10 \\ 10 \\ 0 \end{bmatrix} \tag{5.40}$$

The corresponding initial output shaft response is then as given in Fig. 5.8.

In this example the object was to have the output shaft at rest at the final time t_f. Hence it was necessary to have the input go to zero after the final switching t_3, as was also done in the bang-bang control example. This implied that the fourth component of the input function value h_4 had to be held at zero. From (5.40) it is seen that the initial guess for this component was zero. To keep the value at zero straightforward conjugate gradient descent was done with the gradient as in (5.38); however the component of the gradient corresponding to h_4 was set equal to zero and was held there through all iterations. The component of the gradient corresponding to h_4 was the bottom entry in the gradient as seen in (5.38), that is, $\int_{t_3}^{t_f} 0.1\lambda_3(t)\, dt$.

The output shaft position as a function of time shown in Fig. 5.9 was obtained after 62 CG descent iterations. The program continued descending after this number of iterations. The descent was terminated since it was very slow after this point and it was realized that since there was no bound on the

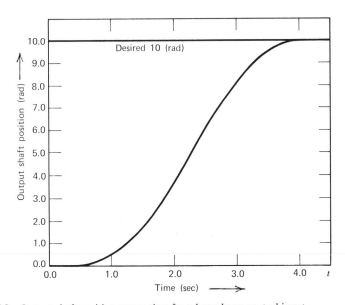

Figure 5.8 Output shaft position versus time for a bang-bang control input.

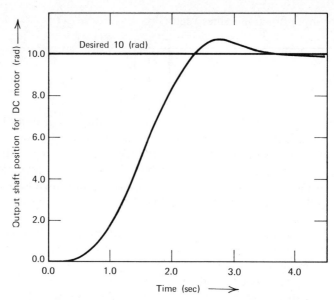

Figure 5.9 Output shaft position versus time with piecewise constant input.

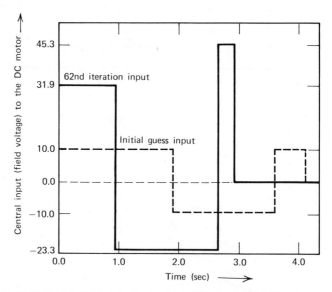

Figure 5.10 Piecewise constant control input versus time for DC motor.

input function magnitude and no weighting in of the input in the criterion
($R = 0$ was assumed), the pulse heights were going off to a limit at infinity
and the switching times were approaching a limit of zero. The input control
function can be seen in Fig. 5.10 to approach this sort of limit. Comparing
Figs. 5.8 and 5.9, we see that the piecewise constant input has resulted in a
quicker responding system. In the limit of course, with unbounded control,
the shaft position should change from 0 to 10 rad in an infinitesimal amount
of time.

The computer program used a final time $t_f = 4.5$ sec as seen in Fig. 5.9.
One hundred and fifty iteration steps were used in Runge–Kutta integration.
$W_1 = W_2 = W_3 = 100$ was used in the penalty function terms of ϕ and $\nabla_x\phi$
of (4.34) and (4.38), respectively. These terms were added to insure that the
output shaft had reached the desired 10 rad displacement and that the motor
was at rest at the final time. To four significant figures the program reached
the switching time and pulse height vectors

$$\tau^{62} = \begin{bmatrix} 1.017 \\ 2.773 \\ 3.116 \end{bmatrix}$$

$$h^{62} = \begin{bmatrix} 31.93 \\ -23.28 \\ 45.28 \\ 0.00 \end{bmatrix}$$

The corresponding piecewise constant control input is given in Fig. 5.10.

5.3. THE GRADIENT OF A COST FUNCTIONAL ON THE SPACE OF PULSE-WIDTH MODULATED CONTROL INPUTS

Statement of the Problem and the System Considered

Again we consider a system whose dynamics are described by

$$\dot{x} = f(x, u): x(t_0) = c \tag{5.41}$$

where $x \in \mathcal{R}^n$ is the system state vector and u the control input. The time
interval of interest is again $[t_0, t_f]$ and the system is in state c at time t_0.
We here consider pulse-width modulated (PWM) control inputs where u,
over the time interval $[t_0, t_f]$, is of the form

$$u(t) = \sum_{k=0}^{N-1} \text{sgn } \tau_k[1(t - t_0 - kT) - 1(t - t_0 - kT - |\tau_k|T)] \tag{5.42}$$

Here $(t_f - t_0) = NT$ where T is the sampling interval, N is the number of sampling intervals considered, and $\tau_0, \tau_1, \ldots, \tau_{N-1}$ give the widths and the sign of the pulses starting at $0, T, 2T, \ldots, \overline{N-1}T$, respectively. $1(t)$ is the unit step function. A typical PWM control input of the type considered here is shown in Fig. 5.11. We assume $f(\cdot, \cdot)$ gives unique, bounded solutions starting at $x(t_0) = c$ for all u as in (5.42). We also assume that f is differentiable w.r.t. all components of x.

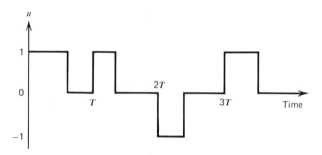

Figure 5.11   A typical PWM control input.

The cost criterion J on the performance of the system is still

$$J = \phi(x(t_f)) \tag{5.43}$$

that is, a function (ϕ) on the space of final states where ϕ is assumed differentiable w.r.t. all components of x.

The optimal control problem for this system is then:

Find u of the form given in (5.42) which when applied to the system, (5.41), produces minimum cost J as given by (5.43).

The Space of PWM Control Inputs to be Considered

From (5.42) it is seen that a control u is specified by the $\tau_0, \tau_1, \ldots, \tau_{N-1}$. Thus if the vector $\tau \in \mathscr{R}^N$ of the form

$$\tau = [\tau_0 \tau_1 \tau_2 \cdots \tau_{N-1}]^+ \tag{5.44}$$

(superscript + indicates transpose) is considered in the set θ where

$$\theta = \{\tau : |\tau_i| \le 1; i = 0, 1, 2, \ldots, N-1\} \tag{5.45}$$

for each $\tau \in \theta$ there corresponds a PWM control as given by (5.42). For this $\tau \in \theta$ there corresponds an $x(t_f)$ that is found by integrating (5.41) using the u corresponding to this τ by (5.43). To this $x(t_f)$ there corresponds a cost $J = \phi(x(t_f))$. Thus functional $J[\tau]$ from $\tau \in \theta$ to the real numbers is defined. The optimal control problem is then:

Find $\tau \in \theta$ that minimizes $J[\tau]$.

The gradient we seek here is the gradient of $J[\tau]$ for $\tau \in \theta$.

The Gradient in the Space of PWM Control Inputs

Now let us consider the computation of the gradient for the PWM control input functional defined from (5.43) as

$$J[\tau] = \phi(x(t_f, \tau)) \tag{5.46}$$

where τ is as given by (5.44) and $x(t_f, \tau)$ is the final state $x(t_f)$, obtained by applying a pulse-width modulated input as in (5.42) corresponding to the vector τ given in (5.44). Integrating (5.41) we obtain

$$x(t_f, \tau) = c + \int_{t_0}^{t_f} \sum_{k=0}^{N-1} \{f(x, \text{sgn } \tau_k)[1(t - t_0 - kT) - 1(t - T_k)]$$

$$+ f(x, 0)[1(t - T_k) - 1(t - t_0 - \overline{k + 1T})]\} \, dt \tag{5.47}$$

where $T_k = t_0 + kT + |\tau_k| T$, that is, the trailing edge of the kth pulse, and T is the sampling interval. Let us consider the construction of the gradient at a given τ using (4.11) and (4.12) and evaluating

$$\frac{dJ[\tau + \varepsilon z]}{d\varepsilon}\bigg|_{\varepsilon=0} = \frac{d}{d\varepsilon} \phi(x(t_f, \tau + \varepsilon z))\bigg|_{\varepsilon=0}$$

$$= \left\langle \nabla_x \phi(x(t_f, \tau)), \frac{dx(t_f, \tau + \varepsilon z)}{d\varepsilon}\bigg|_{\varepsilon=0} \right\rangle$$

$$= \langle g(\tau), z \rangle \tag{5.48}$$

where $\nabla_x \phi$ is the ordinary gradient of the function $\phi(\cdot)$ w.r.t. x. Equation 5.48 reduces the problem to finding

$$\frac{d}{d\varepsilon} x(t_f, \tau + \varepsilon z)\bigg|_{\varepsilon=0} \tag{5.49}$$

This is found by using $\tau + \varepsilon z$ in (5.47), which gives

$$x(t_f, \tau + \varepsilon z) = c + \int_{t_0}^{t_f} \sum_{k=0}^{N-1} \{f(x, \text{sgn}(\tau_k + \varepsilon z_k))$$

$$\times [1(t - t_0 - kT) - 1(t - t_0 - kT - |\tau_k + \varepsilon z_k| T)] + f(x, 0)$$

$$\times [1(t - t_0 - kT - |\tau_k + \varepsilon z_k| T) - 1(t - t_0 - \overline{k + 1}T)]\} dt$$

Differentiating w.r.t. ε and evaluating at $\varepsilon = 0$ gives

$$\frac{dx(t_f, \tau)}{d\varepsilon} = \int_{t_0}^{t_f} \left\{ f_x \frac{dx(t, \tau)}{d\varepsilon} + \sum_{k=0}^{N-1} [f(x, \text{sgn} \tau_k) \right.$$

$$\left. - f(x, 0)]\delta(t - T_k) \text{ sgn } \tau_k \cdot T \cdot z_k \right\} dt \qquad (5.50)$$

where $dx/d\varepsilon$ is assumed evaluated for the arguments as given in (5.49) and f_x is the matrix of partial derivatives whose ijth element is given by

$$(f_x)_{ij} = \frac{\partial f_i(x, u)}{\partial x_j}, \qquad i, j = 1, 2, \ldots, n \qquad (5.51)$$

with u given by (5.42) and where $\delta(t - T_k)$ is a dirac–delta function occurring at time $t = T_k$. Equation 5.50 is an integral equation in $dx/d\varepsilon$ of the same form as (4.20). The solution to this equation may, from (4.23), be written as

$$\frac{dx(t_f, \tau)}{d\varepsilon} = \sum_{k=0}^{N-1} \Phi(t_f, T_k)[f(x(T_k), \text{sgn } \tau_k) - f(x(T_k), 0)] \text{ sgn } \tau_k \cdot T \cdot z_k \qquad (5.52)$$

where $\Phi(t_1, t_2)$ is the $n \times n$ matrix (the state transition matrix) solution to

$$\frac{d}{dt_1} \Phi(t_1, t_2) = f_x \Phi(t_1, t_2) \colon \Phi(t_2, t_2) = I \qquad (5.53)$$

where I is the identity matrix and f_x is as in (5.51). Using (5.52) in (5.48) we obtain

$$\frac{dJ[\tau + \varepsilon z]}{d\varepsilon}\bigg|_{\varepsilon = 0} = \left\langle \nabla_x \phi(x(t_f, \tau)), \sum_{k=0}^{N-1} \Phi(t_f, T_k)[f(x(T_k), \text{sgn } \tau_k) \right.$$

$$\left. - f(x(T_k), 0)] \text{ sgn } \tau_k \cdot T \cdot z_k \right\rangle$$

$$= \sum_{k=0}^{N-1} \lambda^+(T_k)[f(x(T_k), \text{sgn } \tau_k) - f(x(T_k), 0] \text{ sgn } \tau_k \cdot T \cdot z_k$$

$$= \langle g, z \rangle \qquad (5.54)$$

where

$$\lambda(T_k) = \Phi^+(t_f, T_k)\nabla_x\phi(x(t_f, \tau)) \qquad (5.55)$$

and T_k is as given under (5.47). g, the gradient sought, is seen from (5.54) to be the N-vector whose kth component is given by

$$(g)_k = \lambda^+(T_k)[f(x(T_k), \operatorname{sgn} \tau_k) - f(x(T_k), 0)] \operatorname{sgn} \tau_k \cdot T \qquad (5.56)$$

$$k = 0, 1, 2, \ldots, N - 1$$

The construction of the gradient as given in (5.56) is again simplified by the realization (from Appendix D) that $\lambda(t)$ satisfies

$$\dot{\lambda}(t) = -f_x^+\lambda(t): \lambda(t_f) = \nabla_x\phi(x(t_f, \tau)) \qquad (5.57)$$

Remarks

1. To compute the gradient for the criterion functional $J[\tau]$ as given in (5.56) for a given τ the same steps may be used as were given under computation of the Gradient in the Space of Input Control Functions in Section 4.3, the only difference being that the gradient is computed as given by (5.56) instead of by (4.28).

2. $(g)_k$, a component of the gradient can be seen from (5.56) to have a discontinuity at $\tau_k = 0$. A gradient may be defined by taking the limit from the right or the limit from the left. Which one to use in a given instance may be determined, if one is interested in a descent direction, by choosing a variation z such that

$$\delta J = \langle g, z \rangle \leq 0$$

Thus for a $\tau_k = 0$, we let $\tau_k \to z_k$ in (5.54) and choose z_k so that

$$\lambda^+(T_k)[f(x(T_k), \operatorname{sgn} z_k) - f(x(T_k), 0)]|z_k| \cdot T \leq 0$$

or so that

$$\lambda^+(T_k)f(x(T_k), \operatorname{sgn} z_k) \leq \lambda^+(T_k)f(x(T_k), 0) \qquad (5.58)$$

and a minimum principle can be seen here. If no z_k can be found for which (5.58) is satisfied then we choose $z_k = 0$, which implies $(g)_k = 0$, for this component of the gradient.

3. Since the pulse widths of the PWM control cannot be longer than the sampling period T, saturation occurs at $\tau_k = \pm 1$. Thus

$$(g)_k = 0 \qquad |\tau_k| > 1 \qquad (5.59)$$

Example 5.4

As an example of the above-described method of finding the gradient let us consider the PWM modulator operating into the field-controlled DC motor as shown in Fig. 5.12. Values of the pertinent parameters for a motor of approximately 5 hp are shown in the figure. We define the state variables by

$$x_1 = \theta$$
$$x_2 = \dot{\theta} \tag{5.60}$$
$$x_3 = i_f$$

The system differential equations for this choice of state variables are

$$\dot{x}_1 = x_2$$
$$\dot{x}_2 = -\left(\frac{B}{J}\right)x_2 + \left(\frac{K_T}{J}\right)x_3 \tag{5.61}$$
$$\dot{x}_3 = -\left(\frac{R_f}{L_f}\right)x_3 + \frac{u}{L_f}$$

where $u = e_f$ = field voltage is the control input.

Let us consider the problem of making a step change in the position of the output shaft. To make the problem fit the formulation used above, we take a step change of 10 rad as the desired output and we let the cost criterion be the

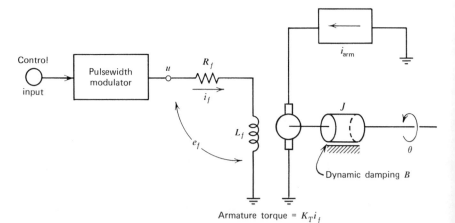

Figure 5.12   PWM applied to a field-controlled DC motor. R_f = 10 ohms, L_f = 10 h, J = 2 kg-m², B = 0.66 kg-m²/sec, K_T = 10 newton-m/A.

integral square of the error between the desired step and the actual shaft position. Thus we consider the criterion

$$J = \int_{t_0}^{t_f} [(\theta - 10)^2 + R(e_f)^2] \, dt$$

$$= \int_{t_0}^{t_f} [(x_1 - 10)^2 + Ru^2] \, dt \qquad (5.62)$$

The $R(e_f)^2$ term is added under the integral to limit the energy (and consequently the magnitude of the pulse widths) applied to the input (the field) of the motor by the PWM modulator.

To handle a criterion of the form of (5.43), the system differential equations are augmented by a new state variable x_4, which satisfies

$$\dot{x}_4 = (x_1 - 10)^2 + Ru^2: x_4(0) = 0 \qquad (5.63)$$

For x_4 defined in this manner

$$J = x_4(t_f) = \phi(x(t_f)) \qquad (5.64)$$

which is the form of the criterion defined in (5.43). Using (5.63) to augment the equations of (5.60) and using the values of the parameters as given in Fig. 5.12, we get

$$\begin{aligned}
\dot{x}_1 &= x_2 \\
\dot{x}_2 &= -\frac{x_2}{3} + 5x_3 \\
\dot{x}_3 &= -x_3 + 0.1u \\
\dot{x}_4 &= (x_1 - 10)^2 + Ru^2
\end{aligned} \qquad (5.65)$$

Under the assumption of quiescence at $t_0 = 0$ and with the initial condition on x_4 as given in (5.63) the initial conditions on the state vector are

$$x(0) = c = \mathbf{0} \qquad (5.66)$$

Equations 5.65 and 5.66 give f and c of (5.41). The adjoint system (5.57) requires f_x and $\nabla \phi$. f_x is found by applying (5.51) to f in (5.65). The result is

$$f_x = \begin{bmatrix} 0 & 1 & 0 & 0 \\ 0 & -\frac{1}{3} & 5 & 0 \\ 0 & 0 & -1 & 0 \\ 2(x_1 - 10) & 0 & 0 & 0 \end{bmatrix} \qquad (5.67)$$

$\nabla\phi$ is the gradient of ϕ as given in (5.64), which is

$$\nabla\phi(x(t_f)) = \begin{bmatrix} 0 \\ 0 \\ 0 \\ 1 \end{bmatrix} \qquad (5.68)$$

The kth component of the gradient, as in (5.56), is then

$$(g)_k = (0.1\lambda_3(T_k)\,\text{sgn}\,\tau_k + R\lambda_4(T_k))\cdot T \qquad (5.69)$$

where T_k is as defined under (5.47).

f, f_x, ϕ, and $\nabla\phi$ as given by (5.65), (5.67), (5.64), and (5.68), respectively, were programmed using $x(0) = 0$ as in (5.66) with $t_0 = 0$, $t_f = 3$ sec, $R = 5$, and $T = 0.3$ so that $N = 10$. From an initial guess of the pulse widths $\tau = 0$, the result shown as curve 1 in Fig. 5.13 was obtained after five conjugate gradient descent iterations. At this number of iterations the decrease in the criterion per step was negligible.

The response obtained with the integral square criterion of (5.62) (curve 1 of Fig. 5.13), was obviously not what was wanted in the way of a step response. Longer time intervals, that is, $t_f > 3$ sec, were tried and the same highly oscillatory type of response still resulted. It was hence decided to add terminal time terms to the criterion of (5.62) to insure that at time t_f the shaft position $\theta = x_1$ would be at 10 rad and that $\dot\theta = x_2$ and $i_f = x_3$ would be at zero. Consequently the criterion

$$J = \int_{t_0}^{t_f} [(x_1 - 10)^2 + Ru^2]\,dt + W_1(x_1(t_f) - 10)^2 + W_2 x_2^2(t_f) + W_3 x_3^2(t_f)$$

$$= x_4 + W_1(x_1 - 10)^2 + W_2 x_2^2 + W_3 x_3^2|_{t=t_f}$$

$$= \phi(x(t_f)) \qquad (5.70)$$

was chosen. This involved no changes except in ϕ and $\nabla\phi$. $\nabla\phi$ for the ϕ of (5.70) is

$$\nabla\phi = \begin{bmatrix} 2W_1(x_1 - 10) \\ 2W_2 x_2 \\ 2W_3 x_3 \\ 1 \end{bmatrix} \qquad (5.71)$$

Using the criterion of (5.70) with $W_1 = W_2 = W_3 = 100$ and $R = 5$ in (5.70) and (5.71) the program with the values of τ_i, $i = 0, 1, \ldots, 9$ as found in the last iteration using the criterion of (5.62) was resubmitted. The result after 10 iterations was the output response, shaft position, shown as curve 2 in Fig. 5.13. The second curve is seen to be more in the manner of what one might desire in a step response. The values of the pulse widths that give the two output curves of Fig. 5.13 are shown in Fig. 5.14.

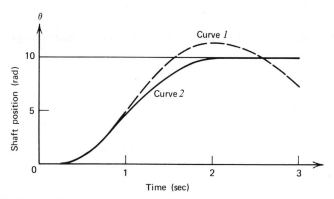

Figure 5.13 Shaft position time responses by minimization of two criteria.

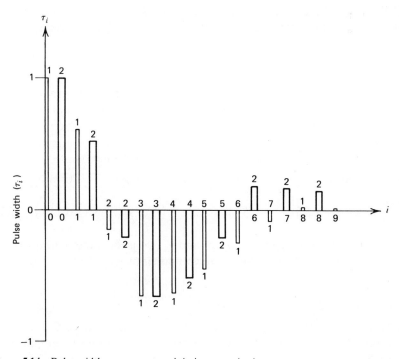

Figure 5.14 Pulse-width sequences to minimize two criteria.

1. $J = \displaystyle\int_0^3 [(\theta - 10)^2 + 5e_f^2]\, dt.$

2. $J = \displaystyle\int_0^3 [(\theta - 10)^2 + 5e_f^2]\, dt + [W_1(\theta - 10)^2 + W_2\theta^2 + W_3 i_f^2]\Big|_{t=t_f}.$

5.4. VARIABLE INITIAL CONDITIONS—PERIODIC BOUNDARY CONDITIONS

We now consider finding the gradient of the cost criterion on the space of initial conditions for the system differential equations. The system is

$$\dot{x} = f(x, u): u_{[t_0, t_f]} \quad \text{fixed, } x(t_0) \text{ arbitrary} \tag{5.72}$$

and the problem is to choose $x(t_0)$ so as to minimize the cost criterion. Here the cost criterion, in the most useful case, takes on a slightly different form from that seen previously. Here we let

$$J[x(t_0)] = \phi(x(t_0), x(t_f)) \tag{5.73}$$

The cost criterion is assumed an explicit function of the final state $x(t_f)$ and also the initial state $x(t_0)$. Here ϕ is a real-valued function from $\mathscr{R}^n \times \mathscr{R}^n$ to $\mathscr{R}^1$. Let us find the gradient of this cost criterion in the space of initial conditions ($\mathscr{R}^n$) at a given $x(t_0)$. We apply (4.4) to this and have directly

$$\left. \frac{d}{d\varepsilon} J[x(t_0) + \varepsilon z_0] \right|_{\varepsilon = 0} = \langle g(x(t_0)), z_0 \rangle \tag{5.74}$$

where now $z_0 \in \mathscr{R}^n$ is a perturbation in $x(t_0)$, and $g(x(t_0))$ is the gradient of the cost criterion at $x(t_0)$, which is being sought. Defining $x(t_f: x(t_0))$ as the state at time t_f starting the system, (5.72), in state $x(t_0)$ at time t_0 and using (5.73), we obtain

$$J[x(t_0) + \varepsilon z_0] = \phi(x(t_0) + \varepsilon z_0, x(t_f: x(t_0) + \varepsilon z_0)) \tag{5.75}$$

Differentiating (5.75) w.r.t. ε and letting $\varepsilon \to 0$, we get

$$\left. \frac{d}{d\varepsilon} J[x(t_0) + \varepsilon z_0] \right|_{\varepsilon = 0} = \langle \nabla_{x(t_0)} \phi, z_0 \rangle + \left\langle \nabla_{x(t_f)} \phi, \frac{d}{d\varepsilon} x(t_f: x(t_0)) \right\rangle \tag{5.76}$$

where now the scalar product is on $\mathscr{R}^n$ and $\nabla_{x(t_0)} \phi$ is the n-vector (the gradient of $\phi(x(t_0), x(t_f))$ w.r.t. $x(t_0)$) whose ith component is given by

$$(\nabla_{x(t_0)} \phi)_i = \frac{\partial}{\partial x_{i\,(t_0)}} \phi(x(t_0), x(t_f: x(t_0)))$$

the partial derivative of ϕ w.r.t. the ith component of $x(t_0)$. $\nabla_{x(t_f)} \phi$ is the n-vector (the gradient of $\phi(x(t_0), x(t_f))$ w.r.t. $x(t_f)$) whose ith component is given by

$$(\nabla_{x(t_f)} \phi)_i = \frac{\partial}{\partial x_{i\,(t_f)}} \phi(x(t_0), x(t_f)) \tag{5.77}$$

that is, the partial derivative of ϕ w.r.t. the ith component of $x_i(t_f)$.

To complete the evaluation of the gradient using (5.76)

$$\frac{d}{d\varepsilon} x(t_f: x(t_0)) = \frac{d}{d\varepsilon} x(t_f: x(t_0) + \varepsilon z_0)\Big|_{\varepsilon=0} \tag{5.78}$$

is required. This can be obtained by integrating (5.72) starting at $x(t_0) + \varepsilon z_0$ at time t_0, which gives

$$x(t_f: x(t_0) + \varepsilon z_0) = x(t_0) + \varepsilon z_0 + \int_{t_0}^{t_f} f(x(t: x(t_0) + \varepsilon z_0), u)\, dt$$

Differentiating now and letting $\varepsilon \to 0$ gives

$$\frac{d}{d\varepsilon} x(t_f: x(t_0)) = z_0 + \int_{t_0}^{t_f} f_x(x, u) \frac{d}{d\varepsilon} x(t: x(t_0))\, dt \tag{5.79}$$

where now $f_x(x, u)$ is, as before, the $n \times n$ matrix whose ijth element is

$$(f_x(x, u))_{ij} = \frac{\partial}{\partial x_j} f_i(x(t: x(t_0)), u) \tag{5.80}$$

Equation 5.79 is an integral equation in terms of $dx/d\varepsilon$. The solution as given in Appendix C is

$$\frac{d}{d\varepsilon} x(t_f: x(t_0)) = \Phi(t_f, t_0) z_0 \tag{5.81}$$

where $\Phi(t_f, t_0)$ is the state transition matrix that satisfies

$$\frac{d}{dt} \Phi(t, t_0) = f_x(x, u)\Phi(t, t_0): \Phi(t_0, t_0) = I$$

Equation 5.81 used in (5.76) permits us to solve for the desired gradient using (5.74). Thus by (5.76)

$$\frac{d}{d\varepsilon} J[x(t_0) + \varepsilon z_0]\Big|_{\varepsilon=0} = \langle \nabla_{x(t_0)} \phi, z_0 \rangle + \langle \nabla_{x(t_f)} \phi, \Phi(t_f, t_0) z_0 \rangle$$

$$= \langle \nabla_{x(t_0)} \phi + \Phi^+(t_f, t_0)\nabla_{x(t_f)} \phi, z_0 \rangle$$

$$= \langle g(x(t_0)), z_0 \rangle$$

where the last equation is (5.74). Thus

$$g(x(t_0)) = \nabla_{x(t_0)} \phi + \lambda(t_0) \tag{5.82}$$

where

$$\lambda(t) \triangleq \Phi^+(t_f, t)\nabla_{x(t_f)} \phi \tag{5.83}$$

which we know from Appendix D satisfies the adjoint system

$$\frac{d}{dt} \lambda = -f_x^+(x, u)\lambda: \lambda(t_f) = \nabla_{x(t_f)} \phi \tag{5.84}$$

Equation 5.82 gives the gradient in the space of initial conditions for the criterion as defined in (5.73), the result desired. To compute the gradient for a given initial condition the procedure is, again, to integrate the system equations, (5.72), forward from the $x(t_0)$ under consideration to t_f. The adjoint system, (5.84), is then integrated backwards in time from t_f to t_0. The gradient at $x(t_0)$ is then found directly from (5.82) using the adjoint solution at time t_0.

Periodic Boundary Conditions

As an example, let us consider the use of the gradient in the space of initial conditions to optimize the performance of a control system to be operated in a periodic mode. This is a frequent problem in practice where a system is designed to perform a task on a continuous basis. In other words, it is to operate cyclically. For the system to begin instantaneously on the next cycle, the initial state must be the same as the final state. Explicitly

$$x(t_0) = x(t_f) \tag{5.85}$$

is desired for the system to operate cyclically with period $T = t_f - t_0$. To enforce such a constraint on a system while operating the system so as to minimize some criterion function, one might consider adding a penalty term to the criterion function. The form of the criterion function might then most logically be of the form

$$J[x(t_0)] = \tilde{\phi}(x(t_f)) + \sum_{i=1}^{n} W_i(x_i(t_f) - x_i(t_0))^2$$

$$= \phi(x(t_0), x(t_f)) \tag{5.86}$$

where $\tilde{\phi}$ is the criterion function that is to be minimized and the summation term is the penalty term added to enforce the periodicity constraint on the state vector trajectory. n is the order of the system under consideration and the W_i are positive constants.

For this case the gradient in the space of initial conditions is using (5.82) on (5.86), the n-vector whose ith component is

$$[g(x(t_0))]_i = 2W_i(x_i(t_0) - x_i(t_f)) + \lambda_i(t_0) \tag{5.87}$$

where $\lambda_i(t_0)$ is the ith component of the adjoint vector $\lambda(t)$ evaluated at $t = t_0$. $\lambda(t)$ satisfies (5.84) with the terminal condition on the ith component

$$\lambda_i(t_f) = (\nabla_{x(t_f)} \phi)_i = \frac{\partial}{\partial x_i} \tilde{\phi}(x(t_f)) + 2W_i(x_i(t_f) - x_i(t_0)) \qquad i = 1, 2, \dots, n$$

Example 5.5

As an example of the use of the gradient as found in (5.82) and (5.87), let us consider finding the steady-state response of a nonlinear electrical circuit. To this end we consider the circuit of Fig. 5.15, which consists of a sine wave source driving a full wave rectifier, the output of which is to be smoothed by a simple filter section, which in turn drives a 1 ohm load. The inductor of the filter section is assumed to be nonlinear; the exact nature of the non-linearity is discussed below, and the problem is now to determine the steady-state response of the circuit. To do this the steady-state current through the inductor and voltage across the capacitor must be found.

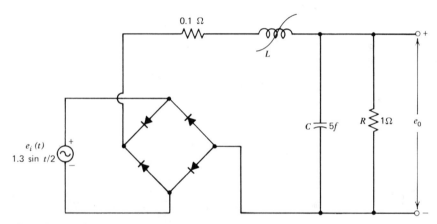

Figure 5.15   DC power supply network.

To analyze the circuit, we assume that the current out of the rectifier never falls to zero, so that the source and rectifier may be replaced by a single source $e(t) = 1.3|\sin t/2|$. The circuit may then be redrawn as in Fig. 5.16. The inductor is assumed to have a flux ϕ, versus current characteristic as shown in Fig. 5.17. It is a typical characteristic curve for an iron core inductor in that after a certain current level is reached, the core begins to saturate and hence more current produces less flux. To good approximation the flux linkages are given by

$$\phi(i) = 2\left(i - \frac{i^3}{3}\right) \qquad |i| \le 0.95$$

$$= 0.2i + 1.14 \, \text{sgn} \, i \qquad |i| > 0.95 \qquad (5.88)$$

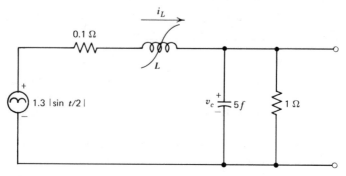

Figure 5.16   Simplified schematic for circuit of Fig. 5.15.

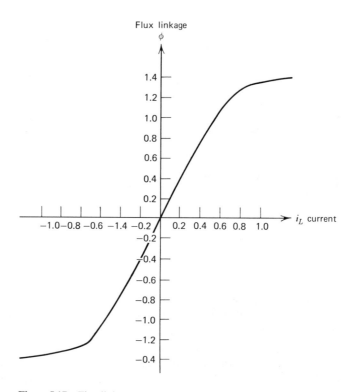

Figure 5.17   Flux linkage versus current for the inductor of Fig. 5.15.

To obtain a set of differential equations for this circuit we write the loop for the circuit loop and the nodal equation for the output node to get

$$-i_L + 5\frac{d}{dt}v_c + v_c = 0$$

$$1.3\left|\sin\frac{t}{2}\right| + 0.1\,i_L + \frac{d\phi\,(i_L)}{dt} + v_c = 0 \qquad (5.89)$$

Now defining a state vector for the circuit by

$$x = \begin{bmatrix} x_1 \\ x_2 \end{bmatrix} = \begin{bmatrix} v_c \\ i_L \end{bmatrix} \qquad (5.90)$$

and using this in (5.89) with $\phi(\cdot)$ as given by (5.88), we obtain

$$\dot{x}_1 = -0.2x_1 + 0.2x_2$$

$$\dot{x}_2 = \frac{-x_1}{2(1-x_2^2)} - \frac{0.1x_2}{2(1-x_2^2)} - \frac{1.3|\sin t/2|}{2(1-x_2^2)} \qquad |x_2| \le 0.95$$

$$\qquad (5.91)$$

$$= -5x_1 - 0.5x_2 - 6.5\left|\sin\frac{t}{2}\right| \qquad |x_2| > 0.95$$

which gives the system differential equations in the desired form.

The circuit here is being driven by a source $|\sin t/2|$ which has a period $T = 2\pi$ secs. In steady state the state of the circuit repeats itself every 2π sec, that is,

$$x(t_0) = x(t_0 + 2\pi) \qquad (5.92)$$

and we seek the solution to the system d.e.'s of (5.91), which satisfies this condition. Picking $t_0 = 0$, which is as convenient as any other, we may seek this solution by defining a criterion

$$\phi(x(0), x(2\pi)) = (x_1(0) - x_1(2\pi))^2 + (x_2(0) - x_2(2\pi))^2 \qquad (5.93)$$

and then looking for the initial conditions $x_1(0)$ and $x_2(0)$ to minimize this criterion. For this case we know that if a steady state solution exists this solution will give a zero value for the criterion, that is, $x^*(0) = x^*(2\pi)$ and hence

$$\phi(x^*(0), x^*(2\pi)) = 0$$

and hence $x^*(0) = x^*(2\pi)$.

The criterion of (5.93) is of the form of (5.86) for which the gradient w.r.t. $x(0)$ is given in (5.87), which is

$$g(x(0)) = \begin{bmatrix} g_1(x(0)) \\ g_2(x(0)) \end{bmatrix} = \begin{bmatrix} 2(x_1(0) - x_1(2\pi)) + \lambda_1(0) \\ 2(x_2(0) - x_2(2\pi)) + \lambda_2(0) \end{bmatrix} \tag{5.94}$$

where λ_1 and λ_2 are components of the vector λ, which satisfies (5.84) with

$$f_x^+ = \begin{bmatrix} -0.2 & -\dfrac{1}{2(1 - x_2^2)} \\[2mm] 0.2 & \dfrac{-0.05}{(1 - x_2^2)} + \dfrac{x_2}{(1 - x_2^2)^2}\left[-x_1 - 0.1x_2 - 1.3\left|\sin\dfrac{t}{2}\right|\right] \end{bmatrix} \tag{5.95}$$

$$\text{for} \quad |x_2| \le 0.95$$

$$= \begin{bmatrix} -0.2 & -5 \\ 0.2 & -0.5 \end{bmatrix} \quad \text{for} \quad |x_2| > 0.95$$

and

$$\nabla_{x(t_f)}\phi = \begin{bmatrix} 2(x_1(2\pi) - x_1(0)) \\ 2(x_2(2\pi) - x_2(0)) \end{bmatrix} \tag{5.96}$$

The system of (5.91) with the gradient of (5.94) was submitted to the conjugate gradient descent program and after 30 iterations the curves of

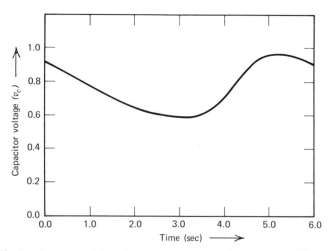

Figure 5.18 Steady-state capacitor voltage versus time for the circuit of Fig. 5.15.

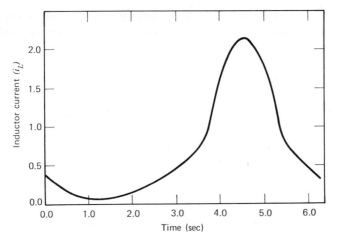

Figure 5.19 Steady-state inductor current versus time for the circuit of Fig. 5.15.

capacitor voltage and inductor current versus time were obtained as seen in
Figs. 5.18 and 5.19, respectively. The initial guess for initial conditions were
taken as the DC values (found by shorting the inductor, opening the capacitor, and setting the source to its average value), which where

$$x_1(0) = 0.75$$
$$x_2(0) = 0.75$$

The criterion at the thirtieth iteration was $7.95E - 12$ and the norm of the
gradient was $1.58E - 5$. One hundred iteration steps were used with fourth
order Runge–Kutta integration.

5.5. SYSTEMS WITH DELAY

A system that frequently occurs in practice is one in which the dynamics of
the system are a function of the state at some previous time. Or looked at
another way, the present state has an effect at some future time. This is in
contrast to the systems considered earlier in which a previous state has no
effect once the system trajectory has carried the system away from that state.

This delay system is handled in the same manner in which systems without
delay were handled in the previous section. The chief difference is an adjoint
system that differs slightly from the one for the nondelay case. We briefly
consider here applying standard gradient techniques to the problem of
optimizing the response of systems with delay. First the gradient of the

system criterion in the space of continuous function inputs is considered, from which we immediately get the gradient in the space of input parameters. An example is considered for the case of a continuous function input.

Finally we consider briefly a special case that occurs only in systems with delay—the problem of optimizing the preconditions of a system. If a system has a delay T, it may be understood that the response of the system after the initial instant t_0 depends not only on the state at time t_0 but also on the precondition—the state in the interval $[t_0 - T, t_0)$. We here consider choosing the precondition to minimize a criterion on the systems response; we begin by defining the system dynamics and the criteria and then go on to the gradient in the space of continuous function inputs.

The Gradient in the Space of Continuous Function Inputs

The system here is assumed to have dynamics as given by

$$\dot{x} = f(x, x_d, u) \tag{5.97}$$

where now $x \in \mathscr{R}^n$ is the state vector, as always, u is the control input, which we here assume is a continuous function, and

$$x_d(t) = x(t - T) \tag{5.98}$$

x_d is thus the delayed state and the delay is assumed to be T sec (or whatever other unit of time is appropriate). The system is to be operated over the time interval $[t_0, t_f]$. f is here an n-vector valued function on $\mathscr{R}^n \times \mathscr{R}^n \times \mathscr{C}_{[t_0, t_f]}$. It should be appreciated that to find a solution $x_{[t_0, t_f]}$ to (5.97), the following items are required:

1. The control input $u(t)$ over $[t_0, t_f]$, that is, $u_{[t_0, t_f]}$.
2. The precondition, that is, $x(t)$ over $[t_0 - T, t_0)$

$$x_{[t_0 - T, t_0)} = x_{d[t_0, t_0 + T)}$$

3. The initial state $x(t_0)$, as before.

Our assumptions here are that with $u_{[t_0, t_f]}$ and $x_{[t_0 - T, t_0)}$ given as continuous functions, then solutions to (5.97) exist for all initial states $x(t_0)$ in the region of state space where it is desired to operate the system. Given the trajectory of the system $x_{[t_0, t_f]}$, the cost criterion on the operation is defined, as before, by

$$J = \phi(x(t_f)) \tag{5.99}$$

where ϕ is a real, scalar-valued function on $\mathscr{R}^n$. f and ϕ are differentiable w.r.t. all arguments. We here consider the problem of finding the gradient of the cost functional of (5.99) in the following two cases:

1. In the space of continuous function control inputs of which $u_{[t_0, t_f]}$ is a member.
2. In the space of preconditions of which $x_{[t_0 - T, t_0)}$ is a member.

Finding the Gradient in the Space of Continuous Function Inputs

To find the gradient in this case, we again make use of the theory developed in Section 4.2, specifically (4.14), which is

$$\frac{d}{d\varepsilon} J[u + \varepsilon z] \bigg|_{\varepsilon = 0} = \langle g(u), z \rangle$$

$$= \left\langle \nabla_x \phi(x(t_f, u)), \frac{d}{d\varepsilon} x(t_f, u) \right\rangle \qquad (5.100)$$

where $g(u)$ is the gradient sought, $x(t_f, u)$ is the state at time t_f obtained by applying a given $u_{[t_0, t_f]}$ [the subscripts have been dropped in (5.100)], and

$$\frac{d}{d\varepsilon} x(t_f, u) = \frac{d}{d\varepsilon} x(t_f, u + \varepsilon z) \bigg|_{\varepsilon = 0} \qquad (5.101)$$

$\nabla_x \phi$ is as always the gradient of ϕ w.r.t. x. To apply (5.100) to obtain the gradient $g(u)$, $dx/d\varepsilon$ of (5.101) must first be evaluated. We use (5.97) evaluated for $u \to u + \varepsilon z$ and differentiate w.r.t. ε. Thus

$$\frac{d}{d\varepsilon} \dot{x}(t_f, u + \varepsilon z) = \frac{d}{d\varepsilon} f(x, (t, u + \varepsilon z), x_d(t, u + \varepsilon z), u + \varepsilon z)$$

where $x_d(t, u + \varepsilon z) = x(t - T, u + \varepsilon z)$ as in (5.98). Performing the operations indicated in the preceding equation and interchanging the order of differentiation w.r.t. ε and t and then evaluating as $\varepsilon \to 0$, we obtain

$$\frac{d}{dt} \frac{d}{d\varepsilon} x(t, u) = f_x \frac{d}{d\varepsilon} x(t, u) + f_{x_d} \frac{d}{d\varepsilon} x_d(t, u) + f_u z(t) \qquad (5.102)$$

where f_x, f_{x_d} are matrices whose ijth elements are given by

$$(f_x)_{ij} = \frac{\partial}{\partial x_j} f_i(x, x_d, u) \qquad (5.103a)$$

$$(f_{x_d})_{ij} = \frac{\partial}{\partial x_{dj}} f_i(x, x_d, u) \qquad (5.103b)$$

and f_u is an n-vector whose ith element is

$$(f_u)_i = \frac{\partial}{\partial u} f_i(x, x_d, u) \tag{5.103c}$$

Equation 5.102 is a linear, time-varying, difference-differential equation of the form

$$\dot{x}(t) = A(t)x(t) + A_d(t)x(t - T) + B(t)u(t) \tag{5.104}$$

where

$$x(t) \leftrightarrow \frac{d}{d\varepsilon} x(t, u)$$

in (5.104) and (5.102), respectively. The solution for (5.104) is given in Appendix E in (E.3), and applied here with the assumption that

$$\frac{d}{d\varepsilon} x(t_0, u) = 0$$

$$\frac{d}{d\varepsilon} x(t - T, u) = \frac{d}{d\varepsilon} x_d(t, u) = 0 \qquad t_0 \leq t \leq t_0 + T$$

that is, under the assumption that the initial condition $x(t_0)$ and the pre-condition $x_{[t_0 - T, t_0)}$ are fixed, gives

$$\frac{d}{d\varepsilon} x(t, u) = \int_{t_0}^{t} \Phi(t, \tau) f_u(\tau) z(\tau) \, d\tau \tag{5.105}$$

where the argument τ has been added to f_u to indicate that x, x_d, and u in (5.104) are evaluated at time $t = \tau$. $\Phi(t, \tau)$, the state transition matrix for the delayed system, by use of (E.4) of Appendix E with the respective quantities in (5.102), satisfies

$$\frac{d}{dt} \Phi(t, \tau) = f_x(t)\Phi(t, \tau) + f_{x_d}(t)\Phi(t - T, \tau)$$

$$\Phi(\tau, \tau) = I \tag{5.106}$$

$$\Phi(t, \tau) = 0 \qquad t < \tau$$

where f_x and f_{x_d} are as in (5.103). Now (5.105) evaluated at $t = t_f$ in (5.100) gives

$$\frac{d}{d\varepsilon} J[u + \varepsilon z] \bigg|_{\varepsilon = 0} = \nabla_x^+ \phi(x(t_f, u)) \int_{t_0}^{t_f} \Phi(t, \tau) f_u(\tau) z(\tau) \, d\tau$$

Transposing the RHS of this and using (5.100), we get

$$\langle g(u), z \rangle = \int_{t_0}^{t_f} f_u^+(\tau)\Phi^+(t_f, \tau)\nabla_x \phi(x(t_f, u))z(\tau)\, d\tau$$

$$= \int_{t_0}^{t_f} f_u^+(\tau)\lambda(\tau)z(\tau)\, d\tau \qquad (5.107)$$

where

$$\lambda(t) = \Phi^+(t_f, t)\nabla_x \phi(x(t_f, u)) \qquad (5.108)$$

Recognizing the scalar product on the RHS of (5.107), we have the gradient

$$g(u) = f_u^+(t)\lambda(t) \qquad t \in [t_0, t_f] \qquad (5.109)$$

which is the desired result—the gradient in the space of continuous functions. It is of the same form as the gradient found for nondelay systems in Section 4.3, (4.28). The difference in the gradient here is in the vector $\lambda(t)$ as given by (5.108). In Appendix E it is shown that the adjoint vector λ must satisfy (E.10). For the system as given by (5.102), the adjoint system corresponding to the one of (E.10) is

$$\frac{d}{dt}\lambda(t) = -f_x^+(t)\lambda(t) - f_{x_d}^+(t + T)\lambda(t + T)$$

$$\lambda(t_f) = \nabla_x \phi(x(t_f, u)) \qquad (5.110)$$

$$\lambda(t) = 0 \qquad t > t_f$$

To compute the gradient of a criterion as in (5.99) at a given input control $u_{[t_0, t_f]}$, the following steps must be taken:

1. Integrate (5.97) forward from t_0 to t_f, using given $x(t_0)$ and precondition $x_{[t_0 - T, t_0)}$, to get $x_{[t_0, t_f]}$.
2. Integrate (5.110) backwards from t_f to t_0 along $x_{[t_0, t_f]}$ to get $\lambda_{[t_0, t_f]}$.
3. Compute $g(u)$ as given by (5.109).

These are the same basic steps as required to compute the gradient of the input control function for a nondelay system.

From (5.107) it is easy to obtain the gradient of the criterion in the space of input control parameters. u is a vector of m control parameters. We may consider u to be a continuous control function input, which is incidentally constant. Thus (5.107) must apply. A variation in the space of input control parameters is also a continuous function of time, which is constant. This means that $z(\tau)$ of (5.107) may hence be taken outside the integral to give

$$\langle g(u), z \rangle = \left[\int_{t_0}^{t_f} f_u^+(\tau)\lambda(\tau)\, d\tau \right]^+ z \qquad (5.111)$$

from which

$$g(u) = \int_{t_0}^{t_f} f_u^+(\tau)\lambda(\tau)\, d\tau \qquad (5.112)$$

the desired gradient in the space of input control parameters for a system with delay.

Example 5.6

As an example of the use of the gradient of (5.109) to find an input control function to optimize the response of a control system, let us consider the rolling mill schematically diagrammed in Fig. 5.20. This is simply a steel strip rolling mill in which the mill rolls down the thickness of the incoming strip. The thickness is detected after the rolling is complete. The signal from the thickness detector is compared to a reference input, and the error signal is used to drive a DC motor that controls the position of the upper rolling cylinder shaft and hence the thickness of the rolled strip. The delay

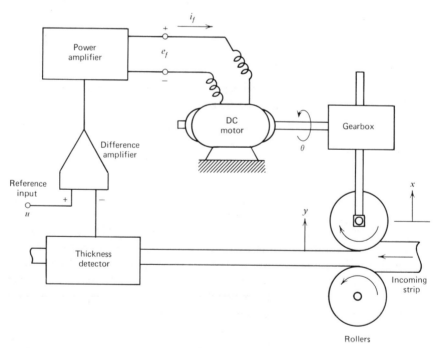

Figure 5.20   Schematic diagram for a DC motor controlled rolling mill.

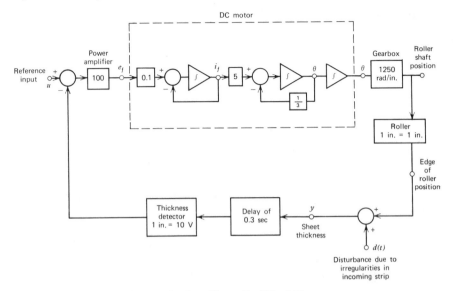

Figure 5.21 Simulation diagram for the rolling mill of Fig. 5.20.

in this system comes from the transport lag in the strip that occurs between the rollers and the thickness detector. Figure 5.21 is a simulation diagram for the strip rolling mill of Fig. 5.20. The DC motor is the same one considered in some of the previous examples. The gearbox on the output shaft of the motor drives the center shaft of the upper roller. Because of compression of the roller, the edge of the roller does not track the center shaft exactly. The block-labeled roller in the diagram takes account of this. The assumption here is, however, that the edge of the roller does track the center shaft, as the gain of this block is taken to be unity. Because of irregularities in the incoming strip, the sheet thickness does not coincide exactly to the distance between the edges of the roller. This is taken into account in the model of Fig. 5.2 by the disturbance signal $d(t)$. After the strip has been rolled a transport lag of 0.3 sec is assumed, after which the thickness is detected and the resulting voltage from the detector is subtracted from the input reference u. This difference drives the power amplifier, which drives the field of the DC motor to complete the loop.

The Problem

As a *problem* here let us consider determining what the reference input of Fig. 5.21 should be to achieve a step change of roller shaft position that is reasonable from the standpoint of time w.r.t. the time constants of the drive motor and assembly and also reasonable w.r.t. the field voltage (e_f) required. We take 20 rad as the desired change in motor shaft position that corresponds to a 0.016 in. change in roller shaft position. Thus let us choose as the criterion

$$J = \int_{t_0}^{t_f} [(\theta - 20)^2 + Re_f^2] \, dt \qquad (5.113)$$

where θ and e_f are as shown in Fig. 5.21. The e_f^2 term is added under the criterion integral to limit the value of the field voltage. Without such a device, e_f may be expected to increase without limit as the optimization progresses. R is again chosen to be a positive constant, the value of which depends on how much limiting of e_f is desired. With the mill operating in steady state with the DC motor at rest, minimization of J of (5.113) should result in a 20 rad change in shaft position with a bound on the field voltage e_f. *We seek the reference input* u *as a function of time that minimizes J of* (5.113).

Formulation of System Differential Equations

For the system of Fig. 5.21, let us define state variables as

$$x_2 = \theta$$
$$x_3 = \dot{\theta}$$
$$x_4 = i_f$$

With this definition of states the criterion of (5.113) becomes

$$J = \int_{t_0}^{t_f} [(x_2 - 20)^2 + Re_f^2] \, dt \qquad (5.114)$$

with

$$e_f = 100(u - 0.008x_{2d} - 0.1 \, d(t - 0.3)) \qquad (5.115)$$

where

$$x_{2d}(t) = x_2(t - 0.3) \qquad (5.116)$$

and $d(t)$ is the disturbance input in Fig. 5.21. For this example $d(t) = 0$ is assumed so that

$$e_f = 100(u - 0.008x_{2d}) \qquad (5.117)$$

To handle a criterion of the form of (5.114) we define the state variable x_1, that satisfies

$$\dot{x}_1 = (x_2 - 20)^2 + Re_f^2: \; x_1(t_0) = 0 \qquad (5.118)$$

so that the criterion of (5.114) becomes $J = x_1(t_f)$. To insure that the system is in the desired state at the final time t_f, that is, $x_2(t_f) = \theta(t_f) = 20$,

$x_3(t_f) = x_4(t_f) = 0$, let us add penalty function terms to the criterion so that

$$J = [x_1 + W_1(x_2 - 20)^2 + W_2 x_3^2 + W_3 x_4^2]_{t=t_f} \quad (5.119)$$
$$= \phi(x(t_f))$$

which is the desired form.

With the states as defined in the text above (5.114) and using (5.118) and Fig. 5.21 we may now write the system differential equations as

$$\begin{aligned}
\dot{x}_1 &= (x_2 - 20)^2 + Re_f^2 \\
\dot{x}_2 &= x_3 \\
\dot{x}_3 &= -\tfrac{1}{3}x_3 + 5x_4 \\
\dot{x}_4 &= -x_4 + 0.1e_f \\
e_f &= 100(u - 0.008x_{2d}) \\
x_{2d}(t) &= x_2(t - 0.3)
\end{aligned} \quad (5.120)$$

Starting from quiescent we have as the initial conditions and preconditions

$$x(t) = 0 \qquad t_0 - 0.3 \le t \le t_0 \quad (5.121)$$

Equations 5.119 and 5.120 are the criterion and system d.e.'s in the form of (5.99) and (5.97), respectively.

The Adjoint System and the Gradient in the Space of Control Inputs

The adjoint system for f as given in (5.120) is found from (5.110)

$$\frac{d}{dt}\begin{bmatrix} \lambda_1 \\ \lambda_2 \\ \lambda_3 \\ \lambda_4 \end{bmatrix} = -\begin{bmatrix} 0 & 0 & 0 & 0 \\ 2(x_2-20) & 0 & 0 & 0 \\ 0 & 1 & -\tfrac{1}{3} & 0 \\ 0 & 0 & 5 & -1 \end{bmatrix}\begin{bmatrix} \lambda_1 \\ \lambda_2 \\ \lambda_3 \\ \lambda_4 \end{bmatrix}$$
$$-\begin{bmatrix} 0 & 0 & 0 & 0 \\ -1.6Re_f(t+0.3) & 0 & 0 & -0.08 \\ 0 & 0 & 0 & 0 \\ 0 & 0 & 0 & 0 \end{bmatrix}\begin{bmatrix} \lambda_{1p} \\ \lambda_{2p} \\ \lambda_{3p} \\ \lambda_{4p} \end{bmatrix} \quad (5.122)$$

where

$$\lambda_p(t) = \lambda(t + 0.3)$$

for which the terminal condition as given in (5.110) and by use of ϕ of (5.119) is

$$\lambda(t_f) = \nabla_x \phi(x(t_f)) = \begin{bmatrix} 1 \\ 2W_1(x_2 - 20) \\ 2W_2 x_3 \\ 2W_3 x_4 \end{bmatrix}_{t=t_f} \quad (5.123)$$

For a solution $\lambda_{[t_0,\,t_f]}$ to the adjoint system of (5.122) with terminal condition of (5.123), the gradient in the space of control inputs as given by (5.109) is

$$g(u) = 200Re_f(t)\lambda_1(t) + 10\lambda_4(t) \qquad t_0 \leq t \leq t_f \qquad (5.124)$$

Results

The system as given by (5.120) and the criterion as in (5.119) with $R = 0.001$ and $W_1 = W_2 = W_3 = 100$ were submitted to the computer for optimization using the gradient as in (5.124). The values for R, W_1, and so on were chosen, by experience with the DC motor without the delayed feedback. $t_0 = 0$ and $t_f = 5.0$ sec were also chosen. Starting from a guess of $u = 0$, the results after 70 iterations are shown in Figs. 5.22 and 5.23. Figure 5.22 shows the output

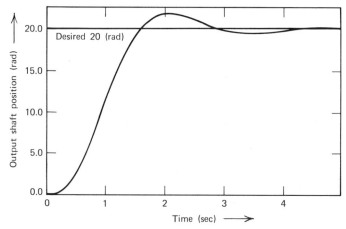

Figure 5.22 Optimized output shaft position versus time for the rolling mill DC motor of Fig. 5.20.

shaft position as a function of time and Fig. 5.23 shows the corresponding input control function required to obtain the output of Fig. 5.22. Seen is a very reasonable step response for a linear system with an overshoot of approximately 8%. The time to the first peak is approximately 2 sec with a quick settling to the final value after that. The value of the criterion of (5.119) with $W_1 = W_2 = 100$ and $R = 0.001$ was 325.6 after the 70 CG descent iterations. The convergence here was rather slow. Two hundred iteration steps with fourth order Runge–Kutta integration were used to integrate the system and adjoint differential equations. Though convergence was slow, it was straightforward.

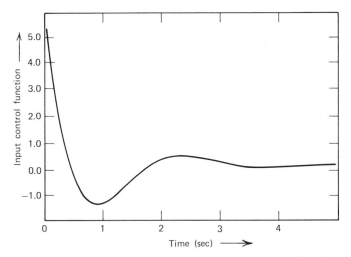

Figure 5.23   Input control function versus time to achieve the output of Fig. 5.22.

The Gradient in the Space of Preconditions

The final state of the system $x(t_f)$, and correspondingly the values of the criterion, as given by (5.99) depends on the precondition for the system, that is, $x_{[t_0-T,\,t_0)}$. It may very well be the case that the control designer has some choice over what this precondition is to be, so logically he would choose it so that the criterion J is minimized. *Hence we here consider the gradient of the cost functional J of (5.99) in the space of preconditions*, for a given control input $u_{[t_0,\,t_f]}$.

We use the notation

$$
\begin{aligned}
x_p &= x_{[t_0-T,\,t_0)} \\
z_p &= z_{[t_0-T,\,t_0)}
\end{aligned}
\tag{5.125}
$$

where x_p and z_p are n-vector valued functions over $[t_0 - T, t_0)$, which we shall assume to be continuous for simplicity. The cost functional is then given by

$$
J[x_p] = \phi(x(t_f, x_p))
\tag{5.126}
$$

where $x(t_f, x_p)$ is the state reached by the system, (5.97), at time t_f starting in precondition x_p and with $x(t_0)$ and $u_{[t_0,\,t_f]}$ assumed given and fixed. Applying (4.14) in the space of preconditions, we seek the gradient of the criterion functional $g(x_p)$ by evaluating

$$
\left. \frac{d}{d\varepsilon} J[x_p + \varepsilon z_p] \right|_{\varepsilon = 0} = \langle g(x_p), z_p \rangle
\tag{5.127}
$$

Using (5.126) we now get

$$\frac{d}{d\varepsilon} J[x_p + \varepsilon z_p]\Big|_{\varepsilon=0} = \frac{d}{d\varepsilon} \phi(x(t_f, x + \varepsilon z_p))\Big|_{\varepsilon=0}$$

$$= \nabla_x^+ \phi(x(t_f, x_p)) \frac{d}{d\varepsilon} x(t_f, x_p) \qquad (5.128)$$

where $\nabla_x \phi$ is again the gradient of ϕ w.r.t. x and

$$\frac{d}{d\varepsilon} x(t_f, x_p) = \frac{d}{d\varepsilon} x(t_f, x_p + \varepsilon z_p)\Big|_{\varepsilon=0} \qquad (5.129)$$

Equation 5.128 reduces the problem to finding $dx/d\varepsilon$ as given by (5.129). To find this quantity, we differentiate (5.97) w.r.t. ε and evaluate at $\varepsilon = 0$. This gives a linear difference-differential equation that is the same as (5.102) except without the f_u term since $u_{[t_0, t_f]}$ has been assumed fixed.

$$\frac{d}{dt}\frac{d}{d\varepsilon} x(t, x_p) = f_x(t)\frac{d}{d\varepsilon} x(t, x_p) + f_{x_d}(t)\frac{d}{d\varepsilon} x(t - T, x_p) \qquad (5.130)$$

where f_x and f_{x_d} are as given in (5.103). The difference-differential equation is of the form treated in Appendix E. The solution to (5.130) may be written from the solution of (E.1) which is given in (E.3) where the correspondence

$$\frac{d}{d\varepsilon} x(t, x_p) \leftrightarrow x(t)$$

$$f_{x_d}(t) \leftrightarrow A_d(t)$$

$$f_x(t) \leftrightarrow A(t)$$

$$\frac{d}{d\varepsilon} x(t - T, x_p) = \frac{d}{d\varepsilon}(x_p(t) + \varepsilon z_p(t)) = z_p(t) \leftrightarrow x(t - T)$$

$$t_0 - T \leq t < t_0 \qquad t_0 \leq t < t_0 + T$$

holds. The solution is then

$$\frac{d}{d\varepsilon} x(t, x_p) = \int_{t_0}^{t} \Phi(t, \tau) f_{x_d}(\tau) z_p(\tau - T)\{1(\tau - t_0) - 1(\tau - t_0 - T)\} \, d\tau$$

or evaluating at $t = t_f > t_0 + T$ with a shift in the integration interval on the RHS, we have

$$\frac{d}{d\varepsilon} x(t_f, x_p) = \int_{t_0 - T}^{t_0} \Phi(t_f, \tau + T) f_{x_d}(\tau + T) z_p(\tau) \, d\tau \qquad (5.131)$$

where $\Phi(t, \tau)$ is the solution of (5.106).

Using (5.131) in (5.128) and with (5.127), we have

$$\langle g(x_p), z_p \rangle = \nabla_x^+ \phi(x(t_f, x_p)) \int_{t_0-T}^{t_0} \Phi(t_f, \tau + T) f_{x_d}(\tau + T) z_p(\tau) \, d\tau$$

$$= \int_{t_0-T}^{t_0} f_{x_d}^+(\tau + T) \Phi^+(t_f, \tau + T) \nabla_x \phi(x(t_f, x_p)) z_p(\tau) \, d\tau$$

$$= \int_{t_0-T}^{t_0} f_{x_d}(\tau + T) \lambda(\tau + T) z_p(\tau) \, d\tau \tag{5.132}$$

where

$$\lambda(\tau) = \Phi^+(t_f, \tau) \nabla_x \phi(x(t_f, x_p)) \tag{5.133}$$

Recognizing the scalar product on the RHS of (5.132), we have

$$g(x_p(t)) = f_{x_d}^+(t + T) \lambda(t + T) \qquad t_0 - T \le t < t_0$$
$$g(x_p(t - T)) = f_{x_d}^+(t) \lambda(t) \qquad t_0 \le t < t_0 + T \tag{5.134}$$

the gradient in the space of preconditions, the desired result. Again $\lambda(t)$ is of the same form as $\lambda(t)$ of (5.108) and hence must satisfy the adjoint system of (5.110), only this time with the terminal condition

$$\lambda(t_f) = \nabla_x \phi(x(t_f, x_p)) \tag{5.135}$$

since x_p, and not u, is the variable here.

Remarks

1. If the initial guess for x_p is a continuous function of time and f of (5.97) is a smooth function of x and x_p (and incidentally $u_{[t_0, t_0+T]}$ is continuous) the gradient as given by (5.134) is also a continuous function of time. If this gradient is used to construct a descent sequence, the result is a sequence of continuous functions, that is, the sequence stays in the space of continuous precondition functions.

2. If $x(t_0)$, the initial condition for the system, is fixed, $x_p(t_0)$ cannot in general be expected to be the same as $x(t_0)$ if x_p is constructed by using the gradient of (5.134) in a descent sequence. Thus $x_d(t) = x(t - T)$, the argument in f of (5.97), can be expected to have a discontinuity at $t = t_0 + T$.

Example 5.7

As an example of the use of the gradient in the space of preconditions as given by (5.134) to optimize a precondition for a system, we consider the steel strip rolling mill of Example 5.5. This mill is shown in Fig. 5.20 with a simulation diagram as given in Fig. 5.21. In Example 5.6 the objective was to find the reference input (u in Fig. 5.21), that would produce a 20 rad change in the shaft position (θ in Fig. 5.21) that corresponded to change in strip thickness of 0.016 in. Let us now assume that the reference input u is held fixed at zero, but the desire is still to change the shaft position by 20 rad and the strip width by 0.016 in. However, this change in shaft position is to be accomplished by suitably choosing the precondition on the system. The dynamics of the system are given in (5.120) where it is seen that the only state variable that is delayed is $x_2 = \theta$, the shaft position. This is also seen in Figs. 5.20 and 5.21.

One might wonder how to use such a precondition to control the response of the system under consideration here. Considering the system of Figs. 5.20 and 5.21 we can see that the delayed state influences the system dynamics through the signal coming from the strip thickness detector. Hence if one knows what the precondition is that produces the response desired, one can design a leader to the strip that passes through the thickness detector in the time interval of interest $[t_0, t_0 + T)$ of such a shape as to accomplish the desired control. Or, alternatively, the reference input u to be applied over the same time interval can be found using the fact that

$$e_f = u - 0.008 x_{2d}$$

from (5.120).

To proceed with the computation of the precondition, let us use the same criterion as in Example 5.6, which is given in (5.119). The system differential equations are then as given in (5.120) (only we now have $u = 0$). The initial condition on the system is

$$x(t_0) = 0 \tag{5.136}$$

which assumes that the system starts from quiescence. The adjoint system remains as given by (5.122) with the terminal condition as given by (5.123). For the system as given by (5.120) we have from (5.103b)

$$f_{x_d} = \begin{bmatrix} 0 & -1.6 Re_f & 0 & 0 \\ 0 & 0 & 0 & 0 \\ 0 & 0 & 0 & 0 \\ 0 & -0.08 & 0 & 0 \end{bmatrix}$$

which gives the gradient in the space of preconditions by (5.134).

$$g(x_p(t)) = \begin{bmatrix} 0 \\ -1.6 Re_f(t + 0.3)\lambda_1(t + 0.3) - 0.08\lambda_4(t + 0.3) \\ 0 \\ 0 \end{bmatrix} \tag{5.137}$$

$$-0.3 \leq t < 0.0$$

We see that all components of this gradient are identically zero except for the second component which corresponds to x_{2d}. This is as it should be since it is only x_2, the second component of x, that has a delayed effect in the system dynamics.

Results

The system and adjoint with the gradient as given by (5.137) were programmed for the computer again with $R = 0.001$ in (5.120) and (5.122) and with $W_1 = W_2 = W_3 = 100.0$. $t_0 = 0$, $t_f = 3.0$ sec was chosen. After 36 CG descent iterations the precondition on x_2 as shown in Fig. 5.24 was obtained.

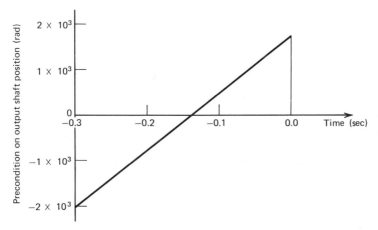

Figure 5.24 Precondition on output shaft position (x_2) for the DC motor in the strip rolling mill of Fig. 5.20.

The corresponding output shaft position obtained with this precondition is shown in Fig. 5.25. It is seen that the output shaft position has indeed changed by 20 rad at time $t - t_f = 3.0$ sec. Also the shaft position has leveled off at the final time t_f. The system and adjoint were integrated by use of fourth order Runge–Kutta integration in 240 integration steps over the 3-sec time interval. The criterion of (5.119) was found to be

$$J = 698$$

to three significant figures. The norm of the gradient was slightly less than unity. Further descent was possible, but improvement in the criterion was so small and as the low value of the gradient indicated the minimum was near, no further improvement was sought.

Remarks

1. The precondition obtained in Fig. 5.24 is interesting in that it is almost a straight line (linear) function of time. For this particular system,

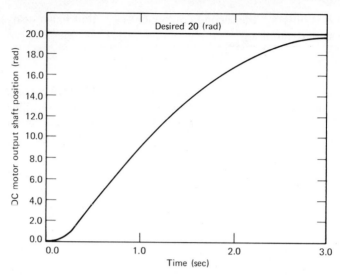

Figure 5.25   DC motor output shaft position versus time with precondition of Fig. 5.24.

precondition control offers a fairly simple to implement method of controlling output shaft (and hence roller) position.

2. Convergence was faster than in the case of the input optimization in Example 5.6, although a considerable number of iterations were still required. The fewer iterations required can of course be attributed to the shorter time interval over which the function was being considered, 0.3 as compared to 5 sec.

3. The precondition on x_2 obtained in Fig. 5.20 is nonzero at the final instant shown, which is at $t = 0$. The initial condition on x_2 from (5.136) is $x_2(0) = 0$. Hence $x_{2d}(t)$ has a discontinuity at time $t = t_0 + T = 0.3$ sec.

4. e_f, the field voltage applied to the DC motor in Fig. 5.20, was found to have a high initial value using the precondition as shown in Fig. 5.24. (It was approximately 1600 V). This high initial value can be reduced by using a higher value of R in the criterion [as seen in the first system differential equation of (5.120)] than the $R = 0.001$ which was actually used. This in turn could be expected to require a larger value for t_f than the 3 sec used.

Summary

The results of Section 5.5 may be put in very compact form by the introduction of the Hamiltonian

$$H(t) = f^+(x, x_d, u)\lambda(t) \tag{5.138}$$

x, x_d, and u are assumed evaluated at time t. The system equations of (5.97) and the adjoint system of (5.110) may now be written as the pair

$$\dot{x} = \nabla_\lambda H(t): x(t_0) \quad \text{and} \quad x_p = x_{[t_0 - T, t_0)} \text{ given}$$

$$\dot{\lambda} = -\nabla_x H(t) - \nabla_{x_d} H(t + T)$$

$$\lambda(t_f) = \nabla_x \phi(x(t_f)) \tag{5.139}$$

$$\lambda(t) = 0 \quad t > t_f$$

The gradient in the space of control function inputs at $u_{[t_0, t_f]}$ as given by (5.109) may be written as

$$g(u) = \frac{\partial}{\partial u} H(t) \quad t \in [t_0, t_f] \tag{5.140}$$

The gradient in the space of system parameters as given by (5.112) may be written as

$$g(u) = \nabla_u \int_{t_0}^{t_f} H(t)\, dt \tag{5.141}$$

The gradient in the space of preconditions as given by (5.134) may be written as

$$g(x_p) = \nabla_{x_d} H(t + T) \quad t_0 \le t < t_0 + T \tag{5.142}$$

Using (5.140) through (5.142) we may write out the results in the form of three minimum principles:

1. The control function input $u_{[t_0, t_f]}^*$, which minimizes $J = \phi(x(t_f))$, with the system that satisfies (5.97), also minimizes $H(t)$, $t \in [t_0, t_f]$.
2. The set of parameters $u^* \in \mathscr{R}^m$, which minimizes $J = \phi(x(t_f))$ with the system that satisfies (5.97), also minimizes

$$\int_{t_0}^{t_f} H(t)\, dt$$

3. The precondition $x_p^* = x_{[t_0 - T, t_0)}$, which minimizes $J = \phi(x(t_f))$ with the system that satisfies (5.97), also minimizes

$$H(t + T) \quad t_0 - T \le t < t_0$$

REFERENCES

[1] Larsen, Andrew, "An Iterative Technique for Extremization of Systems with Delay," Electronics Research Lab. Report No. 63–17, Aug. 1963, Univ. of Calif., Berkeley.

[2] Hasdorff, L. "The Gradient of a Cost Functional on the Space of Pulse-Width Modulated Control Inputs", *Conf. Rec. of JACC, St. Louis, Mo.*, Aug. 1971.

Chapter 6

Design of Controllers
by Gradient Methods

6.1. THE BASIC APPROACH

This chapter presents a brief introduction to the use of gradient methods in the design of controllers for feedback systems. The problem in the design of controllers can be seen by considering the block signal-flow diagram in Fig. 6.1. The plant, which is the object of the control, receives inputs that may in general be classified as control inputs or disturbance inputs. The controller accepts the system control inputs and from observations on the plant and the system inputs it produces the control inputs to the plant. The objective in all this is to make the plant outputs respond in some desired manner. The desired form of plant output is assumed known in advance. If the general configuration of the controller is known, the design problem becomes the determination of a proper choice of controller parameters. Gradient methods are well suited for this and are also useful in choosing the system inputs so as to achieve a desired plant output, but generally this is of less significance.

This chapter in the main considers the problem of determining parameters for several different controller configurations. The basic approach here is to set these parameters by optimizing a criterion on the operation of the system. Gradient methods of course are used to effect this optimization. The controller configurations considered are simple, basic ones shown by experience to generally result in satisfactory control.

The chapter is divided into two parts. First the design of controllers is considered using deterministic inputs; this is for the purpose of introducing the basic concepts in design by gradient methods. Design of controllers

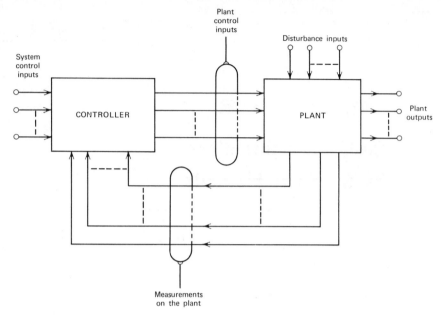

Figure 6.1   A basic configuration in a control system.

using stochastic inputs is considered next. Stochastic inputs offer some unique characteristics that provide real, practical advantages in controller design. Of course there is the added complexity of the additional stochastic concepts that are necessary to describe and to produce the stochastic inputs; hence these are discussed after the basic design concepts have been introduced through the simpler deterministic input case.

6.2.   STATE VARIABLE FEEDBACK CONTROLLER

A simple form of basic controller and one of great practical usefulness is the linear, state variable feedback controller (for examples see [8], [9], and [10]). The signal produced by this controller (see Fig. 6.2), which is the input to the plant, is a linear combination of the state signals from the plant and the system control input. This basic type of controller is shown in Fig. 6.2 for a single-input system. The diagram shows the state variables $x_1, x_2, \ldots, x_n$ detected and fed back (through an inverting summer to give negative feedback) through gains $K_1, K_2, \ldots, K_n$. The result is subtracted from the contribution of the system input $K_0 r$, to produce the input to the plant u_p. The diagram shows all state variables detected and fed back. Of course if it is inconvenient to detect a given state variable x_j, the approach

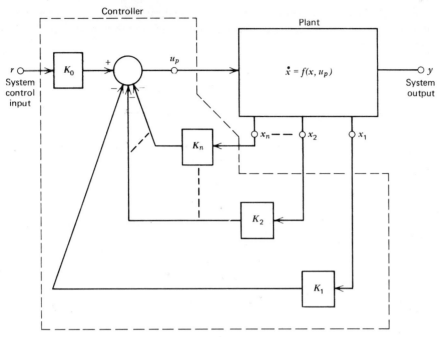

Figure 6.2 Single input state variable feedback controller.

here is to simply choose $K_j = 0$ and to proceed with the design of the controller.

The knowledge of how satisfactory the resulting controller is can then be used to decide whether or not it is worthwhile to detect (or reconstruct from available measurements) state variable x_j.

The problem in the design of the controller is now choosing the gains $K_0, \ldots, K_n$. As mentioned above, the method here is to define a criterion on the operation of the control system and to choose the gains $K_0, \ldots, K_n$ to optimize this criterion. Once the criterion is in hand, choosing the gains to optimize it will proceed as described in Section 4.4, since the $K_0, \ldots, K_n$ may simply be thought of as elements in a parameter space. Since this has already been described in Section 4.4 where the gradient in the space of control parameters is discussed let us now consider briefly the choice of a criterion.

The Choice of a Criterion

In some cases, the use to which the system is to be put may effectively dictate what the criterion should be. For most cases though, the criterion is not definite and one has great flexibility in its selection.

An approach to this problem is to choose a simple input to the system $r(t)$ and to then decide what the desired output $y_d(t)$ is for this input. Knowing the desired output we can define system error as

$$e(t) \triangleq y_d(t) - y(t) \tag{6.1}$$

where $y(t)$ is an actual system response to $r(t)$, (see Fig. 6.2). The criterion is then defined as some positive definite functional on the error, typically integral square error

$$J = \int_{t_0}^{t_f} e^2(t)\, dt$$

$$= \int_{t_0}^{t_f} [y_d(t) - y(t)]^2\, dt \tag{6.2}$$

or integral absolute value, in which case

$$J = \int_{t_0}^{t_f} |e(t)|\, dt$$

or some like functional. If there is concern about the magnitude of the input to the plant becoming too large one may consider adding a term under the integral to get something like

$$J = \int_{t_0}^{t_f} [e^2(t) + Ru_p^2(t)]\, dt \tag{6.3}$$

where $R > 0$ is simply a weighting factor. As we see in Example 6.1, our methods here are flexible enough to permit one to simply clamp the output of the controller u so that the magnitude does not exceed some desired level.

If it is important to have the system in some state x_d at the final time, one may add a term to the criterion based on $\|x(t_f) - x_d\|$. This typically results in a criterion of the form

$$J = \int_{t_0}^{t_f} [e^2(t) + Ru^2(t)]\, dt + g(\|x(t_f) - x_d\|) \tag{6.4}$$

where $g(\cdot)$ is some positive definite function with a minimum at the origin, that is, $g(0) < g(z)$, $z \neq 0$. To apply the methods of Section 4.4, the criterion must be placed into the form

$$J = \phi(x(t_f)) \tag{6.5}$$

as required by (4.10). This, as has also been seen in Chapters 4 and 5, may be accomplished by defining a new state variable x_0, which satisfies

$$\dot{x}_0 = e^2(t) + Ru_p^2(t); \quad x_0(t_0) = 0 \tag{6.6}$$

J of (6.4) then becomes

$$J = x_0(t_f) + g(\|x(t_f) - x_d\|)$$

which is in the form of (6.5).

In using any of the criteria in (6.2) through (6.6) an important consideration is the choice of the time interval $[t_0, t_f]$. Again this may be dictated by the particular problem at hand, but often it comes down to wanting the time interval $t_f - t_0$ as long as possible. The usual rule is to choose t_f so that $t_f - t_0$ is longer than the response times of the system at hand. If the system is a linear one and the largest time constant of the system is τ, one typically chooses

$$t_f - t_0 \geq k\tau$$

where k is generally in the range 3–5. This assures that the system will be very near the steady-state condition by the final instant t_f.

Example 6.1

As an example of the design of a linear, state variable feedback controller, let us consider the DC motor that we have seen before in Chapter 5 and for which a simulation diagram appears in Fig. 6.3. A possible choice of state variables and a feedback controller for this motor are also shown in the figure. Let us now consider the problem of designing the controller so that the motor and controller together form a position control system. The

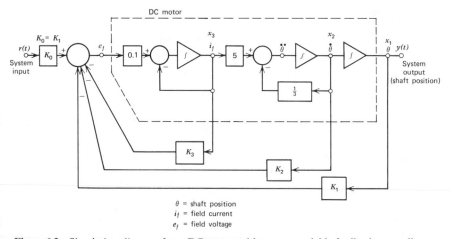

θ = shaft position
i_f = field current
e_f = field voltage

Figure 6.3 Simulation diagram for a DC motor with a state variable feedback controller.

objective is then to have the output shaft position θ track the input $r(t)$. Since $y = \theta$ we wish then to have

$$y(t) = r(t)$$

and thus the desired output is

$$y_d(t) = \theta(t) = r(t) \tag{6.7}$$

for any input. The error for this system is then naturally

$$e(t) \triangleq r(t) - \theta(t) \tag{6.8}$$

In Fig. 6.3, K_0, the gain that multiplies the system input $r(t)$, has been set equal to K_1, which is the gain feeding back output shaft position θ, state variable x_1. This has the desirable effect of producing a controller for which a constant system input r_{ss} results in a constant steady-state shaft position θ_{ss} and

$$\theta_{ss} = r_{ss}$$

that is, a constant system input results in zero steady-state error.

Before presenting the differential equations satisfied by our system and needed to optimize the gains K_1, K_2, and K_3, which is all that is required to complete the design of the controller, we must determine the criterion to be used in this optimization. We have for our system an error defined by (6.8) that arises naturally because the system is to be a position tracking system. From the discussion that resulted in the criteria of (6.2) through (6.6) a natural criteria here is defined as an integral square error one of the form

$$J = \int_{t_0}^{t_f} e^2(t)\, dt = \int_{t_0}^{t_f} [r(t) - \theta(t)]^2\, dt. \tag{6.9}$$

In this case the input to the plant, the DC motor, is the field voltage e_f. To insure that the magnitude of e_f does not become too large, it is reasonable to add a term under the integral of the criterion of (6.9) to give a criterion of the form

$$J = \int_{t_0}^{t_f} [(r(t) - \theta(t))^2 + R e_f^2(t)]\, dt \tag{6.10}$$

where R is a positive constant. This criterion is valid for any input $r(t)$. If the particular $r(t)$ to be used is determined, the desired final state, that is, the state at time t_f, can be determined and suitable terminal terms can be added to the criterion to give one of the form of (6.4). One of the simplest realistic inputs is a step function or

$$r(t) = r_{ss} \cdot 1(t) \tag{6.11}$$

where $1(t)$ is the unit step function and r_{ss} is a constant. For a step input of the form of (6.11), the desired output shaft position at the final time is

$$\theta(t_f) = x_{1_d} = r_{ss} \tag{6.12a}$$

and for the other two state variables

$$\dot{\theta}(t_f) = x_{2_d} = 0$$
$$i_f(t_f) = x_{3_d} = 0 \tag{6.12b}$$

Using the desired final state terms of (6.12) to augment (6.10), we obtain a final criterion

$$J = \int_{t_0}^{t_f} [(r(t) - \theta(t))^2 + Re_f^2(t)]\, dt$$
$$+ W_1(\theta(t_f) - r_{ss})^2 + W_2(\dot{\theta}(t_f))^2 + W_3\, i_f^2(t_f) \tag{6.13}$$

Now defining a new state variable x_0 that satisfies the d.e.

$$\dot{x}_0 = (r - x_1)^2 + Re_f^2 : x_0(t_0) = 0$$
$$e_f = K_1(r - x_1) - K_2 x_2 - K_3 x_3 \tag{6.14}$$

where we have used $x_1 = \theta$ and the expression for e_f from Fig. 6.3. Equation 6.13 hence becomes

$$J = \phi(x(t_f)) = x_0(t_f) + W_1(x_1(t_f) - r_{ss})^2 + W_2 x_2^2(t_f) + W_3 x_3^2(t_f) \tag{6.15}$$

which is a criterion of the form $J = \phi(x(t_f))$ desired. Equation 6.15 uses the state variable definitions as given in Fig. 6.3.

The system differential equations for the system of Fig. 6.3 may now be written from the figure and from (6.14) as

$$\dot{x}_0 = (r - x_1)^2 + Re_f^2$$
$$\dot{x}_1 = x_2$$
$$\dot{x}_2 = -\tfrac{1}{3}x_2 + 5x_3 \tag{6.16}$$
$$\dot{x}_3 = -x_3 + 0.1e_f$$
$$e_f = K_1(r - x_1) - K_2 x_2 - K_3 x_3$$

which is of the form $\dot{x} = f(x, u)$ with

$$u^+ = [K_1, K_2, K_3] \tag{6.17}$$

which is required to apply the gradient in the space of parameters as described in Section 4.4. Initial conditions for the system as given by (6.16) are

$$x(t_0) = [x_0(t_0), x_1(t_0), x_2(t_0), x_3(t_0)]^+ = 0 \tag{6.18}$$

which assumes the motor is in quiescence before the step appears at the input and uses the initial condition on x_0 as given by (6.14).

Results

The system as given by (6.16) and criterion as given in (6.15) were programmed for the computer. The initial condition $x(t_0) = 0$ as given by (6.18) was used. $R = 0.001$ was chosen, since experience with the example showed this to give reasonable values of e_f. Similarly, $W_1 = W_2 = W_3 = 100.0$ were chosen for use in the criterion of (6.15). Since the system was not time varying it was natural to choose $t_0 = 0$ and since the longest time constant of the DC motor plant was 1 sec

$$t_f = 3.3 \text{ sec} \tag{6.19}$$

was guessed and found to be a reasonably long time interval. For an initial guess on the feedback gains

$$K_1 = K_2 = K_3 = 10 \tag{6.20}$$

was chosen since this resulted in a stable closed-loop system and was a convenient value.

With these starting values the system was run using Runge–Kutta integration of the system equations with a step size of 0.05 sec for a step-input of 10 rad, that is, $r_{ss} = 10$. Convergence was straightforward and the results after 22 conjugate gradient descent iterations are shown in Figs. 6.4 and 6.5. The output shaft position and field voltage, respectively, are shown over the time interval of interest. The gradient optimization gave as the optimal values for the feedback gains

$$u^* = \begin{bmatrix} K_1 \\ K_2 \\ K_3 \end{bmatrix} = \begin{bmatrix} 33.34 \\ 20.41 \\ 45.58 \end{bmatrix} \tag{6.21}$$

The step response for the system as seen in Fig. 6.4 shows a well-damped response with an overshoot of approximately 13 %. Settling time is approximately 3 sec. In general the form of the step response in Fig. 6.4 is quite satisfactory. If a faster response is desired, we could consider reducing the value of R in the criterion of (6.15) from the value of 0.001 that was used to obtain the response of Fig. 6.4. A smaller value of R can be expected to result in a higher peak magnitude of the field voltage required as control input to the DC motor. On the other hand, if the response as obtained in Fig. 6.4 is much faster than required for the intended application of the system, we can consider increasing R to a value greater than 0.001 and the result should be a controller that produces a slower response, but one that requires less field voltage magnitude (and energy) to produce a given change in output shaft position.

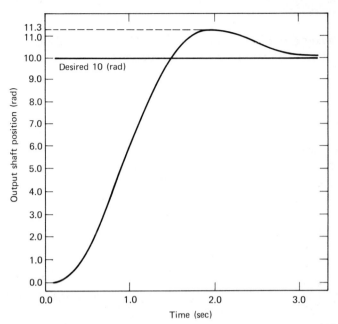

Figure 6.4 Output shaft position versus time for the position tracking system of Fig. 6.3.

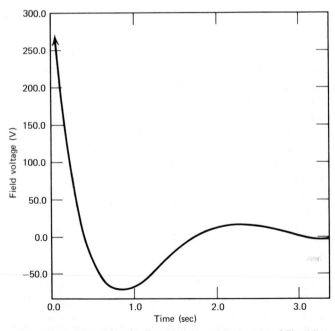

Figure 6.5 Field voltage versus time for the position tracking system of Fig. 6.3.

Let us consider the magnitude of the field voltage applied at the input to the DC motor. By looking at Fig. 6.3 we see that when r is 10 and K_1 as determined in (6.21) is 33, then at the initial instant $(x_1 = x_2 = x_3 = 0)$

$$e_f = K_1 r = 330 \text{ V} \qquad (6.22)$$

This point is out of range of the plot of Fig. 6.5. It can be seen in Fig. 6.5 that this initial instant field voltage is the peak magnitude. It could be that 330 V is more than the field windings of the motor can stand. Thus the output of the controller, the field voltage of the motor, may have to be limited in some ways to something less than 330 V. Realistically, of course, the amplifier that drives the field of the motor would be designed to saturate before it would damage the field winding with an overvoltage or it would be protected in some other way. Let us now suppose that the field winding voltage must be limited to something equal to or less than 100 V, that is, we want

$$|e_f| \le 100 \qquad (6.23)$$

This becomes a limitation on the output of the controller. We can express this analytically in our system equations of (6.16) by making

$$
\begin{aligned}
e_f &= K_1(r - x_1) - K_2 x_2 - K_3 x_3 \\
&\text{for} \quad |K_1(r - x_1) - K_2 x_2 - K_3 x_3| \le 100 \\
&= 100 \text{ sgn} \left[K_1(r - x_1) - K_2 x_2 - K_3 x_3 \right] \quad \text{otherwise}
\end{aligned} \qquad (6.24)
$$

Our approach for determining controller gains K_1, K_2, and K_3 is flexible enough to permit determination of the gains to optimize the criterion of (6.15) in the very same way. Hence the problem was resubmitted to the computer using the criterion of (6.15) and the dynamics of (6.16), but with e_f as given by (6.24). The initial guesses for the gains were taken to be those in (6.21). The problem was run using $R = 0.001$ and all other values used in obtaining the results of Figs. 6.4 and 6.5. The resulting shaft position and field voltage as functions of time are shown in Fig. 6.6 and 6.7, respectively. The feedback gains to be used in the controller of Fig. 6.3 were determined by 20 more conjugate gradient descent iterations to be

$$
u^* = \begin{bmatrix} K_1 \\ K_2 \\ K_3 \end{bmatrix} = \begin{bmatrix} 50.82 \\ 33.90 \\ 47.93 \end{bmatrix} \qquad (6.25)
$$

With these feedback gains, all of which are slightly higher than in the case without saturation, the response shown in Fig. 6.6 is seen to have less over-shoot than in the nonsaturating case. Interestingly enough the response time as measured by the times to the first peak in both cases are very close. As a check on the response of the system for inputs that did not drive the field

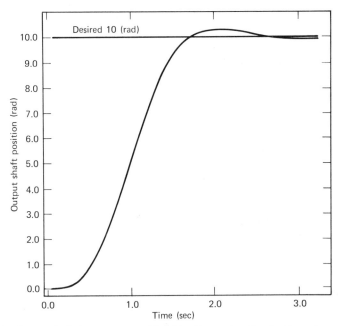

Figure 6.6 Output shaft time response with field voltage saturation for the system of Fig. 6.3.

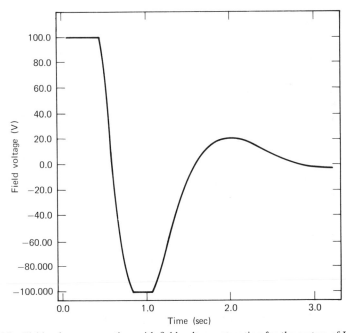

Figure 6.7 Field voltage versus time with field voltage saturation for the system of Fig. 6.3.

voltage into saturation, the response was found for the case of a 1-rad step-input command. The result is shown in Fig. 6.8. We see that the low over-shoot, well damped characteristic of the response was retained even when the field voltage was not being saturated. The peak magnitude of the field voltage for a 1-rad step-input command may be computed in the same way as peak magnitude was found in (6.22). This gives for this case

$$e_{f\,\text{peak}} = 50.8 \cdot 1 = 50.8 \text{ V}$$

which is well below the 100 V taken as the saturation limit. Thus with feed-back gains as given in (6.25) used in the controller of Fig. 6.3 (with saturation of the field voltage at 100 V), the response is well damped for small inputs. For large inputs for which the field voltage goes well into saturation, the response may be expected to degrade gracefully from the linear response obtained with small inputs.

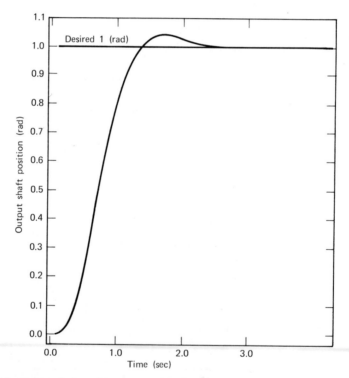

Figure 6.8 Output shaft position versus time for the system of Fig. 6.3 with field voltage saturation.

6.3. THE MODEL FOLLOWER CONTROLLER

Another basic type of controller, for which gradient techniques are useful in the design, is the model follower controller (see [6] and [7]). A basic block diagram for a system that uses such a controller is shown in Fig. 6.9. The key feature in this type of system is the model that appears inside the controller block in the figure. The basic assumption here is that the model has dynamics and performance characteristics that we would like the overall system (i.e., the controller and plant together) to have. *The basic objective of the model follower controller is then to make the output of the plant track the output of the model for any system input* r(t). It is seen in Fig. 6.9 that $r(t)$ drives the model. The output of the controller, which is the plant input, is a linear combination of the system input r, the model state x_m, and the plant state x_p, that is,

$$u_p = k_0 r + k_m^+ x_m - k_p^+ x_p \tag{6.26}$$

There is no particular reason why the plant input should be a linear combination of these quantities; however this is a simple relationship generally shown by experience to give good results and which is also known to be the

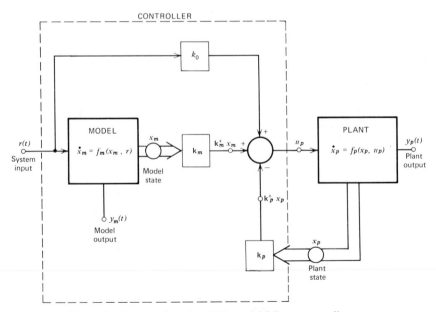

Figure 6.9 Schematic of a control system with a model-follower controller.

right form to minimize quadratic criteria if the system is linear. Under the assumption that the model is known, *the design of a model follower controller, as shown in Fig. 6.9, becomes the choice of the gains* k_0, k_m *and* k_p. Our approach again is to determine these gains by defining a criterion on the operation of the system and to then choose the controller gains so as to optimize this criterion.

Choice of Criterion

For the model follower control system of Fig. 6.9 where the objective is to make the plant output track the model output, error very naturally defines itself as

$$\text{error} = e(t) = y_m(t) - y_p(t) \tag{6.27}$$

Again a reasonable criterion on the operation of this system is integral square error, that is,

$$J = \int_{t_0}^{t_f} e^2(t)\, dt = \int_{t_0}^{t_f} (y_m(t) - y_p(t))^2\, dt \tag{6.28}$$

If, as is often the case, it is necessary to constrain the input to the plant either in magnitude or in signal power, it is reasonable to add a term under the integral of the criterion of (6.28) to get a criterion of the form

$$J = \int_{t_0}^{t_f} [e^2(t) + R u_p^2(t)]\, dt \tag{6.29}$$

where again R is a positive constant. If we are defining a criterion on the operation of the system over the time interval $[t_0, t_f]$, it is natural to want especially good tracking at the final instant t_f. Consequently it is reasonable to add a terminal term to the criterion of (6.29) that involves the state of the model and the state of the plant to give a criterion of the form

$$J = \int_{t_0}^{t_f} [e^2(t) + R u_p^2(t)]\, dt + g(x_m(t_f), x_p(t_f)) \tag{6.30}$$

where $g(x_m, x_p)$ is a function that has a minimum where the states x_m and x_p are such as to imply perfect tracking of the outputs, that is, $y_p = y_m$. One might suppose that what is required is a terminal term involving the difference in the states x_m and x_p. Actually x_m and x_p need not even be of the same order, so the difference may not be well defined. The criterion of (6.30), though it is by no means the only one that could be postulated, is the form used to design the model follower controllers in the examples below.

Formulation of the Design Problem

To use the criterion of (6.30) to design a controller of the form given in Fig. 6.9, which means determining the gain k_0, k_m, k_p, the system differential equations and the criterion must be put into the formulation used in Section 4.4 where optimization in the space of control parameters is considered.

Let us consider the system dynamic equations of Fig. 6.9, that is,

$$\dot{x}_m = f_m(x_m, r): \text{model}$$
$$\dot{x}_p = f_p(x_p, u_p): \text{plant} \qquad (6.31)$$
$$u_p = k_0 r + k_m^+ x_m - k_p^+ x_p$$

Now if we define a state vector

$$x = \begin{bmatrix} x_m \\ x_p \end{bmatrix} \qquad (6.32)$$

Then (6.31) may be put into the form of

$$\dot{x} = \begin{bmatrix} \dot{x}_m \\ \dot{x}_p \end{bmatrix} = \begin{bmatrix} f_m(x_m, r) \\ f_p(x_p, u_p) \end{bmatrix} = f(x, u, r) \qquad (6.33a)$$

where

$$u_p = k_0 r + k_m^+ x_m - k_p^+ x_p$$
$$u = \begin{bmatrix} k_0 \\ k_m \\ k_p \end{bmatrix} \qquad (6.33b)$$

Equation 6.33 gives the system differential equations in the form required in Section 4.4 after r, the system input, is defined, which it of course must be.

To put the criterion of (6.30) in the form required in Section 4.4, which is

$$J = \phi(x(t_f)) \qquad (6.34)$$

we define a new state variable that satisfies

$$\dot{x}_0 = e^2 + R u_p^2 : x_0(t_0) = 0$$
$$= (y_m - y_p)^2 + R(k_0 r + k_m^+ x_m - k_p^+ x_p)^2 \qquad (6.35)$$
$$\dot{x}_0 = f_0(x, u_p, r): x_0(t_0) = 0$$

where u_p is as defined in (6.33b). With x_0 so defined and with x as defined by (6.32), (6.30) may be written as

$$J = x_0(t_f) + g(x(t_f))$$
$$= \phi(\tilde{x}(t_f)) \qquad (6.36)$$

the desired form with

$$\tilde{x} = \begin{bmatrix} x_0 \\ x_m \\ x_p \end{bmatrix}$$

Equation 6.35 now combined with (6.33) gives

$$\dot{\tilde{x}} = \begin{bmatrix} \dot{x}_0 \\ \dot{x}_m \\ \dot{x}_p \end{bmatrix} = \begin{bmatrix} f_0(x, u_p, r) \\ f_m(x_m, r) \\ f_p(x_p, u_p) \end{bmatrix}$$

$$= \tilde{f}(\tilde{x}, u)$$

$$u^+ = \begin{bmatrix} k_0 & k_m^+ & k_p^+ \end{bmatrix}$$

$$u_p = k_0 r + k_m^+ x_m - k_p^+ x_p \tag{6.37}$$

Equations 6.36 and 6.37 give the formulation of the criterion and systems dynamics required to find the optimum system parameters, that is, u, as described in Section 4.4.

Example 6.2

The roll axis of the **X-14** *aircraft*

Let us consider the design of a model follower controller for the roll axis of the X-14 aircraft (see [1], [3], [5]). The X-14 is a vertical takeoff and landing (VTOL) jet aircraft that is capable of hover flight. In hover the attitude of the aircraft is controlled by reaction jet gas nozzles at the extremities of the wing and at the tail of the aircraft. These jets can produce control moments about all three axes of the aircraft. To obtain a problem of reasonable size we shall consider only the roll axis.

In hover the transfer function between degrees of roll of the aircraft (ϕ) and degrees in the space of control nozzle actuator (δ) is to good approximation [1]

$$\frac{\Phi(s)}{\delta(s)} = \frac{4.3}{s(s + 0.447)} \tag{6.38}$$

where s is the Laplace variable. This gives as the differential equation relating roll axis attitude ϕ and nozzle actuator command δ,

$$\ddot{\phi} = -0.447\dot{\phi} + 4.3\delta \tag{6.39}$$

which is used below to set up the system dynamic equations.

Choice of model

It has been found (see [2]) from pilot preference studies that a desirable model for an aircraft roll axis in hover is a simple two pole system with damping $\zeta = 0.7$ and undamped natural frequency $\omega_n \cong 2.0$ rad/sec. Choosing unity steady state gain between pilot's stick position (δ_ϕ) and roll attitude of the model (ϕ_m), we obtain the desired model transfer function

$$\frac{\Phi_m(s)}{\delta_\phi(s)} = \frac{4}{s^2 + 2.8s + 4} \tag{6.40}$$

From this the differential equation relating ϕ_m and δ_ϕ is

$$\ddot{\phi}_m = -2.8\dot{\phi}_m - 4\phi_m + 4\delta_\phi \tag{6.41}$$

which we also use below.

The controller

Using the differential equations for the plant and model, as given in (6.39) and (6.41), respectively, we constructed state diagrams for the model and plant and embedded them into a model follower controller configuration of the type shown in Fig. 6.9. This is shown in Fig. 6.10.

   ϕ and $\dot{\phi}$ were chosen as state variables for the aircraft since these happened to be detected and were hence easily available for use in the control system.

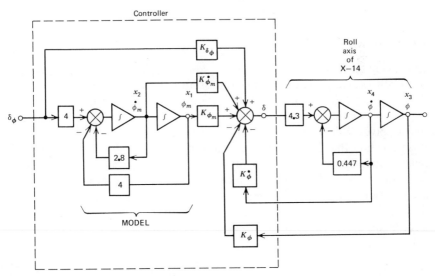

Figure 6.10   Model-follower controller for the X-14 roll axis.

These states are detected and fed back through gains K_ϕ and $K_{\dot\phi}$ in Fig. 6.10. Similarly, for the model it was logical to choose ϕ_m, model attitude, and $\dot\phi_m$, model attitude rate, as the state variables. These states and the pilot's stick position (δ_ϕ) are fed forward through gains $K_{\phi m}$, $K_{\dot\phi m}$, and $K_{\delta\phi}$ in the figure. The configuration of Fig. 6.10 may be recognized as the same one as in Fig. 6.9 with

$$k_0 = K_{\delta\phi} \qquad k_m = \begin{bmatrix} K_{\phi m} \\ K_{\dot\phi m} \end{bmatrix} \qquad k_p = \begin{bmatrix} K_\phi \\ K_{\dot\phi} \end{bmatrix} \tag{6.42}$$

The design problem is now to choose the gains of (6.42) so that good model following performance is obtained.

It may be appreciated that it is desirable to have the steady state response of the aircraft as near as possible to that of the model. Therefore let us consider a constant unit input to the model in Fig. 6.10, that is, $\delta_\phi = 1$. In steady state we then have $\ddot\phi_m = \ddot\phi = 0$, $\phi_m = 1$ and we desire $\phi = 1$. If these values apply, the input to the plant, δ in Fig. 6.10, must be identically zero. This implies

$$K_\phi = K_{\delta\phi} + K_{\phi m}$$

or

$$K_{\delta\phi} = K_\phi - K_{\phi m} \tag{6.43}$$

Equation 6.43 must apply if we are to have zero steady-state error to a constant system input. This relationship is hence assumed as a basic requirement and thus only four gains are left as free variables, $K_{\phi m}$, $K_{\dot\phi m}$, K_ϕ and $K_{\dot\phi}$.

Choice of criterion

In looking for a performance criterion, some decisions had to be made as to what constituted good tracking of the aircraft and model. Ideally, of course, $\phi = \phi_m$ for all time. A further consideration, however, is the fact that ± 20 degrees of command to the nozzles gives maximum control power available, that is, gives wide open nozzle. If the aircraft axis is to track a linear model, it is necessary that it stay out of saturation. Hence it is desirable to keep the maximum magnitude of δ in Fig. 6.10 as low as possible consistent with good tracking. It was also decided, since the pilot could instantaneously feel acceleration of the aircraft and since attitude and rate errors could only be detected visually, to take errors in acceleration between the model and the aircraft as the primary error measure. The result of these considerations led to a criterion of the form

$$J = \int_{t_0}^{t_f} [(\ddot\phi_m - \ddot\phi)^2 + R(\delta)^2]\, dt \tag{6.44}$$

which is exactly the form of (6.29) with

$$e = \ddot{\phi}_m - \ddot{\phi} = y_m - y_p$$

$$\delta = u_p$$

The $R(\delta)^2$ is added to give some control over the maximum magnitude of δ. R is again a positive constant whose value is determined by experience.

To insure good tracking of the roll axis and model it is advisable to add terminal terms to the criterion of (6.44). These make the final criterion take the form of

$$J = \int_{t_0}^{t_f} [(\ddot{\phi}_m - \ddot{\phi})^2 + R\delta^2] \, dt + W_1[\phi_m(t_f) - \phi(t_f))^2 + W_2[\dot{\phi}_m(t_f) - \dot{\phi}(t_f)]^2$$

(6.45)

where W_1 and W_2 are large positive constants. The terminal terms are simply penalty function terms added to insure good tracking at the terminal instant t_f.

Formulation of the problem for computation

From Fig. 6.10 we have the state of the plant and model as

$$x_p = \begin{bmatrix} \phi \\ \dot{\phi} \end{bmatrix} = \begin{bmatrix} x_{1p} \\ x_{2p} \end{bmatrix}$$

$$x_m = \begin{bmatrix} \phi_m \\ \dot{\phi}_m \end{bmatrix} = \begin{bmatrix} x_{1m} \\ x_{2m} \end{bmatrix}$$

(6.46)

To handle a criterion of the form of (6.45), we choose an auxiliary state variable x_0, as in (6.35), that satisfies

$$\dot{x}_0 = (\ddot{\phi}_m - \ddot{\phi})^2 + R\delta^2 : x_0(t_0) = 0$$

(6.47)

Using x_0, so defined, with the states as given in (6.46), we obtain a final system state

$$\tilde{x} = \begin{bmatrix} x_0 \\ \phi_m \\ \dot{\phi}_m \\ \phi \\ \dot{\phi} \end{bmatrix} = \begin{bmatrix} x_0 \\ x_1 \\ x_2 \\ x_3 \\ x_4 \end{bmatrix}$$

(6.48)

Now using the assignment of state variables as in (6.48) (and in Fig. 6.10) the system d.e.'s become (using $\ddot{\phi}$ and $\ddot{\phi}_m$ from (6.39) and (6.41), respectively)

$$\dot{x}_0 = (-2.8x_2 - 4x_1 + 4\delta_\phi + 0.447x_3 - 4.3\delta)^2 + R\delta^2$$

$$\dot{x}_1 = x_2$$

$$\dot{x}_2 = -2.8x_2 - 4x_1 + 4\delta_\phi$$

$$\dot{x}_3 = x_4 \qquad\qquad (6.49)$$

$$\dot{x}_4 = -0.447x_4 + 4.3\delta$$

$$\delta = K_{\phi m}x_1 + K_{\dot\phi m}x_2 - K_\phi x_3 - K_{\dot\phi}x_4 + (K_\phi - K_{\phi m})\delta_\phi$$

where use has been made of (6.43) in the expression for δ. Equation 6.49 is in the form of $\dot{x} = f(x, u)$ where u is the set of parameters

$$u^+ = [K_{\phi m} \quad K_{\dot\phi m} \quad K_\phi \quad K_{\dot\phi}] \qquad\qquad (6.50)$$

To complete the formulation we require the criterion in the form $J = \phi(x(t_f))$ if the gradient as found in Section 4.4 is to be used to optimize the parameters of (6.50). With x_0 as defined in (6.47) and the state variable assignment as in (6.48), the criterion of (6.45) becomes

$$J = x_0(t_f) + W_1(x_1(t_f) - x_3(t_f))^2 + W_2(x_2(t_f) - x_4(t_f))^2$$
$$= \phi(x(t_f)) \qquad\qquad (6.51)$$

The system equations of (6.49) and the criterion of (6.51) are the desired formulation

Results

The problem as formulated in (6.49) and (6.51) was submitted to the computer using a time interval of 3 sec, that is, $t_0 = 0$, $t_f = 3.0$ sec. A unit step input was chosen as the test input, that is $\delta_\phi = 1(t)$ was used in (6.49). $W_1 = W_2 = 100.0$ was used for the values of the weighting factors in the criterion of (6.51). The integration interval used was 0.03 sec, which means there were 100 integration steps in the fourth order Runge–Kutta integration used on the system differential equations. The results for three values of the constant R are shown in Figs. 6.11 and 6.12 where roll altitude ϕ and actuator command δ, respectively, are shown plotted versus time. The initial run with $R = 0.1$ used a guess of zero for all feedback and feed-forward gains in the controller of Fig. 6.10. The result after approximately 20 conjugate gradient descent iterations can be seen in the roll altitude versus time plot in Fig. 6.11. Essentially perfect tracking of the model and the roll axis of the aircraft was obtained for this value of $R = 0.1$. For $R = 10.0$ the final gains obtained for

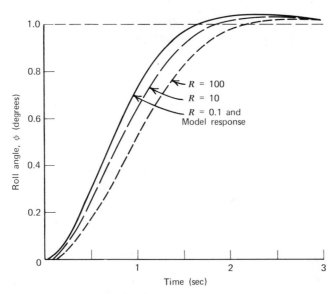

Figure 6.11 Unit step response for the X-14 roll axis with model-follower controller.

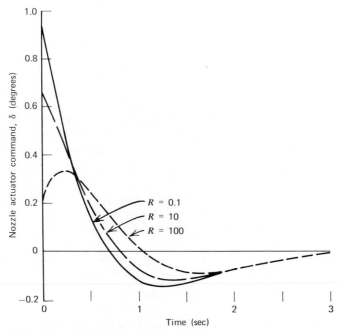

Figure 6.12 Nozzle actuator command for a unit step input.

the $R = 0.1$ run were used as the initial guess. In this case six iterations were sufficient to get satisfactory convergence. The same process was used in the $R = 100$ cases. The gains obtained for all three values of R are shown in Table 6.1.

Comparison of Figs. 6.11 and 6.12 shows that the maximum magnitude of nozzle actuator command δ is reduced as R is increased. The two figures show the trade off that can be achieved between tracking efficiency and maximum magnitude of δ.

Table 6.1 Feedback and Feed-forward Gains for Model Follower Controller for Various Values of R

	$R = 0.1$	$R = 10$	$R = 100$
K_ϕ	0.3386	0.2043	0.1225
$K_{\dot\phi}$	0.7696	0.6854	0.4622
$K_{\phi m}$	-0.5866	-0.4502	-0.1925
$K_{\dot\phi m}$	0.2186	0.3041	0.4144
$K_{\delta\phi}$	0.9252	0.6545	0.3150

6.4. DESIGN OF CONTROLLERS USING STOCHASTIC TEST SIGNALS

In the design of controllers in the preceding sections of this chapter the step function was used in the examples given as the test signal. The step is a historically popular choice for a test signal in classical compensation of linear systems. Performance specifications are generally given in terms of step response characteristics. For example, overshoot, settling time, and rise time to a step input are normal system specifications. Also, experience has shown that if a system (generally linear) has a good step response, it will usually have a transient response that is at least satisfactory for general input. Though step inputs are quite useful as test signals, stochastic test signals offer some advantages that go far beyond the limitations imposed by the step. They offer the very real advantage of allowing the consideration of multi-input systems. Also, they are generally more realistic since few systems encountered operate with strictly deterministic signals. As we shall see, use of stochastic signals allows us to control both the amplitude and frequency bandwidth characteristics of the test signals used in our systems.

The plan is to examine some basic considerations in the choice of a stochastic test signal for a given case and also some considerations in the generation of the chosen signal.

Selection, Generation and Shaping of Stochastic Test Signals

When stochastic inputs to a system are considered and one is making an analytic approach, a very popular type of input to assume and use is white noise (usually Gaussian). However for a numerical approach white noise is not such a desirable signal for several reasons. The most obvious problem is that error goes up rapidly when numerical integration techniques are used to integrate wide-band signals. Another more subtle difficulty found in using such signals occurs when one is using an integral square criterion of the form

$$ J = \int_{t_0}^{t_f} (y_d(t) - y(t))^2 \, dt \tag{6.52} $$

where (see Fig. 6.1) $y(t)$ is the output of the system and $y_d(t)$ is the desired output. The criterion of (6.52) has a relative minimum for $y(t)$ constant at $y(t) = \bar{y}_d$ where $\bar{y}_d$ is the time average value of $y_d(t)$ over the time interval $[t_0, t_f]$. If a system is excited with a stochastic input whose frequency band is much wider than the pass band of the system, optimization of system parameters by gradient methods tend to result in an adjustment of the free parameters such that $y(t) = \bar{y}_d$. The system does not even attempt to track the desired output $y_d(t)$. This phenomena was well noted in early efforts to pick controller parameters by gradient methods.

Consequently if stochastic inputs are to be used as test signals in the design of controllers, some filtering of these signals is necessary. This insures that the frequency band wherein the significant power of the test signal lies does not extend greatly beyond the passband of the system under consideration. If numerical integration is to be used to determine the solution of the system differential equations, the test signal input frequency band must also fall within the passband of the numerical integration technique being used.

The above considerations and the fact that in general our whole approach is to be by digital computer lead quite naturally to the development of a model for the stochastic test signal generator of the form shown in Fig. 6.13. First there is a random number generator, the source of the stochastic process, which can be realized on a computer by use of commonly available library subroutines. The random number generator is followed by a hold, which simply holds the value of the last number generated until the next appears. The output of the hold then feeds directly into the input of the linear filter with transfer function $W(s)$. By control of the probability distribution of the output of the random number generator and of the transfer function of

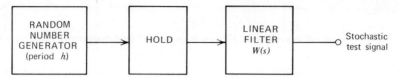

Figure 6.13   Model for computer stochastic test signal generator.

the linear filter $W(s)$, the amplitude characteristic and the frequency band-width characteristics of $r(t)$, the test signal generated may be selected as desired.

Let us consider shaping the frequency characteristics of the generated signal produced by the model of Fig. 6.13. If the period h of the random number generator is small w.r.t. all time constants of the linear filter, the input to the filter is very nearly white noise. In this case the power spectral density (the Laplace transform of the autocorrelation function) of the test signal $r(t)$ is given by

$$\Phi_{rr}(s) = W(s)W(-s)\sigma_{RN}^2 h \tag{6.53}$$

where σ_{RN}^2 is the variance of the numbers produced by the random number generator and s is The Laplace variable. The variance of the test signal is then given by

$$\sigma_r^2 = \frac{1}{2\pi j} \int_{-j\infty}^{j\infty} \Phi_{rr}(s)\, ds = \frac{\sigma_{RN}^2 h}{2\pi j} \int_{-j\infty}^{j\infty} W(s)W(-s)\, ds \tag{6.54}$$

If $W(s)$ is rational, standard tables (see [4]) for the evaluation of the RHS of (6.54) are available. To keep the filtering simple, first and second order filters were chosen of the form

$$W_1(s) = \frac{a}{s + a}$$

$$\tag{6.55}$$

$$W_2(s) = \frac{\omega_n^2}{s^2 + 2\zeta\omega_n s + \omega_n^2}$$

$W_1(s)$ gives a corner frequency of a and $W_2(s)$ has a corner frequency ω_n. These were found to work quite satisfactorily in the examples that follow. For these two cases, using (6.54) and tables from [4], we find that

$$\sigma_{r_1}^2 = \frac{a}{2}\sigma_{RN}^2 h$$

$$\tag{6.56}$$

$$\sigma_{r_2}^2 = \frac{\omega_n}{2\zeta}\sigma_{RN}^2 h$$

where $\sigma_{r_1}^2$ and $\sigma_{r_2}^2$ are the variance of the test signal r using $W_1(s)$ and $W_2(s)$ respectively, from (6.55). Equation 6.56 allows one to choose σ_{RN}^2, the variance of the numbers produced by the random number generator, as a function of the variance of the test signal desired. Typically if $W_2(s)$ is used we choose $\zeta = 0.707$, which gives from (6.56),

$$\sigma_{RN}^2 = \frac{1.414\sigma_{r_2}^2}{\omega_n h}$$

The filtering system, as seen in Fig. 6.13, has been considered in arriving at (6.53) to be a linear system driven by a white noise input. The period of the random number generator h was assumed small relative to the time constants of $W(s)$. The question may arise as to whether the same numerical integration difficulties do not arise that were given as a reason for filtering in the first place. The difference here is that the filter whose transfer function is $W(s)$ is a linear, time-invariant system. If $W(s)$ is rational, a logical choice, state differential equations of the form $\dot{x} = Ax + Bu$ may be written for this system and these may be integrated using (C.2) from Appendix C. This is further simplified if use is made of the fact that the input to the filter is piecewise constant. The point is that the test signal generator as shown in Fig. 6.13 is easily implemented on the computer.

Choice of Criterion with Stochastic Inputs

In general the criterion when a stochastic test input is being used should differ little from that in the case where a deterministic input is used. Thus what was said concerning choice of criterion for controller design in Sections 6.2 and 6.3 is perfectly applicable here. A short comment concerning the length of the time interval used is in order, however. As before we define error for the system of Fig. 6.1 as

$$e(t) \triangleq y_d(t) - y(t)$$

where $y(t)$ is the output of the plant (and hence the system) and $y_d(t)$ is the desired output of the plant. If we choose an integral square error criterion, the basic criterion is of the form

$$J = \int_{t_0}^{t_f} e^2(t)\, dt = \int_{t_0}^{t_f} [y_d(t) - y(t)]^2\, dt \qquad (6.57)$$

which has been seen in (6.2). We note that minimizing this criterion is equivalent to minimizing

$$J = \frac{1}{t_f - t_0} \int_{t_0}^{t_f} e^2(t)\, dt = \overline{e^2} \qquad (6.58)$$

which is the mean square value of error. If we are dealing with a stationary, ergodic process, the time averages over infinite intervals are ensemble averages so that

$$\lim_{(t_f - t_0) \to \infty} J = \mathrm{E}[e^2] = \text{expected value of } e^2 \qquad (6.59)$$

If a stationary process is driven by a stochastic signal that is stationary and ergodic, the output of the system in turn is stationary and ergodic. If the statistics of the random number generator in Fig. 6.13 are stationary and ergodic, then the test signal generated is in turn stationary and ergodic, and if the signal is applied to a stationary controller–plant system, the resulting output is stationary and ergodic. Hence minimizing the criterion of (6.57) results in the minimization of the ensemble average of squared error if the time interval $[t_0, t_f]$ is sufficiently long.

The point of this argument is that if $(t_f - t_0)$ is chosen large enough in the criterion of (6.57), choosing parameters to optimize system response with one test signal from the generator of Fig. 6.13 should optimize system response for all signals from the generator. This is the motivation for choosing $(t_f - t_0)$ as large as possible. For the case here of controller design, this means choosing $(t_f - t_0)$ large w.r.t. the time constants of the linear filter $W(s)$ in Fig. 6.13 and the time constants of the system (the controller and plant) excited by this test signal.

Example 6.3

As an example of the use of a stochastic test signal in the design of a controller, let us consider the design of a state variable feedback controller for a DC motor. This problem was considered and solved using a deterministic input in Example 6.1. A simulation diagram for the motor and associated state variable feedback controller is shown in Fig. 6.14.

The controller has been described in Example 6.1. We note again that the feed-forward gain K_0 multiplying the input signal r, is set so that it is equal to K_1. Thus in steady state a constant input r results in a constant shaft position θ with $\theta = r$. The problem thus reduces itself to finding values for the gains K_1, K_2, and K_3.

The design of the controller here has been complicated, over the case considered in Example 6.1, in that a disturbance input has been assumed.

The motor is assumed to be driving a fluctuating torque load, which leads to a disturbance torque being applied to the output shaft. This is taken into account in Fig. 6.14 by the disturbance input $d(t)$, which adds the disturbance to the acceleration node $\ddot{\theta}$. This assumes that the disturbance torque (T_d) is

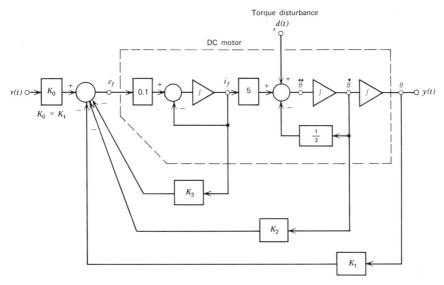

Figure 6.14 Simulation diagram for a DC motor with torque distrubance and state variable feedback controller.

related to angular acceleration of the shaft by $T_d = J\ddot{\theta}$ where J is the moment of inertia of the shaft.

Choice of criterion

Here, as in Example 6.1, the primary objective is to have the output shaft position θ track the system input signal r. A logical criterion is then an integral square error one of the form

$$J = \int_{t_0}^{t_f} (r(t) - \theta(t))^2 \, dt \tag{6.60}$$

which is a valid criterion for all inputs $r(t)$. In any realistic case the input to motor e_f must be constrained in some way. If it is not, the controller may very well be expected to produce excessive values of e_f in order to reduce tracking error. A simple way of taking e_f into account, and one that we have seen before, is to add a term involving e_f under the integral of the criterion. The criterion becomes

$$J = \int_{t_0}^{t_f} [(r(t) - \theta(t))^2 + Re_f^2(t)] \, dt \tag{6.61}$$

where R is a positive constant that can be adjusted by experience to accomplish a tradeoff between tracking efficiency and the power (and hence indirectly the magnitude) of the field voltage e_f, which is the input to the plant.

Choice of the stochastic inputs

The criterion as given in (6.61) requires that the input signal $r(t)$ be defined before optimization can be accomplished. Also, before any response can be determined, the disturbance input $d(t)$ (see Fig. 6.14) must be defined. Here we shall take both of these as stochastic inputs. Both are generated using the test signal generator model as given in Fig. 6.13. For simplicity the random number generator was chosen to have a Gaussian distribution with a mean of zero and variance $\sigma_{RN}^2 = 100$. For the generation of the random test signal that was to be the system input signal $r(t)$, the linear shaping filter was chosen as a second order filter with

$$W(s) = \frac{0.1}{s^2 + 0.448s + 0.1} \tag{6.62}$$

which gives $\zeta = 0.707$, a maximally flat filter, with cutoff frequency $\omega_n = 0.316$ rad/sec. This cutoff frequency was chosen after some trial showed it to work well and because the motor transfer function of the system (see Fig. 6.14) has $\omega = 0.333$ rad/sec as its lowest corner frequency. The frequency spectrum of the test signal then falls within the passband of the motor, which is our plant. For $W(s)$ as in (6.62), using (6.56) with $\sigma_{RN}^2 = 50$ and $h = 0.125$ sec (which was chosen as the integration step size for integrating the system d.e.'s), we get

$$\sigma_r = 1.18 \text{ rad} \tag{6.63}$$

as the standard deviation of the signal $r(t)$.

For the disturbance input (see Fig. 6.14), the generating random number sequence (see Fig. 6.13) was again chosen to have a Gaussian distribution with a mean of zero and variance $\sigma_{RN}^2 = 100$. The first impulse was to choose the disturbance with a flat, white noise spectrum. However, to limit the bandwidth so as not to upset the numerical integration used to calculate system response, a simple first order smoothing filter

$$W(s) = \frac{1}{s + 1} \tag{6.64}$$

was used. This gave a cutoff frequency of $\omega = 1$ rad/sec which means the disturbance spectrum was essentially flat in the passband of the signal exciting the system, $r(t)$ of Fig. 6.14. Using $W(s)$ of (6.64) in (6.56), again with $\sigma_{RN} = 10, h = 0.125$ sec, we obtained

$$\sigma_d = 2.5 \text{ rad/sec}^2 \tag{6.65}$$

as the standard deviation of the disturbance signal. This particular standard deviation was chosen since rough calculation showed it to be about 10% of the standard deviation of the acceleration $\ddot{\theta}$ to be expected without any disturbance.

Formulation of system differential equations

In order to handle a criterion of the form of (6.61), a state variable x_0 was defined to satisfy the differential equation

$$\dot{x}_0 = (r(t) - \theta(t))^2 + R e_f^2(t): x_0(t_0) = 0 \tag{6.66}$$

For x_0 so defined the criterion is then

$$J = \phi(x(t_f)) = x_0(t_f) \tag{6.67}$$

For the other state variables if we let

$$x_1 = \theta$$

$$x_2 = \dot{\theta}$$

$$x_3 = i_f$$

as in Fig. 6.14, the system d.e.'s may be written from (6.66) and Fig. 6.14 as

$$\dot{x}_0 = (r - x_1)^2 + R e_f^2$$

$$\dot{x}_1 = x_2$$

$$\dot{x}_2 = -\tfrac{1}{3}x_2 + 5x_3 + d(t) \tag{6.68}$$

$$\dot{x}_3 = -x_3 + 0.1 e_f$$

$$e_f = K_1(r - x_1) - K_2 x_2 - K_3 x_3$$

The d.e.'s of (6.68) are of the form $\dot{x} = f(x, u)$ and the criterion of (6.67) is of the form $J = \phi(x(t_f))$, which is precisely the form required to optimize parameters by use of the gradient in the space of parameters as described in Section 4.4. In this case the parameters are the gains $K_1, K_2,$ and K_3. With the vector of parameters defined as

$$u = \begin{bmatrix} K_1 \\ K_2 \\ K_3 \end{bmatrix} \tag{6.69}$$

the problem becomes one of finding u of (6.69) which when used in the d.e.'s of (6.68) minimizes the criterion of (6.67).

Results

The problem was submitted to the computer for conjugate gradient descent optimization of the feedback gains. As an initial guess for the gains

$$u^+ = [40 \quad 0 \quad 0] \tag{6.70}$$

was used. These values were chosen because rough calculation showed that the resulting closed-loop poles were in the left half plane. The initial state was chosen as

$$x(t_0) = 0$$

since from (6.66) $x_0(t_0) = 0$ was wanted and since the expected values of the other states were all also zero. The initial time $t_0 = 0$ and final time $t_f = 37.5$ sec were chosen since the system was stationary and since 37.5 sec was long relative to the time constants of the system and to the time constants of the filter transfer functions, (6.62) and (6.64), used in generating the test and disturbance signals. The step size used in the integration of the system d.e.'s was taken as 0.125 sec, which then required 300 iteration steps to achieve $t_f = 37.5$ sec.

The program was run using three values of the parameter R in the criterion of (6.61) and the corresponding d.e. in (6.68). The results of the optimization are shown in Figs. 6.15 through 6.17. The output shaft position and desired output shaft position [the input signal $r(t)$] are shown for two values of R in Fig. 6.15. For $R = 0.001$, the largest value of R used, the tracking is not very good. The output shaft position, as can be seen in Fig. 6.15 for this value of R, on the average tracks the input signal, but the high-frequency components in the disturbance cause the actual shaft position to differ significantly from the desired value at almost all instances of time. For a smaller value, $R = 0.00001$, the result is also shown in Fig. 6.15, where it can be seen that the tracking is actually very good relative to the tracking for $R = 0.001$. We see that the accuracy of tracking can be controlled by choosing different values of the parameter R. However in Figs 6.16 and 6.17 we see the price paid for the better tracking obtained with the smaller value of R. The figures show that the magnitude of the control signal input, the field voltage e_f here, increases with the better tracking accuracy obtained with the smaller values of R. Also for smaller values of R, the control signal e_f bounces around more so that it is evident that there is more high-frequency power being applied to the motor for this case. In summary, better tracking is obtained with smaller values of R, that is, less weighting on the control input e_f in the criterion. The price paid, however to achieve this better tracking is larger control signal magnitudes, more control effort and wider bandwidth.

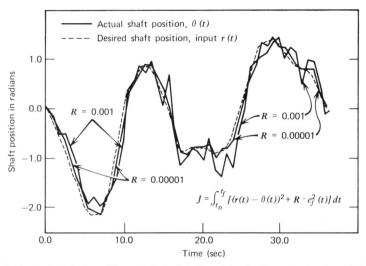

Figure 6.15 Output shaft position and desired shaft position for the control system of Fig. 6.14.

$$J = \int_{t_o}^{t_f} \{[r(t) - \theta(t)]^2 + Re_f^2(t)\} \, dt$$

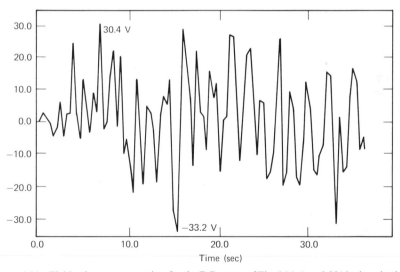

Figure 6.16 Field voltage e_f versus time for the DC motor of Fig. 6.14. $R = 0.001$ in the criterion.

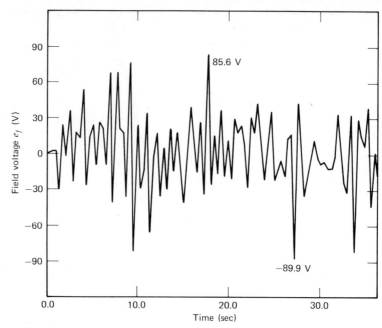

Figure 6.17   Field voltage e_f versus time for the DC motor of Fig. 6.14. $R = 0.00001$ in the criterion.

The values of the feedback gains, K_1, K_2, and K_3 obtained for the different values of R are shown in Table 6.2. Also shown are the values of the criterion of (6.61) obtained for each value of R. In general we see from the table that the feedback gains become larger and the value of the criterion smaller with decreasing R.

Remarks

1. Twenty-four conjugate gradient descent iterations were required to obtain the results shown for $R = 0.001$ with the starting guess as given in (6.70). Subsequently, for the other two values of R, only six iterations were required to obtain satisfactory convergence using the previous values obtained as starting guesses.

2. The gains as given in Table 6.2 were obtained with the disturbance input $d(t)$ in place and accounted for. It may be expected that the resulting controller will be insensitive to torque disturbances on the motor shaft. This kind of optimization in the face of a disturbance is difficult to accomplish using deterministic inputs. One disturbance input was considered; several could as well have been considered in the same manner.

3. The approach to the design of the controller is very flexible in that feedback gains can be added or subtracted at will. There is no requirement that all states be detected and fed back. Also, if the system is nonlinear (as a DC motor is known to be at high field currents) and the nonlinearities are known, they can easily be used in the system modeling equations of (6.68). Optimization of the gains may still go forward so long as the functions obtained are still differentiable w.r.t. x and u [as defined in (6.69)].

4. To check whether or not the time interval of 37.5 sec used was long enough, the optimization was continued using other test signals $r(t)$ and disturbance inputs $d(t)$. These were generated in the same way as the test signals used to obtain the results shown in Figs. 6.15 through 6.17 and in Table 6.2. There was neglible difference in the feedback gains and the value of criterion obtained. No observable difference in the quality of tracking was noted.

5. The gains found in Example 6.1 for this same system, with $R = 0.001$ in the criterion but with a step input rather than a stochastic input, are considerably different than the ones found here. This may be seen by comparison of (6.25) with the corresponding values in Table 6.2. We note especially that the gains obtained using stochastic test signals are in general much higher than the ones obtained using deterministic inputs.

Table 6.2 Feedback Gains and Criterion Value Obtained for Selected Values of the Parameter R

R	K_1	K_2	K_3	Criterion J
0.001	314.9	93.35	213.8	10.17
0.0001	543.5	137.70	180.2	2.670
0.00001	1505.4	247.00	193.9	0.7108

Example 6.4

As a second example of the use of a stochastic input in the design of a controller, let us consider the model follower controller of Section 6.3. In particular let us consider the model follower controller for the X-14 aircraft in hover that was seen in Example 6.2. A simulation diagram for the roll axis of the aircraft and the model follower controller that was proposed for it appear in Fig. 6.18. This diagram is the same as the one seen in Fig. 6.10 with the important exception that a disturbance input $d(t)$ has been added to the summer in the simulation diagram for the roll axis. The disturbance input adds the disturbance directly into the acceleration ($\ddot{\phi}$) node which

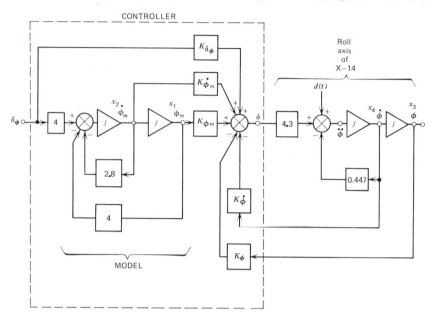

Figure 6.18   Model-follower controller for the X-14 roll axis with a roll moment disturbance.

basically assumes that there is an additional torque disturbance applied to the roll axis of the aircraft. This is a realistic assumption if it is assumed that the aircraft is being operated in an atmosphere subject to wind gusts. Our approach here is to design the controller, that is, determine the gains $K_{\delta\phi}$, $K_{\phi m}$, $K_{\dot\phi m}$, $K_{\dot\phi}$, and K_ϕ by defining a criterion on the response of the system, and then setting these gains to minimize this criterion. We now take the input roll axis command δ_ϕ and the disturbance input $d(t)$ as stochastic inputs with suitably chosen statistical characteristics. Again, the gain parameters are chosen to minimize the criterion by using the gradient in the space of parameters as described in Section 4.4.

Choice of stochastic inputs

For the input to the system, δ_ϕ in Fig. 6.18, we take a stochastic input generated by a model as given in Fig. 6.13. The response of the whole system should in general be approximately that of the model. The model has a transfer function, (6.40), which has a cutoff frequency at $\omega_n = 2$ rad/sec and damping $\zeta = 0.7$. For this case it is reasonable to choose a test signal that is essentially flat and covers this frequency band. Thus it is logical to choose $W(s)$ in the stochastic input generator of Fig. 6.13 as

$$W(s) = \frac{9}{s^2 + 4.24s + 9} \tag{6.71}$$

which gives a flat response ($\zeta = 0.707$) with cutoff frequency of 3 rad/sec. This is slightly higher than the cutoff frequency of the model and should result in the model being excited over the whole band of significant frequencies of the model. For the random number generator of Fig. 6.13, [which excites the linear filter of (6.71)] a Gaussian distribution is a reasonable assumption. Since the system is linear, (6.56) shows how to choose the variance σ_{RN} so that the standard deviation of the test signal is unity, that is,

$$\sigma_{\delta\phi} = 1.0 \text{ degree} \tag{6.72}$$

For the disturbance input the idea was to model wind gust disturbances. The reference for this is Section 9.4 of [4]. The guess for the generator filter transfer function, $W(s)$ in Fig. 6.13, was taken to be simply

$$W(s) = \frac{1}{s + 1} \tag{6.73}$$

which gave a corner frequency of $\omega = 1$ rad/sec which was of the right order of magnitude according to [4]. This results in a disturbance frequency band that falls within the passband of the model, which should hence make it fall within the passband of the overall system. This should hold since the overall system is supposed to follow closely the response of the model. The random number generator (of Fig. 6.13) used in producing the disturbance input was again simply chosen to be Gaussian. The resulting disturbance input $d(t)$ was then also Gaussian. The standard deviation of the disturbance input σ_d was chosen as

$$\sigma_d = 2$$

after a little consideration showed that this would give a significant amount of disturbance to the acceleration $\ddot{\phi}$, which was estimated here as being approximately the same as the acceleration of the model $\ddot{\phi}_m$ (see Fig. 6.18).

Criterion and formulation of system dynamics

The dynamics for the system considered here, the one shown in Fig. 6.18, are the same as the dynamics used in Example 6.2, except that the disturbance $d(t)$ is added to the roll acceleration $\ddot{\phi}$ node. The criterion here was again chosen as a simple integral square one, with the error taken to be the difference between the model attitude ϕ_m and the aircraft roll attitude ϕ. With the addition of a term under the integral involving the control variable (δ here, see Fig. 6.18) to limit the magnitude of δ, the criterion becomes

$$J = \int_{t_0}^{t_f} [(\phi_m(t) - \phi(t))^2 + R\delta^2(t)] \, dt \tag{6.74}$$

where R is now a weighting factor that may be varied to control the magnitude of δ.

To handle this form of criterion we define a state variable by

$$\dot{x}_0 = (\phi_m - \phi)^2 + R\delta^2 \colon x_0(t_0) = 0 \tag{6.75}$$

which puts the criterion in the form

$$\begin{aligned} J &= x_0(t_f) \\ &- \phi(x(t_f)) \end{aligned} \tag{6.76}$$

which is the required form for the gradient optimization. Using (6.75) and the state variable assignment as given in Fig. 6.18, we may write the system differential equations as

$$\begin{aligned} \dot{x}_0 &= (x_1 - x_3)^2 + R\delta^2 \\ \dot{x}_1 &= x_2 \\ \dot{x}_2 &= -2.8x_2 - 4x_1 + 4\delta_\phi \\ \dot{x}_3 &= x_4 \\ \dot{x}_4 &= -0.447x_4 + 4.3\delta + d(t) \\ \delta &= K_{\phi m}x_1 + K_{\dot\phi m}x_2 - K_\phi x_3 - K_{\dot\phi}x_4 + (K_\phi - K_{\phi m})\delta_\phi \end{aligned} \tag{6.77}$$

where in the expression for δ use has been made of (6.43) to determine $K_{\delta m} = K_\phi - K_{\phi m}$. This we recall is done to insure that the system will have zero steady-state error to a constant input.

Equation 6.77 gives the differential equations in the form $\dot{x} = f(x, u)$ where u, the vector of parameters, is

$$u = [K_{\phi m} \quad K_{\dot\phi m} \quad K_\phi \quad K_{\dot\phi}]^+ \tag{6.78}$$

Equation 6.76 gives the criterion in the form $J = \phi(x(t_f))$; thus the problem is properly formulated to determine the parameters of (6.78) so as to minimize the criterion of (6.76) by the gradient method as given in Section 4.4.

Results

The dynamics of (6.77) with the criterion of (6.76) were submitted to the computer using a time interval of 30 sec (so $t_0 = 0$, $t_f = 30.0$ sec was chosen). Thirty seconds here is much longer than any of the time constants of the model, plant, or stochastic input filters. Several values of R were used. The character of the tracking of the model and aircraft [with the gains $K_{\phi m}$,

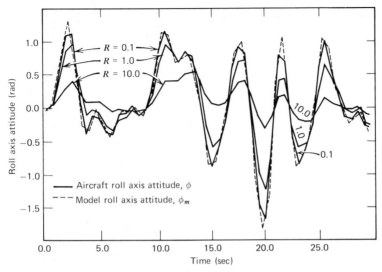

Figure 6.19   Attitude-time response with a model follower controller on the X-14 roll axis.

$$J = \int_{t_0}^{t_f} [(\phi_m(t) - \phi(t))^2 + R_1 \delta^2(t)] \, dt,$$

$K_{\dot{\phi}m}$, K_ϕ, and $K_{\dot{\phi}}$ optimized so as to minimize the criterion of (6.74)] can be seen in Fig. 6.19. The gains found for these values of R are shown in Table 6.3.

All zero initial conditions were assumed for the model and aircraft states as these were the expected values, since the inputs were chosen with mean zero. In Fig. 6.19 we see that the tracking is relatively very good for $R = 0.1$. This degrades to very bad for $R = 10.0$. The price paid for the better tracking at smaller values of R can be seen in the plots of Fig. 6.20 where r.m.s. values of the error $(\phi_m - \phi)$ and the control variable, δ are shown plotted versus the

Table 6.3   Gains Found for the Model Follower Controller on the X-14 Roll Axis

R	J	$K_{\dot{\phi}m}$	$K_{\phi m}$	K_ϕ	$K_{\dot{\phi}}$
0.01	0.135	36.77	16.41	38.31	17.46
0.1	1.268	18.36	4.864	20.79	7.16
1.0	10.69	5.567	3.459	7.816	8.222
10.0	71.9	0.1866	0.3169	0.5591	3.234

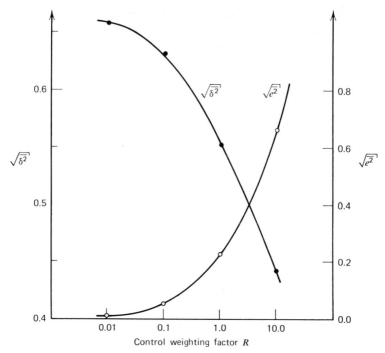

Figure 6.20   Root mean square attitude error and control versus R.

$$\bar{e}^2 = \frac{1}{30} \int_0^{30} [\phi_m(t) - \phi(t)]^2 \, dt; \qquad \bar{\delta}^2 = \frac{1}{30} \int_0^{30} \delta^2(t) \, dt; \qquad J = \int_0^{30} [(\phi_m - \phi)^2 + R\delta^2] \, dt.$$

weighting factor R. Better tracking is seen to require an increase in the r.m.s. value of control δ. It can also be seen in Fig. 6.20 that for a standard deviation of 1 degree on the input (δ_ϕ here, Fig. 6.18) an r.m.s. value of the control variable δ of 0.6 degrees has to be provided or serious tracking divergence between the model and aircraft may be expected.

6.5.   CASCADE-COMPENSATED FEEDBACK TRACKING SYSTEM

One of the oldest and now most classical types of controller is the first order, cascade compensator for a feedback tracking system, designed basically as shown in Fig. 6.21. The output of the plant here is fed back and subtracted from the input. The difference e in the figure is used to control the compensator–plant combination. *The objective here is to have the output y(t) track the input r(t) for all time* t. The effect of the feedback is to continuously drive the

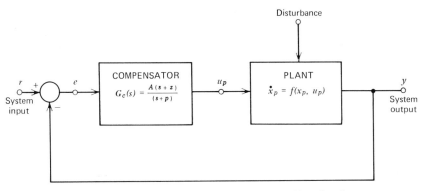

Figure 6.21 A cascade-compensated feedback tracking system with a disturbance.

output in such a direction as to reduce the magnitude of the error signal. It does this if, and this is a very important if, there is no signal sign inversion in going through the compensator–plant combination; that is, a positive change in error $e(t)$ results in a positive change in $y(t)$ and vice versa for negative error. Of course if there is signal sign inversion in going through the compensator–plant, error magnitude is increased and the system does not track. The system is then said to be unstable. Figure 6.21 shows a simple first order compensator. A higher order compensator may be assumed here, and in some cases this gives significantly better performance. But for purposes of illustration the first order case is sufficient and hence what we use here. For a compensator as given in Fig. 6.21, the transfer function is

$$G_c(s) = \frac{A(s + z)}{(s + p)} \qquad (6.79)$$

where s is the Laplace variable. The compensator is called a lead compensator if

$$\left| \frac{z}{p} \right| < 1$$

which means simply that the zero is closer to the origin than the pole in the s-plane. It is called a lag compensator otherwise. In general a lead compensator is required if the response of the plant is to be speeded up, that is, more bandwidth in the loop is required. A lag compensator is required in the opposite case. In particular, a lag compensator is required if high-frequency noise in the loop is a problem. Any undergraduate text on automatic control can provide a much more detailed discussion of the use of lag and lead compensators; Chapter 8 of [8] is an example of such.

As a final note on the first order compensator, a simulation diagram (which is useful in formulating the dynamics of the problém and which is used in the example below) for the compensator is shown in Fig. 6.22. *Design of the controller can be seen from Figs. 6.21 and 6.22 to come down to determining the three parameters* A, z, *and* p. Our approach is again to define a criterion on the operation of the system and then to choose the parameters A, z, and p so as to minimize this criterion by use of the gradient in the space of control parameters as found in Section 4.4.

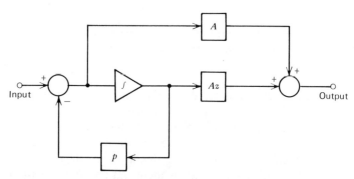

Figure 6.22   A simulation diagram for a compensator with transfer function

$$G_c(s) = \frac{A(s + z)}{(s + p)}.$$

Choice of a Criterion

In choosing a criterion here, considerations are in general the same as in the choice of criterion for state-variable feedback and model-follower controllers as seen in Section 6.2, 6.3, and 6.4. Again here an error is naturally defined since we are using a system from Fig. 6.21

$$e(t) \triangleq r(t) - y(t) \tag{6.80}$$

The desire is to minimize the magnitude of the error at all times. For this purpose the usual integral square error criterion is reasonable. To control the magnitude and energy of the control applied to the plant it is also reasonable to put a square term under the integral involving the plant input. The result is a criterion of the form

$$J = \int_{t_0}^{t_f} [e^2(t) + Ru_p^2(t)] \, dt \tag{6.81}$$

To get good tracking at the final instance t_f, a penalty term of the form $W_1(r(t_f) - y(t_f))^2$ may also be added.

Another consideration here and one that is unique to the cascade compensator case is the problem of keeping the zero of the compensator away from the origin and out of the RHP, that is, keeping $z > 0$. This is especially the case if the plant has a pole at the origin, that is, the signal goes through a pure integration in passing through the plant. Wiener filter theory shows that the minimization of an integral square error criterion results in a compensator that cancels out the LHP and $j\omega$-axis poles of the plant (if the plant is linear) (see Chapter 10 of [8]). Furthermore, experience through computation with a criterion of the form of (6.81) has shown that indeed the compensator zero falls at the origin when the plant has a pole there. This cancellation of the pole at the origin is undesirable first because the steady-state error characteristics of a closed-loop system such as the one shown in Fig. 6.21 depend strongly on the number of forward path poles at the origin. If the system has one forward path (open-loop) pole at the origin, the system tracks a constant input with zero steady-state error. If there are two forward path poles the system tracks a ramp input with zero steady-state error, and so on, provided only that the system is closed-loop stable. Thus so far as the steady-state error characteristics are concerned the system loses tracking capability if poles at the origin are cancelled. Secondly, the cancellation may not be perfect and if the zero should fall into the RHP, a closed-loop RHP pole results and the system becomes closed-loop unstable. In general it is desirable to have no RHP zeroes either from the compensator or the plant. For high values of frequency independent gain in the loop, the resulting closed-loop system is unstable if such RHP zeroes are present. Therefore in general *we desire $z > 0$ in the compensator transfer function of* (6.79). We seek a criterion that will accomplish this.

One that has been found effective in handling this problem is obtained by addition of an integral error squared term to the criterion of (6.81). This results in a criterion of the form

$$J = \int_{t_0}^{t_f} [e^2(t) + Ru_p^2(t)]\, dt + W\left[\int_{t_0}^{t_f} e(t)\, dt\right]^2 \tag{6.82}$$

where W is again a large positive constant. The integral error term in (6.82) is a penalty function term, which, if the constant W is large, results in holding the mean value of the error near zero. If the mean of the input is constant (and since we are free to choose the test signal input, this is a logical choice) and if there is a forward path pole at the origin, the mean of the output is the same as the mean of the input. Thus the mean of the error, e, is zero. If the forward path pole at the origin is cancelled by the zero of the compensator this is no longer true. Thus the mean of the error is not zero and the criterion of (6.82) is increased in value. Therefore minimization of the criterion of (6.82) should result in a compensator that does not cancel the pole at the origin. Thus if we are finding the parameters of the compensator by an iterative gradient method and the initial guess for the parameter z in the transfer function of the compensator, in (6.79), is greater than zero, then $z > 0$ should hold for all subsequent iterations.

To handle a criterion involving a term of the form

$$\int_{t_0}^{t_f} e(t)\, dt \qquad (6.83)$$

we must define a new state variable to put it into the required $J = \phi(x(t_f))$ form that is used in the computation of the gradient. Calling this state variable x_j, let x_j satisfy the differential equation

$$\dot{x}_j = e(t)\text{: } x_j(t_0) = 0 \qquad (6.84)$$

Then we have

$$x_j(t_f) = \int_{t_0}^{t_f} e(t)\, dt$$

and the integral error squared term becomes

$$W\left[\int_{t_0}^{t_f} e(t)\, dt \right]^2 = W x_j^2(t_f)$$

which is of the proper form.

Example 6.5

As an example of the use of a cascade compensator in a feedback tracking system let us consider the position tracking system for which a state variable feedback controller was designed in Example 6.3. A simulation diagram for the system with a cascade compensator in place is shown in Fig. 6.23. This is a DC motor that is preceded by a cascade compensator. The output of the motor, the shaft position θ, is fed back and subtracted from the input $r(t)$ to produce the error signal $e(t)$, which then becomes the input to the compensator. The system corresponds exactly to the block diagram in Fig. 6.21. The simulation diagram for the compensator is the one in Fig. 6.22. A torque distrubance that acts on the output shaft of the motor is assumed. This results, in Fig. 6.23, in the disturbance $d(t)$, which is added to the acceleration ($\ddot{\theta}$) node.

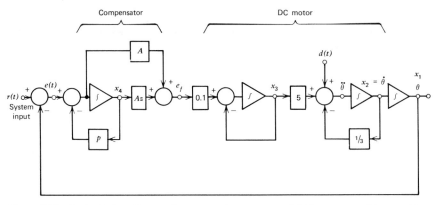

Figure 6.23 A simulation diagram for a cascade-compensated DC motor position tracking system with a disturbance.

Choice of input test signals

Let us use the same basic inputs to the system that were used in Example 6.63. The input $r(t)$ is then generated by a process, modeled in Fig. 6.13, where the random number generator has a Gaussian, mean zero distribution. The linear filter has maximally flat damping $\zeta = 0.707$ with cutoff frequency $\omega_n = 0.316$ rad/sec, which gives the transfer function

$$W(s) = \frac{0.1}{s^2 + 0.1414s + 0.1} \tag{6.85}$$

The variance σ_{RN}^2 of the distribution of the random number generator (see Fig. 6.13) was chosen to produce unity variance of the signal $r(t)$, that is,

$$\sigma_r^2 = 1.0 \text{ rad}^2 \tag{6.86}$$

The disturbance signal $d(t)$ was also assumed to be a stochastic signal generated as shown by the model of Fig. 6.13. The random number generator in this case was also assumed to have a Gaussian, mean zero distribution. The linear filter here was assumed to be first order with cutoff frequency $\omega = 1.0$ rad/sec, which gives

$$W(s) = \frac{1}{s + 1} \tag{6.87}$$

The variance of the random number generator was chosen so that the disturbance signal $d(t)$ would also have unity variance, that is,

$$\sigma_d^2 = 1.0 \tag{6.88}$$

This particular value was chosen because rough calculation showed that it should make a significant (10%) contribution to the acceleration with the compensator as initially guessed.

Formulation of the criterion and system dynamics

The criterion used was exactly as in (6.82). From Fig. 6.23, we see that the error is here

$$e(t) = r(t) - \theta(t)$$

and the plant input is the field voltage e_f. Using these in (6.82) gives the criterion

$$J = \int_{t_0}^{t_f} [(r - \theta)^2 + Re_f^2] \, dt + W \left[\int_{t_0}^{t_f} (r - \theta) \, dt \right]^2 \qquad (6.89)$$

To put this into the proper $J = \phi(x(t_f))$ form we define two new state variables x_0 and x_5 which satisfy

$$\dot{x}_0 = (r - x_1)^2 + Re_f^2 \colon x_0(t_0) = 0$$
$$\dot{x}_5 = (r - x_1) \colon x_5(t_0) = 0 \qquad (6.90)$$
$$e_f = A(r - x_1) + (Az - Ap)x_4$$

where we have used the state variable assignment as seen in Fig. 6.23. With x_0 and x_5 as given by (6.90), the criterion of (6.89) becomes

$$J = x_0(t_f) + Wx_5^2(t_f) \qquad (6.91)$$

which is the desired form.

The system dynamics may now be written in the proper form by use of (6.90) and the simulation diagram of Fig. 6.23,

$$\dot{x}_0 = (r - x_1)^2 + Re_f^2$$
$$\dot{x}_1 = x_2$$
$$\dot{x}_2 = -\tfrac{1}{3}x_2 + 5x_3 + d(t)$$
$$\dot{x}_3 = -x_3 + 0.1e_f \qquad (6.92)$$
$$\dot{x}_4 = -x_1 - px_4 + r$$
$$\dot{x}_5 = -x_1 + r$$
$$e_f = A(r - x_1) + (Az - Ap)x_4$$

Equations 6.91 and 6.92 give the criterion and the dynamics, respectively, in the proper form for the computation of the gradient in the space of system parameters as given in Section 4.4.

Results

The systems dynamics and the criterion as in (6.91) and (6.92) were program-med for the computer, the objective being to determine A, z, and p, the compensator parameters. The vector of unknowns used here was

$$u = \begin{bmatrix} A \\ Az \\ p \end{bmatrix} \qquad (6.93)$$

The choice of Az rather than z as the free parameter was made simply because experience showed that the three unknowns selected as in (6.93) came out to be roughly of the same magnitude and gave better convergence than when z (rather than Az) was chosen as the free parameter. The initial guess for the free parameters was

$$u = \begin{bmatrix} A \\ Az \\ p \end{bmatrix} = \begin{bmatrix} 10 \\ 10 \\ 10 \end{bmatrix} \qquad (6.94)$$

which was chosen simply because rough estimates indicated that they were of the right order of magnitude and stable. The initial state was chosen as $x(t_0) = 0$, that is, quiescence, since this agreed with the initial conditions of (6.90) and since the mean of the input signal was zero and hence the expected value of the system dynamic variables (x_1 through x_4) was also zero. The value of W in (6.91) was chosen as 100. This gave the integral of error over the time interval of interest on the order of 10^{-2} in all cases, which was found to be sufficiently small. Fifteen seconds was chosen as the time interval of interest, that is, $t_0 = 0$ and $t_f = 15.0$ sec, again because trial showed it to work well and because this was a long time relative to all system time constants.

The results for two values of the parameter R [which gives the weight of the field voltage e_f in the criterion, (6.89) and (6.92)] are shown in Fig. 6.24. The output shaft position and the desired shaft position versus time are also shown in this figure. The root mean square value of the field voltage (the control input to the plant) and root mean square tracking error are shown as a function of R in Fig. 6.25. The values of the compensator parameters for three values of R are given in Table 6.4.

Remarks

1. As could be expected, as the parameter R decreases, which means the field voltage e_f is weighted less in the criterion, the better is the tracking obtained. Figure 6.25 shows how this better tracking is paid for in the increased value of field voltages for these same decreasing values of R.

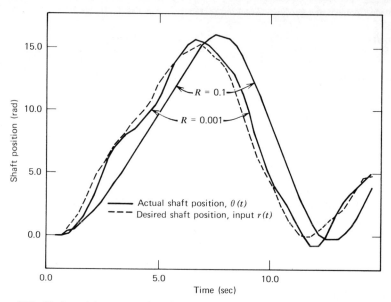

Figure 6.24 Shaft position versus time for the lead-compensated position control system of Fig. 6.23. $W = 100.0$.

$$J = \int_{t_0}^{t_f} \{[r(t) - \theta(t)]^2 + Re_f^2(t)\} \, dt + W\left[\int_{t_0}^{t_f} [r(t) - \theta(t)] \, dt\right]$$

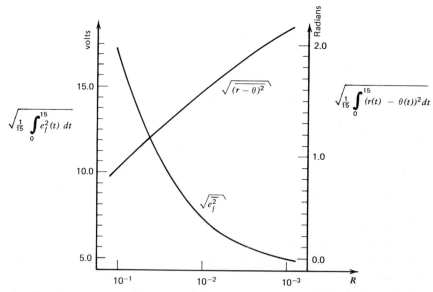

Figure 6.25 Root mean square field voltage and tracking error versus weighting factor R.

Table 6.4 Compensator Parameters for Three Values of the Parameter R

R	A	z	p	J
0.001	164.0	0.2577	14.20	14.94
0.01	94.84	0.2027	19.07	48.30
0.1	53.09	0.2303	20.71	106.2

2. By examining Table 6.4 we see that the compensators are for all values of R, lead compensators, that is, $|z/p| < 1$. We also note that the zero of the compensator (at $s = -z$) is in the LHP for all values of R, that is, $z > 0$, which is as desired and which is the reason for adding the error integral squared term in the criterion of (6.89). The compensator zero is in all three cases very near the plant pole which occurs for this plant at $s = -\frac{1}{3}$. This is in accord with classical compensator design technique which would have begun by putting the compensator zero on top of the LHP plant pole nearest (but not on) the $j\omega$-axis.

3. In glancing at Fig. 6-24 and then at Fig. 6-15 it can be seen that a better feedback tracking system has been obtained using state variable feedback. In general terms this happens because three state variables are being fed back to the controller with state variable feedback as compared to only one in the case of the cascade compensator. If the cascade compensator is to achieve equivalent performance, a higher than first order compensation must be used.

6.6. CONTROLLER DESIGN AND PARAMETER IDENTIFICATION FOR A STIRRED TANK MIXER

As an example of the use of the techniques developed here on a truly non-linear, stochastic problem, let us consider the stirred tank schematically diagrammed in Fig. 6.26†. Seen in the figure are two input flows (with flow rates F_1 and F_2 and concentrations c_1 and c_2, respectively) going in at the top. The two inputs are mixed in the tank to produce output with flow rate F_3 and concentration c_3 out the bottom. The contents of the tank, as indicated by the propeller, are stirred continuously. Hold time in the tank is assumed long enough to produce the desired degree of mixing even with the anticipated

† This example is taken essentially from Kwakernaak and Sivan [10], which is referred to henceforth as K and S.

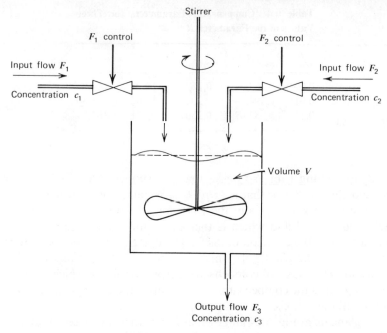

Figure 6.26 A stirred tank mixer.

variations in mixture volume in the tank. The input flow rates F_1 and F_2 are controlled by input valves while the output flow is assumed to be through a constant size orifice. This output flow rate is assumed to vary as the square root of the static pressure head at the orifice. With constant cross-sectional area of the tank this means

$$F_3 = k\sqrt{V} \tag{6.95}$$

where V is the volume of the material in the tank and k is an experimentally determined constant. Following K and S,

$$k = 0.02 \text{ m}^{3/2} \text{ sec}$$

is used here.

The problem here is to control input flows F_1 and F_2 so that the output product concentration c_3 is as near as possible to a desired nominal value c_{3_0}. At the same time the volume of the mixture in the tank (V) is to be maintained at or near a desired nominal value so as to insure both a sufficient hold time in the tank to achieve the desired degree of mixing and also a sufficient, near constant output flow rate F_3.

Dynamics of the Tank

With notation as defined in Fig. 6.26, the dynamics of the tank may be described by the mass balance equations as

$$\frac{d}{dt}(c_3 V) = c_1 F_1 + c_2 F_2 - c_3 F_3$$

$$\frac{dV}{dt} = F_1 + F_2 - F_3$$

(6.96)

These equations simply mean that the rate of change of product in the tank varies with time as the difference between input product rate and output product rate. Volume V in the tank changes as the difference between flow in and flow out. With a few obvious manipulations, (6.96) may be put into the form

$$\frac{dc_3}{dt} = \frac{(c_1 - c_3)F_1 + (c_2 - c_3)F_2}{V}$$

$$\frac{dV}{dt} = F_1 + F_2 - F_3$$

(6.97)

which is the $\dot{x} = f(x)$ form desired here.

The Input Concentrations as Functions of Time

Basically the control problem arises here because input concentration c_1 varies with time in a random manner. Input concentration c_2 is assumed to be adequately approximated by a constant value. For the purposes of controller design the random variations of c_1 are assumed adequately approximated by a Gaussian-distributed white noise process passed through a first order filter (a model as in Fig. 6.13) with variance $\sigma_1 = 0.3$ kmol/m³, mean value 1 kmol/m³, and corner frequency $\omega = 0.05$ rad/sec, which gives a time constant of 20 sec [$a = 0.05$ in W_1 of (6.55)], which is the same order of magnitude as hold time† in the tank. A sample time history from such a stochastic process is shown in Fig. 6.27, which is the concentration c_1 time history used in the design of the controller. For the purposes of design of a controller, this could as well have been recorded from an actual input flow concentration time history.

† Hold time here (again from K and S) is defined as nominal volume V_o divided by nominal flow rate out F_{3_o}, that is, V_o/F_{3_o}.

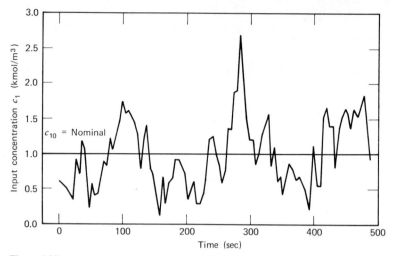

Figure 6.27 Input concentration c_1 versus time over 500 sec.

Nominal Values for the Flow Rates and Concentrations

Nominal values of the input flow rates are assumed adjusted to give the output nominal concentration desired and desired nominal volume V in the tank. These are, using nominal values from [10],

$$
\begin{aligned}
c_{1_o} &= 1 \ \text{kmol/m}^3 \\
c_{2_o} &= 2 \ \text{kmol/m}^3 \\
c_{3_o} &= 1.25 \ \text{kmol/m}^3 \\
F_{1_o} &= 0.015 \ \text{m}^3/\text{sec} \\
F_{2_o} &= 0.005 \ \text{m/sec} \\
F_{3_o} &= 0.02 \ \text{m}^3/\text{sec} \\
V_o &= 1 \ \text{m}^3
\end{aligned}
\tag{6.98}
$$

Subscript o of course indicates nominal value here. F_{3_o} and c_{3_o} were calculated using $k = 0.02$ to relate V and F_3 as in (6.95). F_{3_o} and c_{3_o} are calculated from (6.95) and (6.97) using input nominal flow rates and concentration and constant output concentration c_3 and volume V.

The Configuration of the Controller

In choosing a controller for the tank of Fig. 6.26 it is logical to consider which variables can be controlled and which variables can be measured directly and conveniently, We see from Fig. 6.26 that the input flow rates F_1

and F_2 are the controlled variables. Since measurements are most easily made at the output, measurement of output concentration c_3 and flow rate F_3 is a logical choice. Since F_3 is related to volume V in the tank by (6.95), measuring these two quantities gives the dynamic state of the system. The controller is thus to measure c_3 and F_3 and to produce control variables F_1 and F_2. The simplest type of controller that can be conceived to do this is a linear controller that measures perturbations of the measured variables from nominal and produces linear perturbations of the control variables (again from nominal values). Such a controller is shown in Fig. 6.28. For this controller the control law is

$$\begin{aligned}
F_1 &= K_{11}c_3 + K_{12}F_3 - K_{11}c_{3_o} - K_{12}F_{3_o} + F_{1_o}\\
F_2 &= K_{21}c_3 + K_{22}F_3 - K_{21}c_{3_o} - K_{22}F_{3_o} + F_{2_o}
\end{aligned} \tag{6.99}$$

Realistically the input flow rates can only fall into finite ranges. Here

$$\begin{aligned}
0 \le F_1 \le F_{1\max} &= 2F_{1_o}\\
0 \le F_2 \le F_{2\max} &= 2F_{2_o}
\end{aligned} \tag{6.100}$$

are used. These are simple saturation limits on the control variables and are indicated by the saturation limiters in the controller diagram of Fig. 6.28.

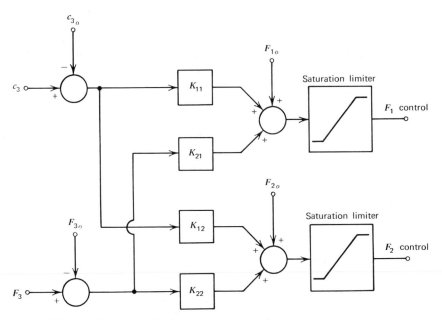

Figure 6.28 A feedback controller for the stirred tank mixer.

Design of the controller now reduces itself to determining the four parameters K_{11}, K_{12}, K_{21}, and K_{22}. The approach here is again to choose a cost criterion on the operation of the system and to then choose the four parameters by gradient optimization to minimize this cost criterion.

The Cost Criterion

The cost criterion here was taken as

$$J = \int_{t_0}^{t_f} [c_3(t) - c_{3_o}]^2 \, dt + R \int_{t_0}^{t_f} [V(t) - V_0]^2 \, dt \qquad (6.101)$$

which can be seen to be a simple integral square error criterion on the error from nominal in output concentration c_3 and volume V. We recall that the objective here was to produce a constant nominal value in output concentration while holding the volume of mixture (and hence output flow rate) at a near nominal constant value. The weighting factor R can be varied to effect tradeoffs in the relative magnitudes of departure from the desired nominal values.

System Dynamics and the Cost Criterion in the Proper Formulation

The tank dynamics of (6.97) plus two new state variables defined to give sum squared error in output concentration c_3 and volume V [which are used in the cost criterion of (6.101)] give the following dynamics

$$\dot{x}_1 = \frac{(c_1 - x_1)F_1 + (c_2 - x_1)F_2}{x_2}$$

$$\dot{x}_2 = -0.02\sqrt{x_2} + F_1 + F_2 \qquad (6.102)$$
$$\dot{x}_3 = (x_1 - c_{3_o})^2$$
$$\dot{x}_4 = (x_2 - V_0)^2$$

where the state variable assignment

$$x_1 = c_3$$
$$x_2 = V \qquad (6.103)$$

has been made. x_3 and x_4 can be seen to give sum squared error in concentration c_3 and volume V, respectively. The criterion of (6.101) is then

$$J = x_3(t_f) + R \cdot x_4(t_f) \qquad (6.104)$$

if $x_3(t_0) = x_4(t_0) = 0$. J of (6.104) is of the desired $J = \phi(x(t_f))$ form.

The control law using the state variable assignment of (6.103) and control law from (6.99) is then

$$F_1 = K_{11}x_1 + K_{12}(0.02\sqrt{x_2}) - K_{11}c_{3_o} - K_{12}F_{3_o} + F_{1_o}$$

$$F_2 = K_{21}x_1 + K_{22}(0.02\sqrt{x_2}) - K_{21}c_{3_o} - K_{22}F_{3_o} + F_{2_o}$$

(6.105)

Saturation limits as in (6.100) now give

$$0 \le F_1 \le 0.03 \text{ m}^3/\text{sec}$$
$$0 \le F_2 \le 0.01 \text{ m}^3/\text{sec}$$

with the nominal values of (6.98) used.

With the dynamics of (6.102) and the control law of (6.105) and with the cost criterion as in (6.104), the problem is in the proper formulation for optimization in the space of control parameters by gradient descent as described in Section 4.4.

Results of the Optimization

The problem was coded for the computer choosing a time interval of interest of 500 sec. This was long relative to the hold time of the tank and the time constants of the stochastic processes that describe the concentration c_1. An integration step size of 2.5 sec was chosen since this was small relative to these same times.

Initial guesses for the controller gains $(K_{11}, K_{12}, K_{21}, K_{22})$ were taken from K and S, [10], where they were found by linearizing this same system about the nominal values and minimizing a similar quadratic criterion by linear quadratic, Gaussian theory as described in that text. A conversion was necessary to account for the fact that in their example tank, volume V was the measured output variable. These gains were chosen since they were known to give a good, stable initial guess and hence the number of iterations in the CG descent sequence could be expected to be small. This expectation was fulfilled. Initial conditions on concentration c_3 and V (state variables x_1 and x_2) were found by running the system over 250 sec (which was long enough to reach steady state) using the initially guessed gains in the controller. These steady-state initial conditions were then used in all subsequent iterations.

The results after nine iterations are shown in Figs. 6.29 through 6.32. Figures 6.29 and 6.30 show the time response of output concentration c_3 and volume V over 500 sec responding to variations in c_1 as shown in Fig. 6.27 with the optimized feedback controller of (6.105). The descent

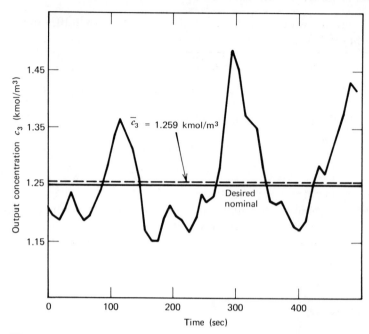

Figure 6.29 Output concentration c_3 versus time over 500 sec.

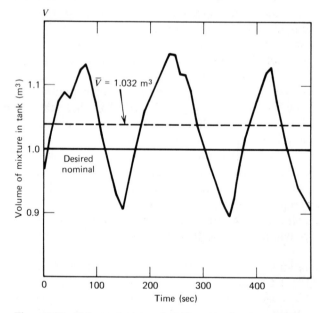

Figure 6.30 Volume of mixture in tank versus time over 500 sec.

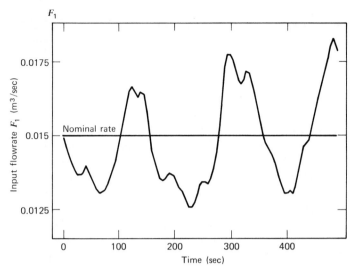

Figure 6.31 Input flow rate F_1 versus time over 500 sec.

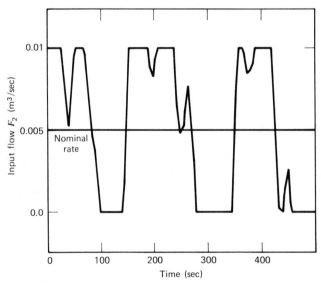

Figure 6.32 Input flow rate F_2 versus time over 500 sec.

227

sequence converged to the following gains:

$$K_{11} = 0.01272 \text{ m}^3/\text{kmol-sec}$$
$$K_{12} = -1.0106$$
$$K_{21} = -0.1276 \text{ m}^3/\text{kmol-sec} \qquad (6.106)$$
$$K_{22} = -1.681$$

K_{11} was the only gain that differed significantly from those obtained by linearization and then optimization. This particular gain increased by a factor of almost 100. The input flow rates F_1 and F_2 are shown in Figs. 6.31 and 6.32, respectively. Though input F_1 never hits the saturation limits, flow rate F_2 is on the boundary most of the time. In fact F_2 is almost of a bang–bang characteristic. For this particular case, a main limitation to the performance of the system would be the saturation limit on F_2.

The constant R, the weighting factor by which integral squared error from nominal in volume V was weighted into the cost criterion of (6.101) and (6.104), was chosen as

$$R = 0.15 \qquad (6.107)$$

This value was chosen to give approximately equal weighting to 0.1 kmol/m^3 errors in concentration c_3 as compared to 0.25 m^3 errors in volume V. This was calculated from

$$[(c_3 - c_{3_o}) = 0.1]^2 \cong R[(V - V_o) = 0.25]^2$$

As before, the value of the weighting factor R could be adjusted to give a different ratio in these two errors if the ratio of errors as seen in Figs. 6.29 and 6.30 is unsatisfactory.

Remarks

Some advantages of the above approach to the design of a controller for this system are as follows:

1. State variables and control variables are actual system quantities and not perturbations.
2. The nonlinear dynamics, including the saturation limits on the input control variables, are handled straightforwardly.
3. The controller followed directly from the available measured and control variables.
4. The criterion reflected as directly as possible what was desired in the operation of the system.
5. The nonlinear system has been optimized on the range of magnitudes of the input over which the system is expected to operate. The optimization has also been over input signals in the frequency band over which the

system is to operate. Ranges in both magnitude and frequency band are freely chosen by the designer. After such an optimization, the designer can expect to have confidence that the controller and the system as a whole will perform as expected.

Identification of Output Parameters of the Stirred Tank Mixer

Parameter optimization methods may be used for the closely related problem of system parameter identification. Basically the idea is to choose the cost criterion so that when it is at a minimum the system parameters to be identified take on their actual values. For example, let us consider a system whose actual input and output signals and dynamics to within a set of parameters are all known. Error may most logically be defined here then as the difference between the output of the system with estimated values for the unknown parameters and the known output of the actual system. Any positive definite functional on the error that has a minimum for zero error will serve as a cost criterion. By use of this cost criterion a descent sequence in the parameter space can be constructed that should converge from estimated values for the parameters to be identified to the neighborhood of the actual values of these parameters. If the presumed dynamics of the system are identical to the actual system dynamics (to within the unknown parameters), bringing the criterion on the error arbitrarily close to its minimum should bring the estimates for the parameter values arbitrarily close to the actual values—at least arbitrarily close to a set for which the output is identical.

As an example of the use of parameter optimization methods to identify system parameters, let us consider the stirred tank example considered earlier in this section and which is shown in Fig. 6.26. Let us take the output concentration c_3 and mixture in the tank volume V as output quantities. These are shown in Figs. 6.29 and 6.30 (over 500 sec) for the random variation in input concentration c_1 shown in Fig. 6.27. As an example of a system parameter identification problem, let us consider finding the average and r.m.s. value of the deviation from average for c_3 and V over the time interval shown. We assume that the feedback controller with optimized gains as given in (6.106) is in place and thus the output c_3 and V are optimized for this controller and the mean and r.m.s. values of these quantities will give a measure of the effectiveness of this controller. To identify the mean and r.m.s. value of the deviations from mean, we use the same form of cost criterion, (6.101), as used in computing the feedback gains in the controller. This is then

$$ J = \int_{t_0}^{t_f} [c_3 - \bar{c}_{3_e}]^2 \, dt + R \int_{t_0}^{t_f} [V - \bar{V}_e]^2 \, dt \qquad (6.108) $$

Here $\bar{c}_{3_e}$ and $\bar{V}_e$ (which are estimated values for the mean of concentration c_3 and volume V, respectively) replace c_{3_o} and V_o, respectively, in (6.101). The criterion of (6.108) was chosen since it is well known that for a given $c_3(t)$ over $[t_0, t_f]$ the average value $\bar{c}_3$ minimizes

$$\int_{t_0}^{t_f} [c_3(t) - \bar{c}_{3_e}]^2 \, dt$$

as a function of $\bar{c}_{3_e}$. Likewise, $\bar{V}$, the average value of $V(t)$ over $[t_0, t_f]$, minimizes

$$\int_{t_0}^{t_f} [V(t) - \bar{V}_e]^2 \, dt$$

as a function of $\bar{V}_e$. Since the first integral term on the RHS of (6.108) is independent of $\bar{V}_e$ and the second integral term is independent of $\bar{c}_{3_e}$, the two terms summed together are minimized by the values of $\bar{c}_{3_e}$ and $\bar{V}_e$, which minimize each term individually. Thus minimization of J of (6.108) w.r.t. $\bar{c}_{3_e}$ and $\bar{V}_e$ simultaneously produces both average values. Also, the r.m.s. value of the deviation from the mean is given by

$$(c_3 - \bar{c}_3)_{\text{r.m.s.}} = \left[\frac{1}{t_f - t_0} \int_{t_0}^{t_f} [c_3(t) - \bar{c}_3]^2 \, dt \right]^{1/2} \tag{6.109}$$

$$(V - \bar{V})_{\text{r.m.s.}} = \left[\frac{1}{t_f - t_0} \int_{t_0}^{t_f} [V(t) - \bar{V}]^2 \, dt \right]^{1/2} \tag{6.110}$$

Thus the value of the square integral terms in the criterion of (6.108) are directly related to the r.m.s. values sought. The approach is then to minimize J of (6.108) w.r.t. $\bar{c}_{3_e}$ and $\bar{V}_e$ to get $\bar{c}_3$ and $\bar{V}$. Then using the value of the integral terms (the minimum values) in (6.109 and 6.110) we obtain the desired r.m.s. values.

To put the problem into the proper formulation to do parameter optimization as described in Section 4.4 requires that the criterion of (6.108) be put into the $J = \phi(x(t_f))$ form. This is done by defining new state variables x_3 and x_4. The dynamics of (6.102) with $\bar{c}_{3_e}$ and $\bar{V}_e$ replacing c_{3_o} and V_o, respectively, give

$$\dot{x}_1 = \frac{(c_1 - x_1)F_1 + (c_2 - x_1)F_2}{x_2}$$

$$\dot{x}_2 = -0.02\sqrt{x_2} + F_1 + F_2 \tag{6.111}$$

$$\dot{x}_3 = (x_1 - \bar{c}_{3_e})^2$$

$$\dot{x}_4 = (x_2 - \bar{V}_e)^2$$

where the state variable assignment $x_1 = c_3$ and $x_2 = V$ has been used as in (6.102). Using the dynamics for x_3 and x_4 as given in (6.111) with zero initial conditions, we obtain

$$x_3(t_f) = \int_{t_0}^{t_f} (c_3(t) - \bar{c}_{3_e})^2 \, dt$$

$$x_4(t_f) = \int_{t_0}^{t_f} (V(t) - \bar{V}_e)^2 \, dt$$

Using these two relationships we can put the criterion of (6.108) into the desired form

$$J = x_3(t_f) + R \cdot x_4(t_f) \tag{6.112}$$

Also using these same two relationships we may write the r.m.s. values of (6.109) and (6.110) as

$$(c_3 - \bar{c}_3)_{\text{r.m.s.}} = \sqrt{\frac{x_3(t_f)}{t_f - t_0}}$$

$$(V - \bar{V})_{\text{r.m.s.}} = \sqrt{\frac{x_4(t_f)}{t_f - t_0}} \tag{6.113}$$

Results

The problem was run using as initial estimates for $\bar{c}_{3_e}$ and $\bar{V}_e$ the values of c_{3_0} and V_0 of the controller design part of the example. $R = 0.15$ was used in the criterion of (6.108 and 6.112) again because it had been used in the controller design. Three iterations brought convergence to

$$\bar{c}_{3_e} \cong \bar{c}_3 \cong 1.259 \text{ kmol/m}^3$$
$$\bar{V}_e \cong \bar{V} \cong 1.032 \text{ m}^3 \tag{6.114}$$

The values have been plotted in Figs. 6.29 and 6.30, respectively. For these values of $\bar{c}_{3_e}$ and $\bar{V}_e$, $x_3(t_f) = 3.067$ and $x_4(t_f) = 2.783$ were found. These values in (6.113) gave

$$(c_3 - \bar{c}_3)_{\text{r.m.s}} = 0.0783 \text{ kmol/m}^3$$
$$(V - \bar{V})_{\text{r.m.s.}} = 0.0746 \text{ m}^3 \tag{6.115}$$

Equations 6.114 and 6.115 give the desired average and r.m.s. values for the output concentration and mixture volume. These quantities tell how well the objectives (in the design of the controller) of obtaining a constant nominal output concentration of 1.25 kmol/m^3 and constant mixture volume in the tank of 1.0 m^3 have been met. The average values of (6.114) can, for this particular input concentration c_1, be brought to the desired nominal values by suitable adjustment of the nominal values in the controller of Fig. 6.28. Some tradeoff in the r.m.s. values of (6.115) can be achieved by adjusting the weighting factor R in (6.101) and (6.104) and evaluating the controller gains accordingly. Significant reduction in these r.m.s. values could only be achieved by getting a more responsive tank. Looking at the dynamics of (6.97), this would mean either a smaller mean value for V (which would mean a smaller hold time and hence a reduced degree of mixing in the tank) or larger values for the input and output flow rates F_1, F_2, and F_3.

REFERENCES

[1]   Northrop-Norair Report NOR 68-134 Section 4, Subsystem Design (LSI).

[2]   Greif, R. K., E. B. Fry, R. M. Gerdes, and T. D. Gossett, "VTOL Control Systems Studies on a Six Degree of Freedom Simulator," *Congr. Int. Council Aero Sci., 5th, London,* **1966**.

[3]   Hasdorff, L., L. D. Corliss, and T. D. Gossett, "Design of a Model Following, State Variable Feedback Controller for the X-14 VTOL Aircraft," *Conf. Rec. Asilomar Conf. Circuits Syst., 4th, Pacific Grove, California,* **1970**.

[4]   Newton, G. C., Jr., L. A. Gould, and J. F. Kaiser, *Analytical Design of Linear Feedback Controls,* Appendix E, Wiley, 1957.

[5]   Corliss, L. D., and T. D. Gossett, "A Study of the Quadratic Performance Index for a VTOL Prefilter Model Reference Attitude Control System," *Proc. Guid., Control Flight Dyn. Conf., Princeton,* **1969**.

[6]   Tyler, J. S., Jr., and F. B. Tuteur, "The Use of a Quadratic Performance Index to Design Multivariable Control Systems," *IEEE Trans. Autom. Control,* **AC-11**, 84 (Jan. 1966).

[7]   Tyler, J. S., Jr., "The Characteristics of Model Following Systems as Synthesized by Optimal Control," *IEEE Trans. Autom. Control,* **AC-9**, 485 (Oct. 1964).

[8]   Gupta, S. C., and L. Hasdorff, *Fundamentals of Automatic Control,* Wiley, 1970.

[9]   Schultz, D. G., and J. L. Melsa, *State Functions and Linear Control Systems,* McGraw-Hill, 1967.

[10] Kwakernaak, H., and R. Sivan, *Linear Optimal Control Systems,* Chapter 1, Wiley-Interscience, 1972.

[11] Hasdorff, L. "The Use of Stochastic Test Signals to Design Controllers by Gradient Methods," *Proc. SWIEEECO, Dellas,* April 1972.

Appendix A

Properties of a Positive-Definite Linear Operator

A.1. EXISTENCE OF AN INVERSE

We here prove the following theorem.

Theorem A.1.   Given a positive-definite linear operator A from Hilbert space $\mathscr{E}$ to $\mathscr{E}$, then the inverse of A, A^{-1}, exists.

Since we can find no proof for this useful theorem we attempt one here.

Lemma A.1.   The range of A is the whole space $\mathscr{E}$.

We assume there exists a vector $y \in \mathscr{E}$ such that no $x \in \mathscr{E}$ exists such that $y = Ax$, that is, y is not in the range of A, which we call RA. The range of a linear operator is a linear subspace. We have assumed then that $RA \subset \mathscr{E}$, that is, it is a proper subspace of $\mathscr{E}$. We have the following theorem†

If $\mathscr{M}$ and $\mathscr{N}$ are subspaces such that $\mathscr{M} \subset \mathscr{N}$ and $\mathscr{M} \neq \mathscr{N}$ then there exists a nonzero vector z in $\mathscr{N}$ such that $z \perp \mathscr{M}$ (z is orthogonal to $\mathscr{M}$).

Applying this theorem we have that a vector z, not zero, exists which is orthogonal to RA. This means $\langle z, Az \rangle = 0$. However this contradicts the positive definiteness of A. Thus the assumption that a vector $y \in \mathscr{E}$ exists that is not in the range of A is wrong, which proves the lemma.

Lemma A.2.   The operator A is a one to one mapping of $\mathscr{E}$ into $\mathscr{E}$, that is,

$$Ax_1 = Ax_2 \Rightarrow x_1 = x_2$$

† Theorem 2 of Section 11 in [6] in References to Chapter 2.

To show this we assume $x_1 \neq x_2$ exist such that $Ax_1 = Ax_2$. Then

$$Ax_1 - Ax_2 = A(x_1 - x_2) = 0$$
$$(x_1 - x_2) \neq 0$$

But then

$$\langle (x_1 - x_2), A(x_1 - x_2) \rangle = 0$$

This again contradicts the assumption of positive definiteness of A which proves the lemma.

By Lemma A.1 the operator A is onto and by Lemma A.2 it is one to one. By definition then the inverse of A exists, which proves the theorem.

A.2. INDEPENDENCE OF CONJUGATE VECTORS

We here consider a set of nonzero vectors $p_0, p_1, p_2, \ldots, p_{n-1}$ that are conjugate w.r.t. a linear, positive-definite operator A from Hilbert space $\mathscr{E}$ to $\mathscr{E}$. By conjugate here we mean

$$\langle p_i, Ap_j \rangle = 0 \qquad \text{if} \quad i \neq j$$
$$\neq 0 \qquad \text{if} \quad i = j$$

Since A is assumed positive $\langle p_i, Ap_i \rangle > 0$. We here show the following theorem:

Theorem A.2.   If the dimension of $\mathscr{E}$ is greater than $n - 1$, then $p_0, p_1, \ldots,$ p_{n-1} are linearly independent if they are conjugate w.r.t. a positive-definite operator A.

If the dimension of $\mathscr{E}$ is equal to or less than $n - 1$, a set of n vectors cannot all be linearly independent, by definition. The proof is by contradiction.

Proof.   Let us assume

$$p_j = \sum_{\substack{i=0 \\ i \neq j}}^{n-1} \alpha_i p_i \tag{A.1}$$

where α_i are not all zero, that is, p_j is linearly dependent. Now evaluating α_i, we have

$$Ap_j = \sum_{\substack{i=0 \\ i \neq j}}^{n-1} \alpha_i Ap_i$$

and

$$\langle p_k, Ap_j \rangle = \sum_{\substack{i=0 \\ i \neq j}}^{n-1} \alpha_i \langle p_k, Ap_i \rangle$$

However $k \neq j$, and use of conjugacy on the above equation gives

$$0 = \alpha_k \langle p_k, A p_k \rangle$$

Now since A is assumed positive-definite $\langle p_k, A p_k \rangle > 0$, which implies therefore that

$$\alpha_k = 0$$

But this is true for $k = 0, 1, \ldots, n - 1, k \neq j$. Therefore the assumption that p_j could be written as in (A.1) with α_k not all zero, that is, p_j is linearly dependent, leads to a contradiction, which proves the theorem.

Appendix B

Some Practical Aspects of the Problem of Finding α to Minimize $F(x_i + \alpha p_i)$ in the Application of Conjugate Gradient Descent

If conjugate gradient descent as described in (3.63) is to be used in producing a descent sequence for a given functional F on Hilbert space $\mathcal{H}$, then at every step in the sequence one is faced with the problem of finding α to minimize $F(x_i + \alpha p_i)$. Here $x_i, p_i \in \mathcal{H}$ are the ith element of the descent sequence and the ith descent direction, respectively. In Section 3.4 where conjugate gradient descent is discussed it is suggested that this may be accomplished by a one-dimensional search. It is our purpose to discuss the method of search used in the conjugate gradient descent program by which the examples in Part Two of this text were calculated, and which is described in Appendix G.

The difficulty of this problem will in general depend on how well the functional F is known. If it is a quadratic functional of the type considered in Section 3.3, that is, of (3.15), then from (3.16c) immediately we have that

$$\alpha_i = \frac{\langle g_i, g_i \rangle}{\langle p_i, A p_i \rangle} \tag{B.1}$$

where A is the second derivative operator of our functional, see (3.15), and $g_i = g(x_i)$ is the gradient at x_i. Of course if the functionals that one is dealing with are quadratic, then α should be determined as in (B.1). The problem

236

arises from the fact that we wish to treat a functional using conjugate gradient descent as described in (3.63), which is not necessarily quadratic. As a practical consideration we would prefer a method of finding the minimizing α for $F(x_i + \alpha p_i)$, which does not require any additional assumption on the functional F beyond those otherwise needed in applying (3.63). These assumptions are basically as follows:

1. F is a smooth functional.
2. $F(x)$ and $g(x)$ can be evaluated for any $x \in \mathcal{H}$.

One method† of finding α_i to minimize $F(x_i + \alpha p_i)$ follows; for convenience we use

$$f(\alpha) \triangleq F(x_i + \alpha p_i) \tag{B.2}$$

1. Estimate the minimum of $f(\alpha)$ by assuming that $f(\alpha)$ is quadratic in α. Call this estimate $\bar{\alpha}_i$.
2. Search for the minimum of $f(\alpha)$ in steps that are powers of two multiples of $\bar{\alpha}_i$. More precisely evaluate $f(\alpha_k)$ for

$$\begin{aligned} \alpha_k &= 2^k \cdot \bar{\alpha}_i &&\text{if} \quad f(\bar{\alpha}_i) < f(0) \\ &= 2^{-k} \cdot \bar{\alpha}_i &&\text{if} \quad f(\bar{\alpha}_i) \geq f(0) \\ k &= 1, 2, 3 \end{aligned}$$

The search is terminated for that value of k for which

$$f(\alpha_k) > f(\alpha_{k-1})$$

3. Fit a third order polynomial through

$$f(\alpha_{k-2}), \; f(\alpha_{k-1}), \; f\left(\frac{\alpha_{k-1} + \alpha_k}{2}\right), \; f(\alpha_k)$$

and find α_i (the end result of the minimizing process) by finding the value of α that minimizes this third order polynomial between α_{k-2} and α_k.

Let us now briefly discuss these three steps.

B.1. ESTIMATING THE MINIMUM OF $f(\alpha) = F(x_i + \alpha p_i)$

As mentioned in step 1, the estimate is made by assuming that $F(x_i + \alpha p_i)$ is quadratic. Truncating the Taylor series of $F(x_i + \alpha p_i)$ about the origin at the second term gives

$$\begin{aligned} F(x_i + \alpha p_i) &= F(x_i) + \alpha F'(x_i)p_i + \tfrac{1}{2}\alpha^2 F''(x_i + \zeta p_i)p_i \cdot p_i \\ &= F(x_i) + \alpha \langle g_i, p_i \rangle + \tfrac{1}{2}\alpha^2 \langle p_i, A(x_i + \zeta p_i)p_i \rangle \quad 0 \leq \zeta \leq \alpha \end{aligned} \tag{B.3}$$

† This method is essentially as suggested in Fletcher and Reeves, [5] in References for Chapter 3.

which is just (3.61). By use of (3.63c) and (3.64), (B.3) becomes

$$F(x_i + \alpha p_i) \cong F(x_i) - \alpha \langle g_i, g_i \rangle + \tfrac{1}{2}\alpha^2 \langle p_i, A(x_i)p_i \rangle \tag{B.4}$$

where we have simply used $\zeta = 0$.

The minimum on the RHS of (B.4) is given by

$$\alpha = \frac{\langle g_i, g_i \rangle}{\langle p_i, A(x_i)p_i \rangle} \tag{B.5}$$

which we have seen already, (B.1), as the value of α that minimizes $F(x_i + \alpha p_i)$ when F is quadratic. Looking at (B.4) and (B.5), at the ith step in the conjugate gradient descent method of (3.63), $F(x_i)$ and g_i are known. However $\langle p_i, A(x_i)p_i \rangle$ is not known. An approximate value for this quantity can be found by evaluating $F(x_i + \alpha p_i)$ for $\alpha = a_0 > 0$, a guessed value, and then evaluating (B.4) for $\langle p_i, A_i(x_i)p_i \rangle$. Thus

$$F(x_i + a_0 p_i) \cong F(x_i) - a_0 \langle g_i, g_i \rangle + \tfrac{1}{2}a_0^2 \langle p_i, A(x_i)p_i \rangle$$

$$\langle p_i, A(x_i)p_i \rangle \cong \frac{2[F(x_i + a_0 p_i) - F(x_i) + a_0 \langle g_i, g_i \rangle]}{a_0^2} \tag{B.6}$$

Equation B.6 used in B.5 gives the value desired

$$\bar{\alpha}_i = \frac{a_0^2 \langle g_i, g_i \rangle}{2[F(x_i + a_0 p_i) - F(x_i) + a_0 \langle g_i, g_i \rangle]} \tag{B.7}$$

The quantities in the expression on the RHS are all available under the assumptions necessary to do conjugate gradient descent, so $\bar{\alpha}_i$ of (B.7) can be evaluated.

A word is in order here about the selection of the value of a_0. Obviously it should be on the same order of magnitude as $\bar{\alpha}_i$. In fact, if $F(x_i + \alpha p_i)$ is symmetrical about the minimum value α^*, that is,

$$F(x_i + (\alpha^* + \varepsilon)p_i) = F(x_i + (\alpha^* - \varepsilon)p_i)$$

then the second order approximation to F has a minimum at α^*, the minimum of F if $a_0 = 2\alpha^*$. This is shown in Fig. B.1. As an estimate for α the program discussed in Appendix G uses the geometric mean of the past values of α_i found by the program; that is, a_0 at the ith step is chosen as

$$a_0 = (\alpha_0 \alpha_1 \ldots \alpha_{i-1})^{1/i} \tag{B.8}$$

For the initial step, that is, $i = 0$, a_0 is chosen so as to give

$$F(x_0 + a_0 p_0) - F(x_0) \cong 0.03\, F(x_0)$$

that is, a 3% change in F. Three percent is a sheer guess. a_0 can then be

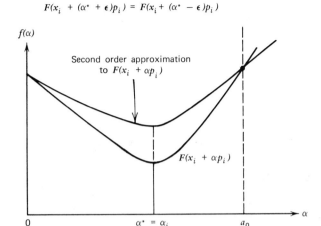

$$F(x_i + (\alpha^* + \epsilon)p_i) = F(x_i + (\alpha^* - \epsilon)p_i)$$

Second order approximation
to $F(x_i + \alpha p_i)$

$F(x_i + \alpha p_i)$

$\alpha^* = \alpha_i$ a_0

Figure B.1 $f(\alpha)$ versus α.

calculated under the assumption that $F(x_0 + a_0 p_0)$ is linear in a_0 near $a_0 = 0$, which gives

$$a_0 = \frac{0.03F(x_0)}{\langle g_0, g_0 \rangle} \tag{B.9}$$

using $p_0 = -g_0$ from (3.63a).

B.2. THE SEARCH FOR THE MINIMUM OF $f(\alpha) = F(x_i + \alpha p_i)$

The search described in step 2 proceeds by doubling the step size of $\bar{\alpha}_i$ as determined in step 1, if

$$f(\bar{\alpha}_i) < f(0)$$

Otherwise the step size is halved at each step. This halving or doubling is continued until the minimum has been passed.

B.3. FITTING THE THIRD ORDER POLYNOMIAL

The third order polynomial is fit to the points as mentioned in step 3 above. The minimum is sought between α_{k-2} and α_k since the search in step 2 indicates that this is where the minimum should occur. If the polynomial found has no minimum in this range, the α_i for this step can be chosen as α_{k-1} or $\frac{1}{2}(\alpha_{k-1} + \alpha_k)$ depending on which of these produces the lower value of the function $F(x_i + \alpha p_i)$.

Appendix C

Solution to the Differential
Equation $\dot{x} = A(t)x + B(t)u$

In considering linear, time-varying systems the underlying differential equation is of the form

$$\dot{x} = A(t)x + B(t)u \tag{C.1}$$

where now x is an n-vector (i.e., $x \in \mathscr{R}^n$), u (the control) is an m-vector (i.e., $u \in \mathscr{R}^m$), and $A(t)$ and $B(t)$ are, respectively, $n \times n$ and $n \times m$ matrix functions of the time variable t. We seek the solution of (C.1) at some general time t, that is, $x(t)$, given, $x(t_0)$ the initial condition at time t_0 and the control input u over the time interval $[t_0, t]$, that is, $u_{[t_0, t]}$. We assume $A(t)$, $B(t)$, and u bounded over all $t \geq t_0$, so that the solution to (C.1) sought does exist.

The solution of the form required here is

$$x(t) = \Phi(t, t_0)x(t_0) + \int_{t_0}^{t} \Phi(t, \tau)B(\tau)u(\tau)\,d\tau \tag{C.2}$$

where now $\Phi(\cdot, \cdot)$ is the $n \times n$ matrix solution of the differential equation

$$\frac{d}{dt}\Phi(t, \tau) = A(t)\Phi(t, \tau): \Phi(\tau, \tau) = I \tag{C.3}$$

where now I is the $n \times n$ identity matrix and A is the system matrix of (C.1). Differentiating (C.2) w.r.t. t and using (C.3) shows straightforwardly that $x(t)$ of (C.2) satisfies (C.1). We also may note that by the initial condition on the defining equation on $\Phi(\cdot, \cdot)$, that is (C.3),

$$\Phi(t_0, t_0) = I$$

and so the solution of (C.2) does pass through $x(t_0)$ for $t = t_0$.

Equations C.2 and C.3 give a closed-form solution to (C.1), however trial will show that these equations are not very suitable for computing or constructing solutions to (C.1). The difficulty is that (C.3) gives a means of finding the matrix $\Phi(t, \tau)$ as a function of the variable t. What is required to find $x(t)$, a solution at time t, by (C.2) is $\Phi(t, \tau)$ as a function of τ for all $\tau \in [t_0, t]$. We seek a defining relationship for $\Phi(t, \tau)$ in terms of the variable τ.

To find this we consider the system of (C.1) unforced, that is, with $u = 0$ for all $t \geq t_0$, or

$$\dot{x} = A(t)x \tag{C.4}$$

Using (C.2) we obtain

$$x(t) = \Phi(t, t_0)x(t_0) \tag{C.5}$$

$$x(\tau) = \Phi(\tau, t_0)x(t_0) \tag{C.6}$$

and also

$$x(t) = \Phi(t, \tau)x(\tau) \tag{C.7}$$

Using $x(\tau)$ from (C.6) in (C.7) and equating (C.7) and (C.5), we get

$$x(t) = \Phi(t, t_0)x(t_0) = \Phi(t, \tau)\Phi(\tau, t_0)x(t_0)$$

which must hold now for arbitrary $x(t_0)$ and thus

$$\Phi(t, t_0) = \Phi(t, \tau)\Phi(\tau, t_0) \tag{C.8}$$

We find now by differentiating w.r.t. τ that

$$0 = \left\{ \frac{d}{d\tau} \Phi(t, \tau) \right\} \Phi(\tau, t_0) + \Phi(t, \tau) \frac{d}{d\tau} \Phi(\tau, t_0) \tag{C.9}$$

Now $(d/d\tau)\Phi(\tau, t_0)$ may be evaluated using (C.3) with $t \to \tau, \tau \to t_0$ to give

$$\left\{ \frac{d}{d\tau} \Phi(t, \tau) + \Phi(t, \tau)A(\tau) \right\} \Phi(\tau, t_0) = 0 \tag{C.10}$$

Equation C.10 must apply for arbitrary t_0 and, in particular, $t_0 = \tau$ so that

$$\frac{d}{d\tau} \Phi(t, \tau) + \Phi(t, \tau)A(\tau) = 0$$

or

$$\frac{d}{d\tau} \Phi(t, \tau) = -\Phi(t, \tau)A(\tau): \ \Phi(t, t) = I \tag{C.11}$$

which is the desired result. The terminal condition in (C.11) is obtained from (C.3) by letting $\tau = t$ in the terminal condition there.

To construct $x(t)$, a solution to (C.1) at time t, we can thus do the following:

1. Integrate (C.11) backwards in τ from t to t_0 to obtain $\Phi(t, \tau)$ for $\tau \in [t_0, t]$.
2. Use $\Phi(t, \tau)$ obtained in step 1 in (C.2) to evaluate $x(t)$.

Appendix D

The Adjoint System

In Section 4.3 the vector function of time $\lambda(t)$ is defined by

$$\lambda(t) \triangleq \Phi^+(t_f, t)\nabla_x \phi(x(t_f, u)) \qquad \text{(D.1)†}$$

where now $\Phi(\cdot, \cdot)$ is $n \times n$ matrix function that satisfies a differential equation of the form

$$\frac{d}{dt}\Phi(t, \tau) = A(t)\Phi(t, \tau)\colon \Phi(\tau, \tau) = I \qquad \text{(D.2)}$$

where $A(t)$ is an $n \times n$ matrix function of time and I is the $n \times n$ identity matrix. $\phi(\cdot)$ is a scalar-valued function on $\mathcal{R}^n$. In (D.1)

$$\nabla_x \phi(x(t_f, u))$$

is the gradient of ϕ w.r.t. x evaluated at $x(t_f, u)$.

We here wish to show that $\lambda(t)$, as defined in (D.1) with $\Phi(\cdot, \cdot)$ satisfying (D.2), satisfies

$$\dot\lambda = -A^+(t)\lambda\colon \lambda(t_f) = \nabla_x \phi(x(t_f, u)) \qquad \text{(D.3)†}$$

To show that we use a result obtained in Appendix C where (D.2) has already been encountered in (C.3). There it is found that $\Phi(\cdot, \cdot)$ satisfying (D.2) or (C.3) also satisfies, from (C.11),

$$\frac{d}{d\tau}\Phi(t, \tau) = -\Phi(t, \tau)A(\tau)\colon \Phi(t, t) = I \qquad \text{(D.4)}$$

---

† Superscript $+$ indicates transpose.

In (D.4) letting $t = t_f$ and $\tau = t$ and taking the transpose gives

$$\frac{d}{dt}\Phi^+(t_f, t) = -A^+(t)\Phi^+(t_f, t): \Phi^+(t_f, t_f) = I$$

Postmultiplying the matrix differential equation by $\nabla_x\phi(x(t_f, u))$ maintains the equality, since it is not a function of t, and gives

$$\frac{d}{dt}\Phi^+(t_f, t)\nabla_x\phi(x(t_f, u)) = -A^+(t)\Phi^+(t_f, t)\nabla_x\phi(x(t_f, u)) \quad \text{(D.5)}$$

The terminal condition is, from (D.1),

$$\begin{aligned} \lambda(t_f) &= \Phi^+(t_f, t_f)\nabla_x\phi(x(t_f, u)) \\ &= \nabla_x\phi(x(t_f, u)) \end{aligned} \quad \text{(D.6)}$$

since $\Phi^+(t_f, t_f) = I$. Using the definition of λ of (D.1) in (D.5) with the terminal condition of (D.6), we get (D.3), the desired result. Equation D.3 is the adjoint system to the one of (C.1).

Appendix E

A State Transition Matrix Solution to a System of Linear, Time-Varying, Difference-Differential Equations

Let us consider the system of linear, time-varying, difference-differential equations of the form

$$\frac{d}{dt} x(t) = A(t)x(t) + A_d(t)x(t - T) + B(t)u(t) \tag{E.1}$$

where now $x \in \mathscr{R}^n$, $u \in \mathscr{R}^m$, T is a positive scalar, $A(t)$ and $A_d(t)$ are $n \times n$ matrices, and $B(t)$ is an $n \times m$ matrix. It is assumed A, A_d, and B are time varying and in general such that (E.1) has a unique solution for an integrable control input. To specify the solution to (E.1) for $t > t_0$ we must know

$$x(t) \qquad \text{for} \qquad t_0 - T \le t < t_0 \tag{E.2}$$

since it can be seen from (E.1) that $\dot{x}(t)$ for $t_0 \le t < t_0 + T$ depends on $x(t)$ as given in (E.2). $x(t)$ defined in the interval given by (E.2) is termed the precondition for the solution of (E.1).

The solution of (E.1) with a precondition as in (E.2) may be written in terms of a state transition matrix for (E.1) as

$$x(t) = \Phi(t, t_0)x(t_0) + \int_{t_0}^{t} \Phi(t, \tau)B(\tau)u(\tau) \, d\tau$$

$$+ \int_{t_0}^{t} \Phi(t, \tau)A_d(\tau)x(\tau - T)\{1(\tau - t_0) - 1(\tau - t_0 - T)\} \, d\tau \tag{E.3}$$

244

where $1(t)$ is the unit step function and thus

$$1(\tau - t_0) - 1(\tau - t_0 - T) = 1 \qquad t_0 < \tau < t_0 + T$$
$$= 0 \qquad \text{otherwise}$$

$\Phi(t, \tau)$ here is the state transition matrix that satisfies

$$\frac{d}{dt}\Phi(t, \tau) = A(t)\Phi(t, \tau) + A_d(t)\Phi(t - T, \tau)$$

$$\Phi(\tau, \tau) = I \tag{E.4}$$

$$\Phi(t, \tau) = \mathbf{0} \qquad t < \tau$$

That (E.3) is a solution to (E.1) may be checked simply by differentiation of (E.3) w.r.t. t using (E.4) to evaluate $d\Phi(t, \cdot)/dt$.

To evaluate $x(t)$ for a given input control $u_{[t_0, t]}$ and precondition as given by (E.2), $\Phi(t, \tau)$ must be known as a function of the second variable τ for $t_0 \le \tau \le t$. Equation E.4 is not well suited for the production of $\Phi(t, \tau)$ as a function of the variable τ since it is a difference-differential equation w.r.t. the first variable t. So let us seek a relationship by which $\Phi(t, \tau)$ may be found explicitly as a function of the variable τ.

To do this, we consider a solution to (E.1) with the control input null, that is, $u(t) = 0$ for all t, and also $x(t) = 0$ for $t < t_0$, that is, with zero precondition, and $x(t_0)$ arbitrary. Under this assumption, (E.3) gives

$$x(t_f) = \Phi(t_f, t_0)x(t_0) \tag{E.5a}$$

$$x(t) = \Phi(t, t_0)x(t_0) \tag{E.5b}$$

where we assume $t_0 \le t \le t_f$. The solution at time t_f may also be written starting at time t. Using (E.3) we get

$$x(t_f) = \left(\Phi(t_f, t)x(t) + \int_t^{t_f} \Phi(t_f, \tau)A_d(\tau)x(\tau - T)\{1(\tau - t) - 1(\tau - t - T)\}\, d\tau \right)$$

Using (E.5b) to evaluate $x(t)$ and $x(t - T)$ and recognizing that the integrand on the RHS just above is null for $\tau < t$ we have

$$x(t_f) = \left(\Phi(t_f, t)\Phi(t, t_0) + \int_{t_0}^{t_f} \Phi(t_f, \tau)A_d(\tau)\Phi(\tau - T, t_0)\{1(\tau - t)\right.$$
$$\left. - 1(\tau - t - T)\}\, d\tau \right)x(t_0)$$

Comparing this result with (E.5a) and realizing that $x(t_0)$ is arbitrary, we get

$$\Phi(t_f, t_0) = \Phi(t_f, t)\Phi(t, t_0) + \int_{t_0}^{t_f} \Phi(t_f, \tau)A_d(\tau)\Phi(\tau - T, t_0)\{1(\tau - t)$$
$$- 1(\tau - t - T)\}\, d\tau \tag{E.6}$$

Now the LHS of (E.6) does not involve t. Thus differentiating (E.6) w.r.t. t and using (E.4), we get

$$0 = \left(\frac{d}{dt}\Phi(t_f, t) + \Phi(t_f, t)A(t) + \Phi(t_f, t + T)A_d(t + T)\right)\Phi(t, t_0) \quad (E.7)$$

Equation (E.7) must hold for arbitrary $t_0 \le t \le t_f$, and particularly for $t_0 = t$; hence

$$0 = \frac{d}{dt}\Phi(t_f, t) + \Phi(t_f, t)A(t) + \Phi(t_f, t + T)A_d(t + T)$$

Now letting $t \to \tau$, $t_f \to t$ and using the terminal conditions of (E.4), we have

$$\frac{d}{d\tau}\Phi(t, \tau) = -\Phi(t, \tau)A(\tau) - \Phi(t, \tau + T)A_d(\tau + T)$$

$$\Phi(t, t) = I \qquad\qquad\qquad (E.8)$$

$$\Phi(t, \tau) = 0 \qquad \tau > t$$

The last relationship implies

$$\Phi(t, \tau + T) = 0 \qquad \tau > (t - T) \qquad (E.8a)$$

Equation E.8 is the desired result.

To produce a general solution for a system (linear, time-varying, difference-differential) as in (E.1) the following steps must be taken:

1. Integrate (E.8) from t to t_0, that is, backwards.
2. Using the so-found $\Phi(t, t_0)$ and $\Phi(t, \tau)$, $t_0 \le \tau \le t$ write the solution as in (E.3) for general input $u(t)$, $t_0 \le \tau \le t$, precondition $x(\tau)$, $t_0 - T \le \tau < t_0$ and initial condition $x(t_0)$.

E.1. THE ADJOINT SYSTEM

Let us consider the system of (E.1) now with state transition matrix $\Phi(\cdot, \cdot)$ satisfying (E.4) and (E.8) and let us consider the vector-valued function of time τ.

$$\lambda(\tau) = \Phi^+(t_f, \tau)\lambda(t_f) \qquad (E.9)$$

where now $t_f \ge \tau$ and $\lambda(t_f)$ is an n-vector, that is, $\lambda(t_f) \in \mathscr{R}^n$. From the terminal condition of (E.4) and (E.8) and with (E.9)

$$\lambda(t_f) = \Phi^+(t_f, t_f)\lambda(t_f)$$
$$= \lambda(t_f)$$

since $\Phi(t_f, t_f) = \Phi^+(t_f, t_f) = I$.

We seek the system satisfied by $\lambda(\tau)$ over the interval $t_0 \leq \tau \leq t_f$, which is the adjoint system. This we find by transposing (E.8) and evaluating at $t = t_f$, which gives

$$\frac{d}{d\tau} \Phi^+(t_f, \tau) = -A^+(\tau)\Phi^+(t_f, \tau)$$

$$-A_d^+(\tau + T)\Phi^+(t_f, \tau + T) \qquad \Phi^+(t_f, t_f) = I$$

Postmultiplying the above differential equation by the constant vector $\lambda(t_f)$, which is admissible since $\lambda(t_f)$ is not a function of τ, we get

$$\frac{d}{d\tau} \Phi^+(t_f, \tau)\lambda(t_f) = -A^+(\tau)\Phi^+(t_f, \tau)\lambda(t_f)$$

$$-A_d^+(\tau + T)\Phi^+(t_f, \tau + T)\lambda(t_f)$$

$$\Phi^+(t_f, t_f)\lambda(t_f) = \lambda(t_f)$$

and using (E.9) on this equation we get

$$\frac{d}{d\tau} \lambda(\tau) = -A^+(\tau)\lambda(\tau) - A_d^+(\tau + T)\lambda(\tau + T)$$
(E.10)

$$\lambda(t_f) = \Phi^+(t_f, t_f)\lambda(t_f) = \lambda(t_f)$$

$$\lambda(\tau) = \mathbf{0}, \tau > t_f$$

which is the system adjoint to (E.1).

Appendix F

Solution to the Discrete, Linear System $x_{k+1} = A_k x_k + B_k u_k$

Let us consider the discrete, linear system

$$x_{k+1} = A_k x_k + B_k u_k: k = 0, 1, 2, \ldots \tag{F.1}$$

where $x_k \in \mathcal{R}^n$, $u_k \in \mathcal{R}^m$, and A_k and B_k are, respectively, $n \times n$ and $n \times m$ matrices for all $k \geq 0$. We assume that for $k = 0$ the system is in a known state x_0 and that u_k, the control input, is known for all $k \geq 0$. We seek an explicit solution for (F.1), by which is meant that for a general $N > 0$ we seek x_N in terms of A_k, B_k, u_k, and x_0 for $0 \leq k \leq N$.

The solution is obtained by iteration, as follows:

$$x_1 = A_0 x_0 + B_0 u_0$$

$$x_2 = A_1 x_1 + B_1 u_1 = A_1 A_0 x_0 + A_1 B_0 u_1 + B_1 u_1$$

$$x_3 = A_2 x_2 + B_2 u_2 = A_2 A_1 A_0 x_0 + A_2 A_1 B_0 u_0 + A_2 B_1 u_1 + B_2 u_2$$

$$\vdots \quad \vdots \quad \vdots \quad \vdots \quad \vdots$$

$$x_N = A_{N-1} x_{N-1} + B_{N-1} u_{N-1} = \left(\prod_{k=0}^{N-1} A_k \right) x_0 + \sum_{i=0}^{N-1} \left(\prod_{k=i+1}^{N-1} A_k \right) B_i u_i$$

$$\tag{F.2}$$

The notation on the RHS of (F.2) requires some explanation of the matrix product notation used. Here

$$\prod_{k=0}^{N-1} A_k = A_{N-1} A_{N-2} A_{N-3} \ldots A_1 A_0 \tag{F.3}$$

that is, the product is such that the index decreases monotonically to the right. This is important here because matrix multiplication generally is not commutative. Also we have used the convention

$$\prod_{k=N-1}^{N-1} A_k = A_{N-1}$$

and

$$\prod_{k=N}^{N-1} A_k = I \tag{F.4}$$

for any A_k and where I is the $n \times n$ identity matrix. Expansion of the RHS of (F.2) for $N = 1, 2, 3, \ldots$ with the conventions on the matrix product as given in (F.3) and (F.4) gives the sequence obtained above (F.2), which is the desired result.

F.1. THE ADJOINT SYSTEM

Just as the continuous time system $\dot{x} = Ax + Bu$ (considered in Appendix C) has an associated adjoint system (considered in Appendix D), the discrete system of (F.1) also has an associated adjoint system. The system that is adjoint to the discrete system of (F.1) is given by

$$\lambda_k = A_k^+ \lambda_{k+1} \tag{F.5}$$

where now $\lambda \in \mathscr{R}^n$ is the adjoint state vector and A_k is the $n \times n$ system matrix of (F.1). We note the similarity of the adjoint system here as compared with the adjoint system for the continuous time case ($\dot{x} = Ax + Bu$), which is

$$\dot{\lambda} = -A^+\lambda \tag{F.6}$$

We also note that (F.5) is in a form to produce the adjoint vector λ_k for decreasing values of the index k.

We consider now the solution of the adjoint system of (F.5). Assuming that the adjoint vector is λ_N for $k = N$, we have from (F.5)

$$\lambda_{N-1} = A_{N-1}^+ \lambda_N$$

$$\lambda_{N-2} = A_{N-2}^+ \lambda_{N-1} = A_{N-2}^+ A_{N-1}^+ \lambda_N$$

$$\lambda_{N-3} = A_{N-3}^+ \lambda_{N-2} = A_{N-3}^+ A_{N-2}^+ A_{N-1}^+ \lambda_N$$

$$\vdots \qquad\qquad \vdots \qquad\qquad \vdots$$

$$\lambda_i = A_i^+ \lambda_{i+1} \quad = \left(\prod_{k=i}^{N-1} A_k \right)^+ \lambda_N \tag{F.7}$$

Equation F.7 is the solution of the adjoint system of (F.5) for $k = i$ with λ_N given, and it is the desired result.

Appendix G

A Program for Conjugate Gradient Descent

G.1. INTRODUCTION

The examples as given in this text with the exception of the ones with delay in the dynamics have all been computed with a single general purpose computer program. The purpose of this appendix is to show the general formulation for the problem attacked by the program as an illustration of one way of implementing the theory presented in this text.

G.2. STATEMENT OF THE PROBLEM

The program considers a system with state vector $x \in \mathscr{R}^n$. System trajectories are assumed to satisfy

$$\dot{x} = f(x, u): x(t_0) = c \tag{G.1}$$

where $f(\cdot, \cdot)$ is a function whose range is in $\mathscr{R}^n$ and u is the control input, which may be any of the several forms specified below. t_0 is the initial time. A criterion J on the operation of the system is assumed of the form

$$J = \phi(x(t_f)) \tag{G.2}$$

where $\phi(\cdot)$ is a real-valued function on $\mathscr{R}^n$ and where $x(t_f)$ is the state of the system at time t_f, the final time. The time interval of interest is thus $[t_0, t_f]$. The basic assumptions made here are as follows:

   1. f is such that unique, bounded solutions (starting at $x(t_0) = c$) exist for

bounded $\|u\|$ and can be found by numerical integration of the differential equation (G.1).

2. f has partial derivatives w.r.t. all components of x and u for $\|x\|$ and $\|u\|$ bounded.

3. ϕ has partial derivatives w.r.t. all components of x for $\|x\|$ bounded.

The basic problem considered by the program is then to find u such that J is a minimum.

The program considers this problem in the basic three cases where u is

1. A piecewise continuous function over $[t_0, t_f]$,
2. A set of system parameters.
3. A set of initial conditions for (G.1).

G.3. BASIC METHOD OF SOLUTION

The basic method of solution used by the program is to construct a conjugate gradient descent sequence u^0, u^1, ... starting at an initial guess u^0. The number of terms constructed is specified by the user. The program stops if no u^{i+1} can be found such that

$$J(u^{i+1}) < J(u^i)$$

In general with conjugate gradient descent this should not occur unless the gradient is null, which indicates that a relative minima of J has been reached. The program is designed to do all this automatically once the function f of (G.1), ϕ of (G.2) with the initial condition c on (G.1), and the initial guess u^0 and subsidiary functions and information required in the computations are submitted.

G.4. CONJUGATE GRADIENT DESCENT ALGORITHM

The algorithm used by the program considers a real-valued functional $F(\cdot)$ on a Hilbert space $\mathscr{H}$ with typical element U. We seek $U \in \mathscr{H}$ that minimizes $F(U)$. With conjugate gradient descent a sequence U_0, U_1, ..., is constructed such that $F(U_{i+1}) < F(U_i)$. If G_i is the gradient of F evaluated at U_i, then the CG descent algorithm used is

$$S_1 = -G_1$$
$$S_{i+1} = -G_{i+1} + \beta_i S_i$$
$$\beta_i = \frac{\langle G_{i+1}, G_{i+1} \rangle}{\langle G_i, G_i \rangle}$$
$$U_{i+1} = U_i + \alpha_i S_i$$

(G.3)

where α_i is chosen to minimize $F(U_i + \alpha_i S_i)$ and $\langle \cdot, \cdot \rangle$ is the scalar product on $\mathscr{H}$. It is shown in Chapter 3 that the so-constructed sequence converges to U^*, the minimizing argument of F, if the initial guess is chosen in a region R which contains U^* and if in that region the second derivative of F is bounded and positive definite.

The CGD program evaluates the gradient of F on the space of input controls for the system and criterion of Section G.2, where the control inputs are of the form described in Section G.3. The so-found gradient is used to construct the CG descent sequence as in (G.3).

G.5. REPRESENTATION OF A PIECEWISE CONTINUOUS INPUT FUNCTION

A piecewise continuous input function is represented as the sum of a continuous function and a piecewise constant function. This is as shown in Section 5.2. Repeating (5.3) here, the piecewise continuous control input is of the form

$$u(t) = c(t) + \sum_{i=0}^{M} h_i[1(t - t_i) - 1(t - t_{i+1})] \qquad \text{(G.4)}$$

$$t_{m+1} = t_f$$

where now $c(t)$ is a continuous function over $[t_0, t_f]$, $1(t)$ is the unit step function, and the h_i are constants. It may be seen that $u(t)$ as given by (G.4) has jumps (discontinuities) of height h_i that occur at time t_i. The CGD program handles an input $u(t)$ of the form seen in (G.4) in three separate parts as follows:

1. The continuous function $c(t)$ over $[t_0, t_f]$.
2. The vector of jump times

$$t = [t_1, t_2, \ldots, t_M]^+ \qquad t \in R^M \qquad \text{(G.5)}$$

3. The vector of values of the piecewise constant portion of the input

$$h = [h_0, h_1, \ldots, h_M]^+ \qquad h \in R^{M+1} \qquad \text{(G.6)}$$

The program, for a given run, may optimize on any or all of these different parts.

G.6. THE GRADIENT OF THE COST FUNCTIONAL

The gradient of the cost functional J as defined in Section G.2 has been found for the cases used in the program in Chapters 4 and 5. Before giving the gradient for each case let us define terms. The vector λ is the adjoint vector and is the solution to the system adjoint to (G.1), which is

$$\dot{\lambda} = -f_x^+ \lambda; \ \lambda(t_f) = \nabla\phi(x(t_f)) \tag{G.7}$$

Here superscript $+$ indicates transpose and f_x is the matrix of partial derivatives whose ijth element is

$$(f_x)_{ij} = \frac{\partial f_i}{\partial x_j} \qquad i,j = 1, 2, \ldots, n \tag{G.8}$$

where f_i is the ith component of f of (G.1), x_j is the jth component of the state vector x, f_x in (G.7) is evaluated along the trajectory found by integrating (G.1) with a given control input and initial condition c, and $\nabla\phi(x(t_f))$ is the gradient of the cost function ϕ of (G.2) evaluated at the state $x(t_f)$ found by integrating (G.1). From the solution to (G.7) over the time interval $[t_0, t_f]$, the gradient of the cost functional may be written as follows:

1. u a continuous function over $[t_0, t_f]$,

$$g(t) = f_u^+ \lambda(t) \qquad t \in [t_0, t_f] \tag{G.9}$$

where f_u is the vector of partial derivatives whose ith component is

$$(f_u)_i = \frac{\partial f_i}{\partial u} \qquad i = 1, 2, \ldots, n \tag{G.10}$$

evaluated with $x(t)$ obtained from integration of (G.1) and $u(t) = c(t)$.
   2. u a set of parameters $u_1, u_2, \ldots, u_m$

$$g = \int_{t_0}^{t_f} f_u^+ \lambda(t) \, dt \tag{G.11}$$

where

$$(f_u)_{ij} = \frac{\partial f_i}{\partial u_j} \qquad \begin{matrix} i = 1, 2, \ldots, n \\ j = 1, 2, \ldots, m \end{matrix} \tag{G.12}$$

evaluated along the trajectory obtained by integrating (G.1).
   3. u a set of initial conditions, that is, c of (G.1)

$$g = \lambda(t_0) \tag{G.13}$$

The program also handles the case where the criterion function is a function of the initial state, that is, the criterion is of the form

$$J = \phi(x(t_0), x(t_f)) \tag{G.14}$$

From Section 5.4, the gradient is thus

$$g = \lambda(t_0) + \nabla_{x(t_0)} \phi(x(t_0), x(t_f))$$ (G.15)

where $\nabla_{x(t_0)} \phi$ is the gradient of $\phi(x(t_0), x(t_f))$ w.r.t. $x(t_0)$.

4. u a set of jump times (discontinuities), that is, t of (G.5).
In this case the gradient (from Section 5.2) is a vector with M components, the ith of which is (corresponding to jump time t_i)

$$g_i = \lambda^+(t_i)\{f(x, u)|_{t_{i-}} - f(x, u)|_{t_{i+}}\}$$ (G.16)

5. u, a set of values of the piecewise constant function that is added to the continuous function input to achieve a piecewise continuous input, that is, h of (G.6). In this case the gradient is an $M + 1$ vector whose ith component is

$$g_i = \int_{t_i}^{t_{i+1}} f_u^+ \lambda(t)\, dt$$ (G.17)

where f_u is as given by (G.10).

The program is written to compute the gradients for the five cases given above and to simultaneously optimize on any or all of these sets of control inputs.

Answers to Selected Problems

Chapter II

2.

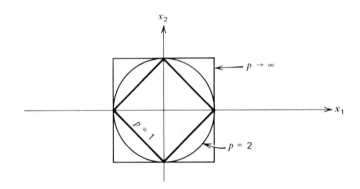

3. $0[ax + by] = a0[x] + b0[y] = 0$, the null element in the range space.

4. By definition of the norm

$$\|A(x - x_0)\| \leq \|A\| \cdot \|x - x_0\|$$

$$\lim_{x \to x_0} \|Ax - Ax_0\| \leq 0 \qquad \text{if} \quad \|A\| \text{ is bounded}$$

$$\lim_{x \to x_0} Ax = Ax_0$$

5. Consider

$$\langle x + ay, x + ay \rangle \geq 0$$

Equality holds for $x + ay = 0$. Multiplying out the above scalar product gives

$$\langle x, x \rangle + 2a\langle x, y \rangle + a^2\langle y, y \rangle \geq 0$$

Letting

$$a = -\frac{\langle x, y \rangle}{\langle y, y \rangle}$$

gives

$$\langle x, x \rangle - \frac{\langle x, y \rangle^2}{\langle y, y \rangle} \geq 0$$

which with a little rearrangèment gives

$$|\langle x, y \rangle| \leq \|x\| \|y\|$$

for $\|x\|^2 \triangleq \langle x, x \rangle$.

6. $\|x + y\|^2 = \langle x + y, x + y \rangle = \langle x, x \rangle + \langle y, y \rangle + 2\langle x, y \rangle$
    $$= \|x\|^2 + \|y\|^2 + 2\langle x, y \rangle$$
    $$\leq \|x\|^2 + \|y\|^2 + 2|\langle x, y \rangle|$$

which by use of Schwarz's inequality gives

$$\|x + y\|^2 \leq \|x\|^2 + \|y\|^2 + 2\|x\| \|y\| = (\|x\| + \|y\|)^2$$

or

$$\|x + y\| \leq \|x\| + \|y\|$$

9. $F'(x_0) \cdot z = \langle g(x_0), z \rangle \ \forall z \in \mathcal{H}$
    $F'(x) \cdot z - F'(x_0) \cdot z = \langle g(x), z \rangle - \langle g(x_0), z \rangle$
    $(F'(x) - F'(x_0)) \cdot z = \langle g(x) - g(x_0), z \rangle$
    $\|F'(x) - F'(x_0)\| = \|g(x) - g(x_0)\|$

Therefore if g is continuous at x_0, F' is also continuous and vice versa.

10. If it is assumed that $F'(x_0)$ exists, then

$$\|F(x) - F(x_0)\| - \|F'(x_0) \cdot (x - x_0)\|$$
$$\leq \|F(x) - F(x_0) - F'(x_0) \cdot (x - x_0)\|$$
$$\|F(x) - F(x_0)\| \leq \|F'(x_0) \cdot (x - x_0)\|$$
$$+ \frac{\|F(x) - F(x_0) - F'(x_0) \cdot (x - x_0)\|}{\|x - x_0\|} \|x - x_0\|$$

Taking the limit $x \to x_0$ on both sides gives

$$\lim_{x \to x_0} \| F(x) - F(x_0) \| = 0$$

Therefore

$$\lim_{x \to x_0} F(x) = F(x_0)$$

11. (a) $A \cdot t$

(b) $\langle t, A(x_0 + \zeta t) \rangle + \langle x_0 + \zeta t, At \rangle$

(c) $B \cdot (t, y_0 + \zeta s) + B \cdot (x_0 + \zeta t, s)$

12. $F(x) = F(x_1, x_2, \ldots, x_n) = [F_1(x), F_2(x), \ldots, F_m(x)]^+$

$\quad y = y_1 e_1 + y_2 e_2 + \cdots + y_n e_n$

Since $F'(x_0)$ is a linear operator

$$F'(x_0) \cdot y = y_1 F'(x_0) \cdot e_1 + y_2 F'(x_0) \cdot e_2 + \cdots + y_n F'(x_0) \cdot e_n$$

and

$$F'(x_0) \cdot e_i = \lim_{t \to 0} \frac{F(x_0 + te_i) - F(x_0)}{t} = \frac{\partial F(x)}{\partial x_i}$$

$$= \left[\frac{\partial F_1(x_0)}{\partial x_i}, \frac{\partial F_2(x_0)}{\partial x_i}, \ldots, \frac{\partial F_m(x_0)}{\partial x_i} \right]^+$$

Therefore

$$y_1 F'(x_0) \cdot e_1 + y_2 F'(x_0) \cdot e_2 + y_n F'(x_0) \cdot e_n = \text{RHS of equation of}$$
$$\text{Problem 12}$$

13. $F(x) = F(x_0) + \displaystyle\int_a^b g_{x_0}(t) [x(t) - x_0(t)] \, dt$

$$+ \tfrac{1}{2} \int_a^b [x(\tau) - x_0(\tau)] \left\{ \int_a^b k_{x_0}(\tau, t) [x(t) - x_0(t)] \, dt \right\} d\tau$$

15. (a) $(1/n)\sqrt{2/3}$.

(b) n.

(c) 0.

(d) ∞.

Chapter III

1. (a) By induction $p_{k+1}^+ A p_j = 0$ for $1 \le j \le k$.
    $p_{k+1}^+ A p_{k+1} > 0$ because A is positive definite and $p_{k+1} \ne 0$ since it is a
    linear combination of $d_0, d_1, \ldots, d_{k+1}$, which are linearly independent
    by assumption.
    (b) Hint: Use $A = I =$ identity matrix.

2. If $u_i =$ the ith eigenvector of A, then $A u_i = \lambda_i u_i$, $u_i \ne 0$. $u_i^+ A u_j =$
    $\lambda_j u_i^+ u_j = \lambda_i u_i^+ u_j$ by symmetry. If the eigenvalues are distinct then
    $\lambda_j \ne \lambda_i$, which means therefore that $u_i^+ u_j = 0$ if $i \ne j$. Thus $u_i^+ A u_j = 0$
    for $i \ne j$.

3. $P = [p_0, p_1, \ldots, p_{n-1}]$.

9. Hint: Use p_k as defined in (3.81) and then apply (3.82).

10. Hint: Use α_k as given by (3.16c).

13. $\|x_n - x^*\| \le 2 \sqrt{\dfrac{M}{m}} \left(\dfrac{1 - \sqrt{m/M}}{1 + \sqrt{m/M}} \right)^n \|x_0 - x^*\|$

$\|g(x_n)\| \le 2 \sqrt{\dfrac{M}{m}} \left(\dfrac{1 - \sqrt{m/M}}{1 + \sqrt{m/M}} \right)^2 \|g(x_0)\|$

Chapter IV

1. Hint: Use the second order expansion about x_0

$$F(x_0 + \varepsilon z) = F(x_0) + \varepsilon \langle g(x_0), z \rangle + \tfrac{1}{2}\varepsilon^2 \langle z, F''(x_0) \cdot z \rangle + o(\varepsilon^2)$$

2. (a) A.
    (b) The $n \times n$ matrix whose ijth element is

$$\dfrac{\partial^2 \phi(x)}{\partial x_i \partial x_j} \bigg|_{x=x_0}$$

where $x_i = i$th component of x.

    (c) $F''(x_{1_o}, x_{2_o}) = \begin{bmatrix} 6(x_{1_o} + 1) & 0 \\ 0 & 12(x_{2_o} + 2) \end{bmatrix}$.

    (d) $F''(x_0) \cdot = \displaystyle\int_a^b \cdot \, dt \int_a^b k(t, s) \cdot ds$.

3. (a) $w(t) = \delta(t) + (b - a)e^{-at}1(t)$.

   (b) 0.

   (c) No.

4. For the following, from Appendix F, λ_k is found by solving

$$\lambda_{k-1} = f_x^+(x_{k-1}, u_{k-1})\lambda_k; \ \lambda_N = \nabla_x\phi(x)|_{x=x_N} \qquad k = 1, 2, \ldots, N$$

   (a) $u = [u_o, u_1, \ldots, u_{N-1}] \qquad u_k \in \mathscr{R}^m$

$$g(u_k) = f_u^+(x_k, u_k)\lambda_{k+1} \qquad k = 0, 1, \ldots, N-1$$

   (b) $u = [u_1, u_2, \ldots, u_m]^+ \qquad u_i \in \mathscr{R}^1,$

$$g(u) = \sum_{k=0}^{N-1} f_u^+(x_k, u)\lambda_{k+1}$$

   (c) $u = [u_1, u_2, \ldots, u_{p_{\max}}] \qquad u_p \in \mathscr{R}^m,$

$$g(u_p) = \sum_{k=(p-1)M}^{pM-1} f_u^+(x_k, u_p)\lambda_{k+1}$$

   (d) $g(x_0) = \lambda_0$.

5. $\lambda(t)$ satisfies $\dot{\lambda} = -f_x^+(x(t))\lambda$

$$\lambda(t_f) = \nabla_{x(t_f)}\phi(x_0, x(t_f))$$

$$g(t_0, t_f, x_0) = \{-[\nabla_{x_0}\phi(x_0, x(t_f))]^+ f(x_0)$$
$$\times [\nabla_{x(t_f)}\phi(x_0, x(t_f))]^+ f(x(t_f))$$
$$\times [\lambda(t_0) + \nabla_{x_0}\phi(x_0, x(t_f))]\}$$

Index